THREE, FOUR AND MORE

A Study of Triplet and Higher Order Births

Edited by: Beverley J Botting
Alison J Macfarlane
Frances V Price

LONDON: HMSO

© Crown copyright 1990
First published 1990

ISBN 0 11 691270 7

Preface

The Study of Triplet and Higher Order Births was undertaken by a Steering Group which comprised:

BEVERLEY BOTTING	Statistician, Office of Population Censuses and Surveys (OPCS)
PATRICK BOWER	General practitioner and parent of twins
ELIZABETH BRYAN	Paediatrician, and honorary consultant at Queen Charlotte's Maternity Hospital and to the Twins and Multiple Births Association
TED DAW	Obstetrician, North Manchester General Hospital
JUDI LINNEY	Health education officer, and parent of twins
ALISON MACFARLANE	Medical Statistician, National Perinatal Epidemiology Unit (NPEU), Oxford
SARAH MOORES	Teacher and parent of triplets
MICHAEL MURPHY	Epidemiologist, Department of Community Medicine and General Practice, University of Oxford
EILEEN OCKWELL	Teacher, parent of triplets, and Supertwins Co-ordinator of the Twins and Multiple Births Association
FRANCES PRICE	Medical Sociologist, Child Care and Development Group (CCDG), University of Cambridge
MARTIN RICHARDS	Psychologist, Child Care and Development Group (CCDG), University of Cambridge

The Study would not have been possible without the help of the many people contributing to the various stages. We are particularly grateful to:

All the parents of triplets, quadruplets and quintuplets who made time to complete a lengthy questionnaire and to be interviewed in their homes. Hazel Ashurst (NPEU) for organising data entry and analysis, John Waterman, David Fitzgerald and Nirupa Lakhani (Medical Statistics Unit, OPCS) for sending and receiving questionnaires, Jean Martin (Social Survey Division, OPCS), Lesley Mutch (NPEU) and Myrna Holmes (NPEU) for questionnaire design, David Elliot (Social Survey Division, OPCS) for help with sampling, Annette Magner, Janet Stokes, Patrick Walsh, Rose Marx, Kate Beckett, Clare Sanderson and the other midwives who completed outstanding obstetric questionnaires, Jill Brown (CCDG) and Jini Hetherington (NPEU) for administrative help, Brenda Childs-Barry and Paula Wybrew for coding the doctor's questionnaires, Carole Harris, Sarah Barlow and Sarah Ayers who entered the data onto the computer, Jane Elliott (CCDG) for statistical advice and setting up the data analysis for the parents' study, the OPCS Typing Pool for typing much of the text and to Jourdanne Morgan (OPCS), and Sally Roberts (CCDG) for excellent and very extensive secretarial support.

Frances Price is very grateful for help with the parents' study also provided by Emily Caston, Vanessa Coupland, Lesley Day, Harriet Elson, Janet Hall, Alison Harrison, Amy Iverson, Shirley Prendergast, Chris Walker and Nina, Tom and, most of all, John Wakeford. She is grateful for advice concerning the survey of community nursing provision from Morris Robinson and Peggy Gordon.

In addition to those already mentioned, we should like to thank colleagues in the National Perinatal Epidemiology Unit and the Office of Population Censuses and Surveys for their help, advice and support.

We thank Paul Cain for permission to quote from his unpublished autobiography, Alan Bowness for permission to quote from Barbara Hepworth's autobiography, and to the Oxford Mail, Sarah and Nigel Moores, Eileen and Andrew Ockwell, Wendy Varley and Ian Winter for permission to reproduce photographs.

Alison Macfarlane, Hazel Ashurst, Ann Johnson and Miranda Mugford are funded by the Department of Health as core staff of the National Perinatal Epidemiology Unit. Frances Price was funded by the Department of Health under its Small Grants Scheme.

Contents

Preface   3

Introduction – Beverley J Botting, Alison J Macfarlane, Frances V Price,   13
    Martin P M Richards

Chapter 1 – Background – Beverley J Botting, Alison J Macfarlance,   15
    Elizabeth Bryan, Michael G F Murphy,
    Martin P M Richards
Triplets and higher order births in the past   15
The incidence of multiple births   17
Survival chances of multiple birth children   22
The processes resulting in a multiple birth   24
The role of fertility treatment   27

Chapter 2 – Design and response – Beverley J Botting,   31
    Alison J Macfarlane, Hazel Ashurst
Introduction   31
Design of the study   31
Population of multiple births covered by the study and their mortality   35
Response rates   36
    Obstetric questionnaire   37
    GP questionnaire   37
    Parents' questionnaire and interviews   38
    Data from all sources   38
    Surveys of health and personal social services provision 41
Possible biases in the surveys   41

Chapter 3 – Infertility drugs and procedures – Alison J Macfarlane,   46
    Frances V Price, E G Daw
Associations between infertility treatment and multiple birth   47
Background of parents who had infertility treatment   47
Patterns of infertility care   50
In-vitro fertilisation   55
Discussion between parents and doctors about the possibility of a multiple
birth   55
Conclusions   57

Chapter 4 – Antenatal care – Alison J Macfarlane, Frances V Price,   59
    E G Daw
Diagnosis of multiple pregnancy   60
Parents' experiences of diagnosis   62

Chapter 4 – continued

Infertility treatment and the diagnosis of multiple pregnancy   66
Booking for delivery and changes in booking   68
Special help for parents with multiple pregnancies   69
Obstetric problems during multiple pregnancy   70
Admission to hospital during pregnancy   75
Conclusions   77

Chapter 5 – The delivery – Alison J Macfarlane, Frances V Price,   80
                                E G Daw
Discussions with hospital staff about the birth   80
Gestational age at birth   85
Labour and delivery   86
Policies about methods of delivery   90
Examination of placentas and assessment of zygosity   93
Parents' experience of the birth   93
Conclusions   97

Chapter 6 – Early days – Alison J Macfarlane, Frances V Price,   99
                             Elizabeth Bryan, Beverley J Botting
After the birth – the early days and weeks   99
Mothers' medical problems in the neonatal period   99
The babies   102
Mortality rates   105
Babies' problems immediately after birth   107
Apgar scores   110
Babies' problems in the neonatal period   113
Congenital malformations   117
Admission to special care   119
Mothers' discharge from hospital   122
Feeding   123
Parents' views about hospital care   125
Preparation for discharge of babies   127
Discharge of the babies   128
Conclusions   128

Chapter 7 – Who helps? – Frances V Price   131
Help and support from relatives   132
Help from friends and neighbours   134
Intensity of help and support required   134
Night nursing help from statutory and other sources   135
Help from local authority social services   136
Help from general practitioners   141
The role of health visitors   143
Help from students, trainees, volunteers and support groups   147
Conclusions   150

Chapter 8 – Disabilities and health problems in childhood – Alison J   153
Macfarlane,
Ann Johnson,
Patrick Bower

Cerebral palsy   153
Vision, hearing and speech problems   154
Convulsions   154
Illness and hospital admissions   154
Congenital malformations   157
Interpretation of the findings   158
Assessing the impact of disability on adult triplets   159
Conclusions   160

Chapter 9 – Consequences – Frances V Price   161
Introduction   161
Publicity   161
Benefits, gifts and loans   163
Housing status, moves and extensions   166
Transport   168
Access to car or van   169
Access to telephone   172
Getting out: visits to clinic   172
Babysitting   173
Holidays in the first year   173
Overnight visits by children away from home   174
Conclusions   175

Chapter 10 – Pre-schooling – Frances V Price   177
Introduction   177
Pre-school provision   177
Costs and difficulties encountered   184
Access to pre-school   186
Conclusions   187

Chapter 11 – Schooling – Frances V Price, Sarah Moores, Eileen Ockwell,   189
Bride Stokes
Introduction   189
Entry to school   190
Separate or together?   191
Language development and communication   192
Involvement of specialists   193
Conclusions   196
Case Studies   196

Chapter 12 – The costs of a multiple birth – Miranda Mugford   205
Introduction   205
Conception   205

Chapter 12 – continued
Out-patient antenatal care   207
In-patient antenatal care   208
Delivery   209
Postnatal hospital care   210
Neonatal care in hospital   211
Rehospitalisation   211
At home   213
Childcare and home help   214
Paying the costs   214
Conclusions   215

Chapter 13 – Conclusions and recommendations – Alison J Macfarlane,   218
                                                    Frances V Price,
                                                    Beverley J Botting

Conclusions
Before conception   218
Pregnancy   219
Delivery   219
After the birth   220
Help for parents after the babies went home   220
Health and disability in childhood   221
Press publicity and gifts   221
Housing and mobility   222
Pre-school provision   222
School   222
Costs   223

Recommendations
Recommendations for health and social services   224
Recommendations for research and data collection   226

Copies of questionnaires used in the study have not been reproduced in this book, but are available from the authors on request.

Tables and figures

Tables

1.1 Numbers and incidence of multiple deliveries in England and Wales, 1938–89   19

1.2 Mortality rates for singleton and multiple births in England and Wales born in the years 1975–86, excluding 1981   23

2.1 Number of multiple maternities and rate per 1,000 maternities, 1980 and 1982–85 England and Wales   34

2.2 Births and deaths of triplets 1980, 1982–85 England and Wales   34

2.3 Response to questionnaires 1980, 1982–85, England and Wales   36

2.4 Maternities with triplet and higher order births by mother's age 1980, 1982–85 England and Wales   39

2.5 Live and stillborn triplets, and quadruplet and higher order births by birthweight, 1980, 1982–85   40

2.6 Mother's family situation   42

2.7 Fathers' employment   42

2.8 Social class of father   43

2.9 Previous pregnancies   43

2.10 Living children at time of study pregnancy   44

2.11 Sex combinations of triplets, comparing registration with survey data, England and Wales   45

3.1 Investigations and treatment for infertility   47

3.2 Demographic characteristics and infertility treatment for mothers of triplets   49

3.3 Infertility treatment and social class of parents of triplets   50

3.4 Types of surgery for investigation and treatment of infertility   51

3.5 Drugs prescribed for infertility   52

3.6 Where drug treatment for infertility was initiated   53

3.7 Type of drug treatment for mothers of triplets and above   54

4.1 Method of diagnosis of multiple birth   59

4.2 Serum alpha-fetoprotein tests   60

4.3 Sources of information about gestational age   61

4.4 Detection of multiple birth at first scan   62

4.5 Detection of triplet and higher order births detected at first scan by gestational age   62

4.6 Gestational age at diagnosis of multiple birth   63

4.7 Numbers of scans reported by parents and obstetricians   64

4.8 Comparison of parents' and obstetricians' replies about numbers of scans   65

4.9 Correct diagnosis of triplets and infertility treatment   68

4.10 Reasons for change in booking   69

4.11 Women with obstetric problems during pregnancy   71

4.12	Obstetric problems among women expecting triplets and higher order births according to infertility treatment and previous pregnancies	72
4.13	Numbers of antenatal admissions to hospital	73
4.14	Reasons for antenatal admissions to hospital	74
4.15	Length of antenatal stay in hospital	75
5.1	Gestational age at delivery, cumulative distribution	82
5.2	Gestational age by multiplicity, comparison with singletons	84
5.3	Did spontaneous labour occur?	84
5.4	Estimated gestational age at first onset of spontaneous labour	85
5.5	Induction rates	86
5.6	Method of delivery of multiple births	87
5.7	Method of delivery within triplet sets	88
5.8	Presentation prior to delivery	89
5.9	The use of anaesthesia in labour and delivery	92
5.10	Description of placenta	93
5.11	Determination of zygosity	94
5.12	Relationship between placenta and zygosity	94
6.1	Obstetricians' reports of mothers' problems after the birth	100
6.2	Comparison of obstetricians' and parents' replies about mothers' problems after the birth	101
6.3	Comparison of birthweights of triplet and higher order births with singletons and twins	103
6.4	Comparison of birthweights of triplets by order of birth within each set	105
6.5	Birthweights, of triplets by birth order and method of delivery	106
6.6	Outcome at one year for twins and triplets by birth order	107
6.7	Mortality by birthweight	109
6.8	Outcome of triplet sets at one year, obstetric survey data	111
6.9	Percentage of babies resuscitated after live birth	113
6.10	Method of resuscitation of triplets	113
6.11	Medical problems in the neonatal period	117
6.12	Recorded malformations in multiple births	118
6.13	Numbers of malformed multiple births by birth order and type of delivery	119
6.14	Length of stay in special care	121
7.1	Provision of local authority night nurse	136
7.2	Provision of local authority home help	140
7.3	Parents' views of the care, advice and help received from their GP in first year	142
7.4	Visits from health visitor	144
7.5	Parents' comments about help provided by health visitor by frequency of visits	145
8.1	Vision problems reported by general practitioners	155
8.2	Children who had been admitted to hospital at least once	156
8.3	Children who had had surgery	157
8.4	Congenital malformations recorded by general practitioners	158
9.1	Publicity and its consequences	162
9.2	Gifts received from commercial companies	166
9.3	Access to telephone	171

10.1	Use of mother and toddler group by age of children at time of survey	178
10.2	Use of playgroup by age of children at time of survey	179
10.3	Use of nursery school by age of children at time of survey	180
10.4	Use of nursery class by age of children at time of survey	181
11.1	Arrangements at school	189
12.1	Health service costs of hospital care for mothers with triplet and higher order births	206
12.2	Health service costs of hospital care for babies born in triplet and higher order births	207
12.3	Samples of monthly expenditure on food and nappies for triplets	212
12.4	Examples of expenditure on equipment for triplets	213

Figures

1.1	General fertility rates, England and Wales, 1838–1988	18
1.2	Proportion of all maternities which resulted in a multiple birth, England and Wales 1939–1989	20
1.3	Proportion of all maternities which resulted in a triplet or higher order birth, England and Wales, 1970–1989	21
1.4	Infant mortality for singleton and multiple births, England and Wales, 1975–1986	22
1.5	The origins of fraternal and identical twins	25
1.6	Types of triplets and quadruplets	26
2.1	Study design and response	33
3.1	Infertility investigations and procedures	46
3.2	Treatment for infertility	48
3.3	Number of living children at the time of birth of triplets and use of infertility drugs and procedures	49
3.4	Trends in infertility treatment amongst mothers of triplets	53
4.1	Numbers of ultrasound scans in multiple pregnancies	64
4.2	Gestational age at first scan and infertility treatment, mothers of triplets	67
4.3	Ultrasound scans for triplet pregnancies and infertility treatment	67
4.4	Antenatal admissions, length of stay	73
4.5	Infertility treatment and antenatal stay, mothers of triplets	77
5.1	Gestational age at delivery	83
5.2	Infertility treatment and age at delivery, mothers of triplets	83
5.3	Method of delivery of multiple and singleton births	87
5.4	Caesarean rates and infertility treatment	91
6.1	Birthweight distributions of singleton and multiple births	101
6.2	Birthweight of triplets by birth order	102
6.3	Birthweight distribution of triplets by method of delivery	103
6.4	Birthweight by birth order and method of delivery	104
6.5	Very low birthweight triplets by method of delivery	112
6.6	Resuscitation of triplets by method of delivery	112
6.7	Apgar score at one minute for triplets by method of delivery	114
6.8	Apgar score at five minutes for triplets by birth order and method of delivery	115
6.9	Apgar scores at one and five minutes by method of delivery	116
6.10	Admission to special care and length of stay	120

Introduction

Beverley J Botting, Alison J Macfarlane, Frances V Price, Martin P M Richards

Despite their rising numbers, higher order multiple births, that is, triplets, quadruplets, quintuplets and sextuplets, remain rare. In 1988, 166 sets of triplets, 14 sets of quadruplets and one set of quintuplets were born in the United Kingdom. That is approximately three sets of triplets and higher order births in every 10,000 deliveries. In the same year 8,445 sets of twins were delivered, so nearly 47 sets of twins were born for each higher order multiple birth.

Higher order multiple births, or 'grand multiples' as they are sometimes called, are not only unusual. In addition to all the problems the parents may experience in coping with three or more children of the same age, these babies are frequently born early, which means that they are likely to have problems in the early days and weeks of life. Furthermore, since these births are rare, there are few professionals or parents from whose experience others can draw. Only a small minority of health visitors or general practitioners will ever encounter triplets or quadruplets. Even neonatal paediatricians, who specialise in the hospital care of preterm babies, may not see a triplet or higher order multiple birth every year. Consequently, public knowledge about these children and the problems they may pose is limited. Apart from mutual support between parents, the information and support available to parents and professionals may be far less than that expected or needed.

It was to try and fill this gap that we set up a national study of triplet and higher order births. We set out to collect information about all such babies born in the United Kingdom over a five year period in 1980 and from 1982 to 1985. Although we did not manage to cover them all, we have information from the obstetricians about a total of 340 sets (75 per cent of all such births in these years). For many of these sets we also have information from questionnaires completed by the mother's general practitioner and by the parents themselves. Some parents were also visited. One hundred and fifty three parents who had triplet or higher births outside the main study years also completed questionnaires, and several adult triplets and quadruplets wrote letters describing their lives.

A central aim of our study has been to identify problems which have arisen for parents and for professionals and to learn how they have tried to resolve them. As births from several years are included, the study covers families with multiple birth children aged from a few months old up to school age. We have, as a result, a fairly full picture of the early years of life of these children. Other parts of the survey are concerned with the medical care mothers received before conception, during pregnancy and at birth, and that of their children, both in the critical period immediately after birth and subsequently. Our aim has been to reflect both parents' views and those of the professionals who supported these families and provided care.

As our work got underway, it took on a new urgency. This was because the number of triplet and higher order multiple births began to rise quite sharply as a result of increasing use of fertility drug treatment and assisted conception. This has raised many questions about the ways in which these techniques are being employed, as well as about the resources required to care for these babies. Many require a period of intensive care in a neonatal unit. The increasing numbers of these births is putting a great strain on facilities and has led to calls from paediatricians, among others, that steps should be taken to prevent such multi-fetal pregnancies arising in the first place.

Our research project and this book were collaborative efforts involving the Office of Population Censuses and Surveys (the government office which collects and compiles medical and social statistics), the Child Care and Development Group of the University of Cambridge (a group undertaking research into the concerns of parents and the development of children), and the National Perinatal Epidemiology Unit (a Department of Health funded research unit concerned both with the social and economic context of childbearing and with evaluating the care parents and babies receive before, during and after birth). Research workers from these groups, together with the medical professionals and parents in the steering group, have contributed their particular expertise to make the study much more wide-ranging than it would have been otherwise. It provides a unique view of what may be anticipated with triplets, quadruplets, quintruplets and sextuplets. We hope it will lead to improvements in the care and support that these households receive in the future.

Chapter 1 – Background

Beverley J Botting, Alison J Macfarlane,
Elizabeth Bryan, Michael G F Murphy, Martin P M Richards

> 'Among women, the birth of twins occurs once in about eighty deliveries.
> Triplets, quadruplets, quintuplets and even higher figures are occasionally
> observed; they are very uncommon, and the rarity is progressive with the
> number.'
>
> J Matthews Duncan, 1866[1]

Triplets and higher order births in the past

When J Matthews Duncan, a well-known Edinburgh obstetrician, read a paper on
'some laws of the production of twins' to the Medico-Chirurgical Society in February
1865[2] he was unable to find any reliable estimates of the frequency of triplets and
higher order births. In order to refute the claim made by the physiologist Burdach
that, 'We scarcely ever encounter the births of three or four children except in women
who have passed the thirtieth year'[2], Matthews Duncan hastily collected 'the
following ten authentic cases of triplets' from other writers on multiple births and
from his own notebook to show that '. . . triplets are by no means exclusively confined
to women above thirty years of age. Yet it is noticeable that not one occurs among the
younger childbearing women and not one in a first pregnancy'.[1] To underline this
point he also reported that 'An interesting fact in connection with this subject is
mentioned in Hugenberger's report of the St Petersburg Midwives' Institute (1863).
Three women admitted there between 1845–59 in their fifteenth pregnancies had
triplets, and each went on to have triplets three times in succession'.[2]

Although Scandinavian countries have been collecting statistics about multiple
births since the mid-eighteenth century, this was not the case in Britain. Scotland
started collecting statistics about 'plural births' when its birth registration system was
set up in 1855 although stillbirths were not included. In England and Wales collection
of statistics about multiple births did not start until the late 1930s. Before this, births
from a multiple delivery were registered independently and the fact that the children
were from the same delivery was not recorded.

This lack of statistics did not imply a lack of interest. Multiple births have long
been the object of public and medical curiosity and of scientific research. This interest
has continued to the present day.[3]

In the 1920s the Royal Society commissioned Ronald Fisher, a prominent
statistician, to undertake a survey of 166 sets of triplets born in Britain and Ireland
between 8 October 1917 and 28 September 1920.[4] Fisher traced the surviving triplets
at the age of six through the records of the 'King's Bounty' for triplets. This was a
payment at birth of a special crown bounty of one guinea for each child of a triplet or
quadruplet set, an arrangement instituted by Queen Victoria in 1839. The survey was
fairly limited in the subjects it covered and focussed largely on survival rates,
measurements of stature and family histories of multiple births.

Other contemporary accounts of individual higher order births highlight issues
which are still with us today. A report in the British Medical Journal of a set of

quadruplets born at term in 1919 in Hamilton, Scotland mentioned that the parents had two previous children and 'live in a single apartment. Each baby weighed at least 5lbs and all survived'

One of a set of quadruplets born in 1935 in Eynesbury, near St Neots in Huntingdonshire wrote and told us about their birth, at home, because their mother could not reach hospital in time, and about their early days.

'My parents lived in a council house two up and two down, so there wasn't much room for us, so we only stayed there for a few days till we were moved to Dr E Harrison's house. He was the doctor who brought us into the world with two district nurses, Nurse Mailing and Nurse Daniels. The doctor then hired four nurses from Great Ormond St Hospital to look after us for the first six months. Then this was cut down to one plus my mother as my parents couldn't cope with the cost.'[6]

Writing in the British Medical Journal shortly after the birth of these quadruplets, Dr Harrison commented that:

'I am grateful to Dr Donald Paterson for the valuable help he has given me, and to the management committee of Great Ormond Street for supplying four nurses gratis during the time of emergency. This act of generosity is all the more appreciated when I know they can ill afford it, having to make a great effort on their own behalf for funds for rebuilding.'[7]

Even though the quadruplets' father earned only £3 a week, this family eventually managed, with the help of fees from press publicity, to buy a larger house in St Neots.

'The people of St Neots raised £450 to build a sun-parlour on to the house, also a nursery. It seems a small amount today but fifty two years ago it was a large sum. Visitors paid 1/- a time to view us in our prams. This helped also to pay the cost of bringing us up.'[6]

Although their circumstances were somewhat different, the sculptor Barbara Hepworth and her partner the painter Ben Nicholson, whose triplets were also born in the 1930s, found that their unexpected arrival brought financial problems, but also help.

As Barbara Hepworth wrote in her autobiography:[8]

'On October 3rd Ben and I went to the cinema in Belsize Park, and my life-long friend Margaret Gardiner had supper with us. Ben had complained a little bit that I seemed withdrawn and concentrated over my pregnancy. But suddenly I said, "Oh dear", and in next to no time I saw three small children at the foot of my bed – looking pretty determined and fairly belligerent. This was an event even my doctor did not suspect, and we had only a basement flat, no washing in the garden, and a kitchen-bathroom, and £20 in the bank and only one cot.

Ben was superb. The day before he had done a three-form white relief. At dawn he did another relief. He was a tower of strength, and rang round our immediate friends at dawn, who said, "Shut up Ben, this is no time for jokes".

16

I, myself, knew fear for the first time in my life, as I was very weak, and wondered how on earth we were to support this family on white reliefs and the carving I was doing.

Ben was entirely right and, supported by his faith, our work strengthened in the right direction, and miraculously we made our way, due to the wonderful help given to us by our friends and patrons.

The children were an inspiration, each one giving us a very great joy.

It seemed as though it might be impossible to provide for such a family by the sale of abstract paintings and white reliefs, which Ben Nicholson was then doing, and by my sculptures; but the experience of the children seemed to intensify our sense of direction and purpose, and gave us both an even greater unity of idea and aim.

When I started carving again in November 1934, my work seemed to have changed direction, although the only fresh influence had been the arrival of the children.'

In Britain many families with multiple births have had extensive press coverage. Amongst much other publicity the Good quadruplets, born in 1949, made the cover story in Picture Post.[9] Their parents and older sister lived in one council house and the quadruplets, together with two nurses, lived next door. Despite the gifts received after the birth, including £100 in War Savings for each quadruplet raised in subscription by their local Rural District Council and a substantial donation from a baby food firm, much of the article is taken up describing the high costs of bringing up the children and the difficulties the family had in meeting these.

While public interest and curiosity has tended to be centred on the higher multiples, it is twins which have been the main object of research.[10] Twins may or may not have all their genes in common and may or may not grow up together, and therefore, they have been seen as the ideal test situation in which estimate the extent to which genetic and environmental factors contribute to the development of IQ, personality and the tendency to mental illness.

Our study focuses on two main themes; first, the problems in providing appropriate medical care and other services, and second, the situation of and demands made upon parents of triplets and higher order births. To put our study in a wider context, the remainder of this chapter examines trends in the frequency of triplet and higher order births, changes in their survival rates, and ends by discussing what is known about how multiple births can occur.

The incidence of multiple births

Trends in the multiple birth rate need to be seen in the context of changing patterns in all births.

The number of women in the fertile age group has changed over the years, so a better picture of changing child bearing patterns over time is obtained by expressing the number of live births in relation to the total number of women who might become pregnant. Figure 1.1 illustrates trends in child bearing by showing the general fertility rate in England and Wales since records began in 1838 until 1989. It has to be assumed that the proportion of 15–44 year olds who cannot or do not want to become pregnant has remained constant over time, although with the

17

Figure 1.1   General fertility rates, England and Wales, 1838–1988

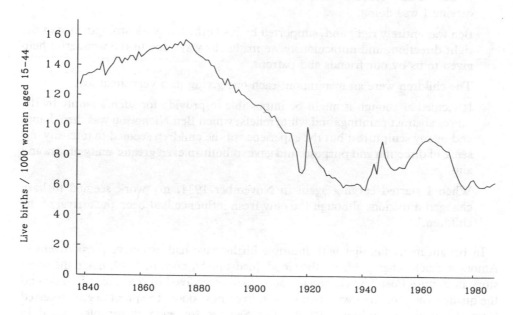

Source: OPCS Birth statistics. Series FM1

increasing use of infertility treatment this is probably no longer a correct assumption.

Figure 1.1 shows a pattern of increasing fertility between 1838 and 1880, although birth registration was incomplete at this time. The deficit of registrations reduced between 1840 and 1870[11] accounting for much of the increase in rates. Fertility rates then fell sharply until the early 1940s with the exception of a brief increase after the First World War. There was a similar increase after the Second World War followed by a gradual increase in rates until the early 1960s. Fertility rates declined between the mid 1960s and 1977, since which time they have fluctuated around a level of 60 births per thousand women aged 15–44.

Recent patterns of fertility are likely to have been affected by the availability of effective contraception, which means that most people are now able to decide on the number and spacing of their pregnancies. Over the last few years the trend has been for women to delay having their first baby until they are older, perhaps to fit in better with their career and to allow some time for life as a couple before coping with child care. This has happened across the social spectrum, though more so amongst couples where the male partner is in an occupation classified by the Registrar General as non-manual compared with those whose occupation is classified as manual.[12]

Patterns in the incidence of twin and higher order births have not followed that of overall fertility. When the collection of data about multiple births in England and Wales began in July 1938 the prime reason was to monitor trends in fertility. The

Population (Statistics) Act was passed at a time of public concern about falling birth rates, to collect additional data so that parents' fertility rates could be monitored more fully. The reason for analysing multiple births was given as follows:

'Although fertility is usually measured by the number of children born rather than by the number of maternities experienced, it is necessary to remember that the former is a composite total made up of the number of maternities, which is susceptible to voluntary control and the number of extra children born in multiple maternities which cannot be so readily controlled.'[13]

Table 1.1 shows the number and incidence of multiple deliveries in England and

Table 1.1

Numbers and incidence of multiple deliveries in England and Wales, 1938–1989†

Years	All mater-nities	Singleton births	Twins	Triplets	Quad-ruplets	Quin-tuplets	Sex-tuplets	Sep-tuplets
1938–40*	1,546,780	1,528,175	18,451	153	1			
1941–45	3,409,944	3,368,744	40,849	343	8			
1946–50	3,950,343	3,900,340	49,551	444	8			
1951–55	3,412,386	3,368,755	43,225	401	4	1		
1956–60	3,732,859	3,687,188	45,240	427	4			
1961–65	4,267,306	4,217,736	49,116	448	6			
1966–70	4,097,511	4,053,556	43,533	413	6	1	2	
1971–75	3,433,182	3,398,786	34,020	353	19	4		
1976–80	3,040,236	3,010,581	29,253	373	24	4	1	
1982–85	2,536,895	2,511,022	25,515	332	22	2	2	
1986–89	2,706,907	2,677,086	29,186	588	40	5	1	1

Rates per 1,000 deliveries:

Years		Singleton births	Twins	Triplets
1938–40		988.0	11.9	0.10**
1941–45		987.9	12.0	0.10
1946–50		987.3	12.5	0.11
1951–55		987.2	12.7	0.12
1956–60		987.8	12.1	0.11
1961–65		988.4	11.5	0.11
1966–70		989.3	10.6	0.10
1971–75		990.0	9.9	0.11
1976–80		990.2	9.6	0.13
1982–85		990.0	10.1	0.14
1986–89		989.0	10.8	0.24

† Data on multiple births in 1981 are not available due to industrial action in that year by local registrars of births and deaths.
* From July 1938 onwards.
** Triplets and above.
Source: OPCS Birth Statistics Series FM1.

Wales between 1938–89. While twin births are quite common at about one per cent of all deliveries, the higher order births are much less so. The ratios of higher order multiple births to twins has reduced in recent years such that by 1989 one in 44 multiple births was a triplet or higher order delivery. This means that twins dominate the pattern of all multiple births.

Figure 1.2 shows the proportion of all maternities in England and Wales between 1939 and 1989 which resulted in a multiple birth. The proportion of all pregnancies which were a twin or higher order delivery rose from 1939 until the early 1950s and then fell until the late 1970s before starting to increase again. The increase in rate from the late 1970s is, at least in part, a consequence of the growing use of 'fertility' or ovulation stimulating drugs and, in the most recent years, various techniques of assisted conception such as IVF and GIFT.

Since the incidence of twins has not changed markedly over the period, the recent increase in the incidence of multiple births is much more marked if triplets and higher order births are looked at separately. Figure 1.3 shows the increase over time in the numbers of triplet and higher order births as a proportion of all pregnancies. The striking feature of this graph is the huge increase in triplet and higher order births since 1970. These higher order birth rates showed a marked increase in 1986 when a record 123 sets of triplets were born in England and Wales. A similar level was recorded in 1987, but the rate then increased again. In 1989 183 sets of triplets were registered. This was the most in any year since multiple birth statistics were first com-

Figure 1.2 Proportion of all maternities which resulted in a multiple birth, England and Wales, 1939–1989

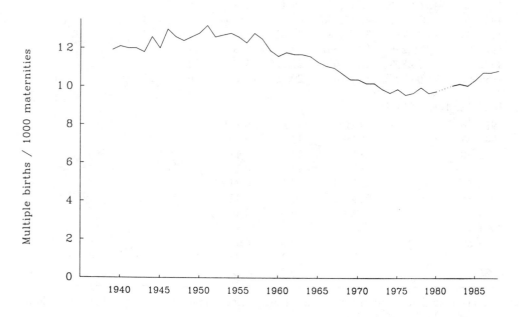

Source: OPCS Birth statistics, Series FM1

Figure 1.3   Proportion of all maternities which resulted in a triplet or higher order birth, England and Wales, 1939–1989

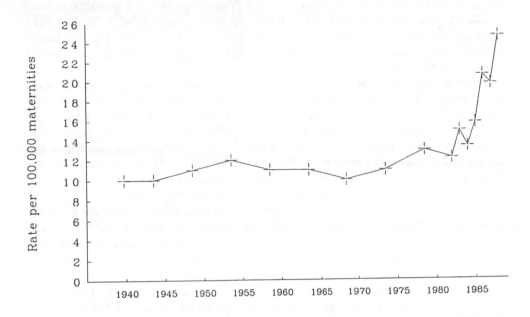

Source: OPCS Birth statistics, Series FM1

piled, and represented a rate of 27 sets of triplets per 100,000 maternities (pregnancies leading to a registrable birth) compared with a rate of 14 in 1985.

These trends seem to indicate that whether a conception results in a single or multiple delivery is dependent on different factors to those which influence overall fertility. The graphs must be interpreted with care, however, because they present statistics of registered births, not of babies conceived. Although counts of live and stillbirths are known to be very accurate, if a multiple birth is delivered before 28 weeks and at least one fetus is born dead, then the dead fetuses should not be registered. This is discussed in Chapter 2.

A further factor which can affect both singleton and multiple pregnancies, is that birth statistics exclude induced abortions which currently account for about 20 per cent of the total number of conceptions each year[14], and miscarriages, which can occur very early in pregnancy, even before the woman knows she is pregnant. A considerable number of pregnancies begin with two or more fetuses but deliver as fewer. Ultrasound scan studies have shown this to be the case. For instance one fetus may die or fail to develop after an early stage in the pregnancy and the result is a singleton delivery. This is known as 'the vanishing twin syndrome'. Similarly, in triplet or higher order pregnancies one or more fetuses may die or fail to develop.[15] Very occasionally, an operation is performed to selectively reduce the number of fetuses in a higher order pregnancy to improve the survival chances of the remaining fetuses. Although no statistics are kept about this, it is probably too uncommon to affect the figures given here, except possibly in the most recent years.[16]

21

Survival chances of multiple birth children

The risk of the babies in a multiple pregnancy being stillborn or dying during infancy is higher than that for a singleton birth. Figure 1.4 shows infant mortality among singleton and multiple births in England and Wales between 1975 and 1986.

The chances that multiple birth children survive through infancy has increased more rapidly in recent years than the chances of survival of singletons, but the risks of stillbirth and infant death are still about five times higher for multiple birth babies than for singletons.[17]

The risk of stillbirth or death during the first year after birth is greater the larger the number of babies delivered. Table 1.2 shows the risk of death in differently-sized pregnancies in England and Wales for 1975 to 1986. Twins were three times more likely to die during infancy than singletons, and the death rates among triplets and higher order births were higher than those among twins. The rates for quadruplet and higher order births are generally greater than those in triplets but are based on very small numbers of births and therefore should be assessed with caution.

The 1958 British Perinatal Mortality Survey showed that preterm delivery was a major factor associated with deaths in twins.[18] Being born too soon may mean that the babies are not ready to function independently and will need very careful medical and nursing care. Despite improvements in neonatal care the problems of immaturity continue to be a main reason for the high mortality, and this fear of losing some or all of her babies increases anxiety for the mother during pregnancy.

An analysis of mortality among twins, by age and cause, in England and Wales for 1979–84[17] showed that the most commonly attributed causes of stillbirth were

Figure 1.4 Infant mortality for singleton and multiple births, England and Wales, 1975–1986

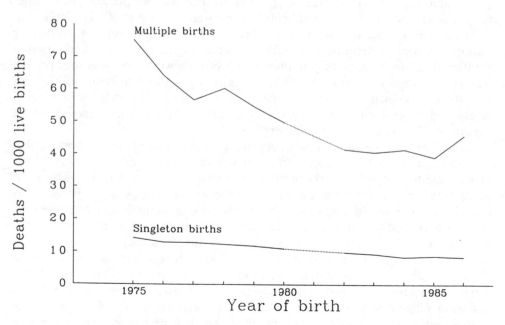

Source: OPCS Mortality statistics, Series DH3

Table 1.2

Mortality rates for singleton and multiple births in England and Wales born in the years 1975–86, excluding 1981

Type of birth	Stillbirths*	Perinatal*	Neonatal**	Postneo-natal**	Infant**	Number of total births (live and still)
Singleton	7.7	13.8	7.4	4.3	11.7	4,845,382
Twin	25.4	63.2	43.9	9.1	52.9	95,312
Triplet	47.5	164.5	135.0	12.7	147.7	1,812
Quadruplet and higher order births	30.5	219.5	207.5	12.6	220.1	164

* Rates per 1000 total births.
** Rates per 1,000 live births.
Source: OPCS series FM1 and DH3 Annual Reference Volumes.

complications of the placenta and cord. Respiratory distress syndrome was the most commonly given cause of neonatal death. In the postneonatal period the most commonly cited causes of death were the same as for singletons: respiratory conditions, sudden infant deaths and congenital anomalies. Unfortunately many deaths of multiple birth children were simply attributed to 'multiple pregnancy'. The underlying cause of death among triplets showed a similar pattern to that for twins.

Respiratory distress results from underdevelopment of the lungs and may often require intensive care with artificial ventilation. Mortality rates are high and even for survivors there is an increased chance of lung problems in childhood and later life. For reasons that are not well understood, the incidence of respiratory distress syndrome is higher among multiple birth children than among singletons even when gestational age has been taken into account.[19]

The analysis mentioned above also showed that there were differences in mortality when this was analysed by birth order. The higher mortality of second twins and of second and third triplets might be due to their less favourable position in the uterus, or womb, during labour, rendering them more liable to direct trauma from the contracting womb during delivery.[20] Another factor for vaginal deliveries is the reduction of uterine capacity following delivery of the first child, which might alter the blood flow in the placenta and thus cause anoxia, or shortage of oxygen, in the remaining babies. This could be aggravated by the cumulative effect of prolonged anaesthesia. Such differential effects are likely to be reduced or eliminated when multiple sets are delivered by caesarean section.

The higher mortality among sets of the same sex compared with those born in mixed sets may be due to differences in zygosity. Monochorionic monozygous twins (identical twins with the same placenta) share the same placental blood vessels which may be to their disadvantage. Dichorionic monozygous pairs which are identical but have separate placentae, and dizygous or fraternal pairs, have separate blood supplies.

23

Parents who had experienced one or more stillbirths, neonatal deaths or infant deaths and who did not take home three or more of their higher order birth children were not included in the parents' study. During the course of our study, however, we came in contact with some parents who had experienced such loss. A mother whose higher order multiple birth babies only survived for a few days wrote:

'My babies only lived for between 12 and 36 hours. Nevertheless every effort was made to help them in the [regional hospital's] SCBU. We were actively encouraged to stay with them throughout and we even held [first born's] hand. Soft music played in the background and the staff were all very kind, gentle, sensitive and caring. We were kept informed throughout about their condition. We held them for a long time after they had died – very important.'

The trauma is compounded when babies are transferred after birth to another hospital and subsequently die. A mother whose triplets were delivered by emergency caesarean at 32 weeks wrote about her feelings after the babies were transferred to different hospitals within hours of their birth and a day later one baby died:

'Dreadful feelings of isolation and confusion because we were all in three separate hospitals. These feelings brought to a head when [second born] died and the birth hospital could not get me to her before her death.'

Another mother wrote that her experience of the birth of triplets followed by the death of one baby very soon afterwards was 'extremely hard to handle':

'The birth of the triplets [at 29 weeks' gestation] in the local hospital posed problems for the paediatric staff who only had one intensive care "set up". Consequently they had to be immediately sent to another hospital 30 miles away. Being alone in hospital after the birth was very difficult for me and I think the local staff were unused to the situation and found it difficult to help me.'

Often the feelings of grief did not come out until some months or years afterwards and it was only then that the parents were able to let themselves mourn.[21]

The processes resulting in a multiple birth
Factors which affect the processes of ovulation (the release of a woman's eggs), fertilisation of the eggs by sperm, implantation in the womb and then intrauterine growth and survival determine whether there will be a multiple birth. Although the exact mechanism by which female hormones control ovulation is not clear, generally only one egg (ovum) is released. If this is fertilised, further ovulation is inhibited so that only one baby develops. A multiple birth occurs when either more than one ovum is released and fertilised at around the same time, leading to non-identical births, or the cells developing from a fertilised ovum separate at one of their early divisions so that two, or more, cell masses (embryos) develop independently. At this early stage of development each cell mass has the potential to become a fetus.

Figure 1.5 illustrates the processes resulting in the two types of twins. Fraternal (or non-identical) twins occur when more than one egg is produced and each is fertilised separately in the same menstrual cycle. The eggs and sperm involved will vary genetically so that resulting children will be no more alike than any brother and sister.

If a single ovum is released as usual and fertilised by one sperm, (fertilisation of one egg by more than one sperm is very rare indeed) the cells may then divide at least once to produce genetically identical (monozygotic) twins, triplets etc. Identical twin or higher order births always have the same physical features such as eye and hair colour and bone structure. They will not, however, necessarily be indistinguishable. Identical multiple birth children will be the same sex while non-identical ones may or may not be.

It is possible for both the processes described above to happen in the same pregnancy. So, for example, two ova might be released and fertilised and one of these fertilised eggs might then divide to become two embryos. Thus there would be two identical and one non-identical triplet. Matters can become a little more complicated, however, because not all early embryos survive. In any pregnancy, multiple or singleton, there is a relatively high chance that a fertilised embryo will not survive the first days or weeks' gestation. Such early miscarriages are generally unnoticed or at most may result in a slightly late menstrual period that is heavier than usual. So a triplet pregnancy could, for example, be the result of two divisions of a single fertilisation into four embryos followed by the loss of one of the resulting embryos. Figure 1.6 illustrates the basic processes (without embryo loss) which can result in a triplet or quadruplet pregnancy.

Figure 1.5   The origins of fraternal and identical twins

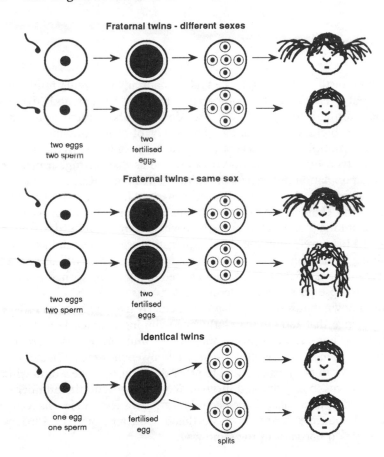

25

Figure 1.6 Types of triplets and quadruplets

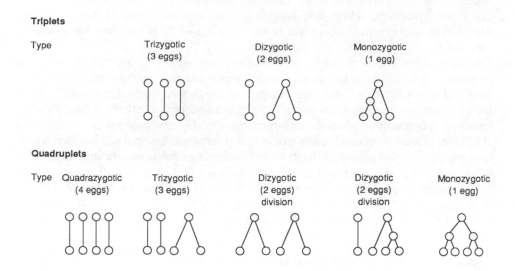

A nonuplet birth[22] (9 babies) is the highest naturally occurring multiple birth ever recorded, but even today, the comparative rarity of triplets and higher multiples makes them difficult to study.[23] What we do know about them comes mainly from studies of the biology of twinning. The study of twins provides information of relevance to multiplicity in general, though as already seen, the increase in the frequency of twin births has not been as marked as that for higher order births.

There are population differences in multiple birth rates. Rates are particularly high in Africa, a fact that was noticed as long ago as the tenth century by the Arab geographer, Ibn Hauqal. He reported that in Egypt multiple births were believed to arise from drinking of the waters of the Nile which were thought to contain a feminine principle.[24] This purely environmental explanation seems most unlikely, however, as women living in many other parts of Africa far away from the Nile also have high rates of multiple birth, as do Afro-Caribbean women living in the United States. Diet may play a role in these population differences.[25]

It is well-known that some women are particularly likely to have non-identical twins but the evidence that fathers may influence twinning is much less clear.[25] It seems likely that for non-identical twins and higher multiple births there is a genetic predisposition, which may possibly be modified by environmental factors, to multiple ovulation. This can perhaps also lead to other differences in the womb which make it easier for embryos to implant and survive. Women's age and the number of previous children (parity) have also long been known to affect their chances of having non-identical multiple births as J Matthews Duncan noted in 1865.[26] Identical twinning rates do not vary in the same way.

Women's chances of non-identical twinning seem to increase with age until their late 30s, and then decreases again. Possibly this depends on the age when childbearing begins. Women who have had twins tend to have an early menopause.[27] One suggested explanation is that the ovaries become 'exhausted' as a result of greater stimulation throughout life.[27, 28] Changes in the average age of women at childbirth, or in the number of times women give birth during their lifetime therefore influence the overall rates of non-identical twinning and higher order births, directly or through the indirect selection of women who have differently sized and spaced families.

Women's height and weight (perhaps as 'weight for height' or body mass) is also related to the probability of twinning, with taller and heavier women being more likely to have twins.[29, 30] As body mass is related to age and parity, however, it is impossible to identify a single factor which is ultimately responsible.

Whether taking hormones, particularly oral contraceptives, before conception can directly affect twinning has been much debated but remains uncertain.[31] Cigarette smoking before conception may affect hormone levels and thus may decrease fertility[32], but smoking has also been reported to increase the chance of non-identical twinning.[33]

A study of multiple births in Scotland during 1962–64 suggested that the proportion of births of dizygotic twins was associated with social class, being highest among women with husbands in partly skilled or unskilled manual occupations.[34] Suggestions have also been made that a number of other factors, such as exposure to pesticides and hormone implants in beef cattle could have contributed to the changes in twin and higher multiple birth rates[35, 36], but these are even more speculative than some of the other factors discussed in this chapter.

The role of fertility treatment

Recent increases in the number of multiple births are due in part to treatment for sub-fertility. In Britain it is believed that more than one in 10 couples experience difficulty achieving either pregnancy or having a liveborn child.[37] Whether this has varied much over time is not known. Even estimating the current number of these couples is difficult.[38]

Some infertility is the result of a failure of ovulation and the woman can be prescribed drugs which stimulate ovulation. The most commonly used such drug is clomiphene citrate (known by the trade names Clomid (R) or Serophene (R)). This drug, and others such as the hormone human menopausal gonadotrophin (HmG, known by trade names such as Pergonal (R)) have the serious disadvantage that under some conditions more than one ovarian follicle ripens to produce multiple ova with a resulting higher risk of multiple births. It has been estimated that six to eight per cent of pregnancies following treatment with clomiphene led to multiple births.[39] The risks with gonadotrophins were higher with estimates ranging from 18 to 54 per cent.[40] The percentages varied according to the reasons for infertility and the dosage and timing of the drugs used. The majority of these multiple births will be twins, but a small proportion will be triplets and higher multiples.

More recently, multiple births have been the result of assisted reproduction techniques such as in-vitro fertilisation (IVF) and gamete intra fallopian transfer (GIFT), since the first 'test tube baby' resulting from the IVF procedure was born in July 1978. In these procedures the ovary is stimulated with drugs or hormones to produce multiple ovulation. In IVF the unfertilised eggs are collected from the ovaries, fertilised and replaced, whereas in GIFT programmes the unfertilised eggs are transferred to the fallopian tube together with sperm. The pregnancy rates associated with these techniques are low.[41] Until recently it was believed that the chances of a successful pregnancy increased with the number of embryos or unfertilised eggs transferred. The consequence is an increased risk of multiple pregnancies.

The higher multiple pregnancy rate achieved with these assisted reproduction techniques is greater than expected.[42] Replacing more than one egg only provides solid evidence for trends in non-identical children from a multiple birth. There is evidence from the results of artificial induction of ovulation, IVF and GIFT programmes, however, that these techniques result in more identical children from higher order multiple pregnancies than would be expected.[43, 44] Variation in the results achieved with different drug regimens suggest that aspects of the processes concerned with ovulation induction and in-vitro fertilisation in some way promote the splitting of embryos to produce two identical embryos.

The Interim Licensing Authority (ILA) (formerly the Voluntary Licensing Authority) was set up to regulate the activities of clinics practising techniques of IVF and other related procedures. There had been concern about the growing number of higher order multiple births and the difficulties that these births were causing to the families and to the health services, as well as the risks to the children. As a result the ILA issued a guideline that usually a maximum of three, and only exceptionally four, embryos, should be transferred in IVF, otherwise there is a disproportionately greater increase in multiple pregnancies relative to the increased success in achieving pregnancy. In 1989 the guideline was extended to include GIFT.[41]

These are only voluntary guidelines, but they must be followed by any clinic which wishes to continue to be licensed by the ILA. However, many people feel that the licensing authority should have legal backing, and as we go to press, a Human Fertilisation and Embryology Bill,[45] with provisions to set up a statutory authority, the Human Fertilisation and Embryology Authority is going through Parliament.

References

1. Duncan J M. Fecundity, fertility, sterility and allied topics. Edinburgh: Adam and Charles Black, 1866.

2. Duncan J M. On some laws of the production of twins. Edinburgh Medical Journal 1865; 10: 767–781.

3. Clay M M. Quadruplets and higher multiple births. London: Mackeith Press, 1989.

4. Fisher R A. Triplet children in Great Britain and Ireland. Proceedings of the Royal Society 1928; B: 286–311.

5. Loudon J I H. A case of quadruplets. British Medical Journal 1919; 2: 802.

6. Browning A. Personal communication.

7. Harrison E H. The Eynesbury quadruplets. British Medical Journal 1935; 2: 1207–1208.

8. Bowness A. Barbara Hepworth: a pictorial autobiography. London: Tate Gallery, 1985.

9. Picture Post 1949; 5(3): 1.

10. MacGillivray I, Campbell D M, Thompson B, eds. Twinning and twins. Chichester: John Wiley, 1988.

11. General Register Office, Thirty-fifth Annual Report of the Registrar General for the year 1872, London: HMSO, 1874.

12. Werner B. Fertility trends in different social classes 1970–83. Population Trends 1985; 41: 5–13.

13. General Register Office. Registrar General's statistical review for the year 1938. Part III, Civil. London: HMSO 1944.

14. OPCS Abortion Statistics 1987. Series AB No. 17. London: HMSO, 1988.

15. Goldman G A, Dicker D, Feldberg D, Ashkenazi J, Yeshaya A, Goldman J A. The vanishing fetus. A report of 17 cases of triplets and quadruplets. J Perinat Med 1989; 17: 157–161.

16. Selective fetal reduction. Lancet 1988, ii: 773–775.

17. Botting B, Macdonald Davies I, Macfarlane A. Recent trends in the incidence of multiple births and associated mortality. Arch Dis Child 1987; 62: 941–950.

18. Butler N R, Alberman E D. Perinatal problems – the second report of the 1958 British Perinatal Mortality Survey. Edinburgh: E&W Livingstone, 1969.

19. Keirse M J N C, Kanhai H H H. An obstetrical point on preterm birth with particular reference to perinatal morbidity and mortality. In Aspects of Perinatal Morbidity. Huisjes H J, ed Groningen: Universitaire Boekhandel Nederland, 1981.

20. Kurtz G R, Davis L L, Loftus J B. Factors influencing the survival of triplets. J Obstet Gynaecol 1958; 12: 504–8.

21. Bryan E. Twins in the family. A parent's guide. London: Constable, 1984.

22. Carey H M. Induction of ovulation resulting in a nonuplet pregnancy. Australian and New Zealand Journal of Obstetrics and Gynaecology 1976; 16: 200.

23. Benirschke K, Kim C. Multiple pregnancy. New Engl J Med 1973; Med 1973; 288: 1276–1284, 1329–1336.

24. Hauqal I, Kitab Surat Al-Ard. French translation by J H Kramers, G Weit. Beyrouth: Commission Internationale Pour la Traduction des Chefs-D'Oeuvre, 1964.

25. MacGillivray I, Samphier M, Little J. Factors affecting twinning. In: Twinning and Twins. MacGillivray I, Campbell D M, Thompson B. eds Chichester: John Wiley, 1988.

26. Duncan J M. On the comparative frequency of twinbearing in different pregnancies. Edinburgh. Med J 1865; 10: 928–929.

27. Bulmer M G. The biology of twinning in man. Oxford: Clarendon Press, 1970.

28. Wyshak G. Menopause in mothers of multiple births and mothers of singletons only. Social Biology. 1978; 25: 52–61.

29. Bonnelykke B. Predictors of human twinning: an epidemiological study of medical, social and demographic factors in human twinning. Cytogenetic Laboratory, Arhus Psychiatric Hospital, Risskov, Denmark, 1988.

30. Hemon D, Berger C, Lazar P. The aetiology of human dizygotic twinning with special reference to spontaneous abortions. Acta Genet Med Gemellol 1979; 28. 253 258.

31. Murphy M, Campbell M, Bone M. Is there an increased risk of twinning after discontinuation of the oral contraceptive pill? J Epid Comm Hlth 1989; 43: 275–279.

32. Howe G, Westhoff C, Vessey M, Yeates D. Effects of age, cigarette smoking and other factors on fertility: findings in a large prospective study. Br Med J 1985; 290: 1697–1700.

33. Olsen J, Bonnelykke B, Nielsen J. Tobacco smoking and twinning. Acta Med Scand 1988; 224: 491–494.

34. Smith A. Observations on the determinants of human multiple birth. In: Annual Report of the Registrar General for Scotland 1964. Edinburgh: HMSO, 1966: 70–82.

35. James W H. Recent secular trends in dizygotic twinning rates in Europe. J Biosoc Sci 1986; 18: 497–504.

36. Little J, Thompson B. Descriptive epidemiology. In Twinning and Twins. MacGillivray I, Campbell D M, Thompson B, eds. Chichester: John Wiley, 1988; 37–66.

37. Page H. The increasing demand for fertility treatment. Health Trends 1988; 115–118.

38. Greenhall E. Sub-fertility in the community. Thesis submitted for membership of the Faculty of Community Medicine. Oxford 1987.

39. Merrell Pharmaceuticals Ltd. Clomid Data Sheet Compendium. London: Data pharm, 1981.

40. Schenker J G, Yarkoni S, Granat M. Multiple pregnancies following induction of ovulation. Fertility and Sterility 1981; 35: 105–123.

41. The fourth report of the Voluntary Licensing Authority for human in vitro fertilisation and embryology. London: Interim Licensing Authority, 1989.

42. MRC Working Party on Children Conceived by In Vitro Fertilisation. Births in Great Britain resulting from assisted conception, 1978–87. British Medical Journal 1990; 300: 1229–33.

43. Derom C, Derom R, Vlietinck R, Van Den Berghe H, Thiery M. Increased monozygotic twinning after ovulation induction. Lancet 1987; i: 1236–1238.

44. Edwards R, Mettler L, Walters D. Identical twins and vitro fertilisation. J In Vitro Fertil Embryo Transfer 1986; 3: 114–117.

45. Human Fertilisation and Embryology Bill. London: HMSO, 1989.

Chapter 2 – Design and Response

Beverley J Botting, Alison J Macfarlane, Hazel Ashurst

Introduction

Before discussing the replies we received from doctors, parents and others, we explain in this chapter the methods we used in the study. As there are no straightforward ways to find parents of triplet and higher order births and their doctors, these methods were inevitably complex. The chapter also discusses the response rates achieved for the different stages of the study. Parents of triplet or higher order births became known to the study through different routes, so the replies were examined to see whether those replying were typical of parents of all triplet and higher order births born in the study years.

Design of the study

The study consisted of a series of linked surveys of triplet and higher order births in 1980 and 1982–85 identified from birth registration records received by the Office of Population Censuses and Surveys (OPCS). Unfortunately multiple births in 1981 cannot be identified due to industrial action in that year by local registrars of births, marriages and deaths. So that comparisons could be made, a singleton and a twin 'control' were also selected, matched to each triplet and higher order birth. The survey methods were piloted on 1979 births, selected in the same way. Some parents with triplet and higher order births born outside the study years also wanted to participate and so completed questionnaires. These additional data provided more recent information about such families.

Originally, the study was restricted to births registered in England and Wales, which are processed by OPCS. Subsequently Scotland and Northern Ireland, whose birth registrations are dealt with by separate General Register Offices in Edinburgh and Belfast respectively, joined the study, extending its coverage to the whole of the United Kingdom.

Confidentiality was maintained at all stages of the study. The questionnaires sent to obstetricians and general practitioners had a detachable covering sheet which gave personal details so that case notes could be identified. Once this was detached the completed questionnaire contained only the mother's unique study number with no personal details or other identifiable information.

Confidentiality restrictions meant that it was not possible for OPCS to provide a list made up solely of triplet and higher order births. Instead a longer list of births was provided. This included all triplet and higher order births in 1980 and 1982–1985 in England and Wales, together with matched twin and singleton controls. The controls were matched according to the district health authority where the mother lived, her age, whether the birth was inside or outside marriage, and, for babies born inside marriage, how many previous births the mother had had whilst married. Similar lists of triplet and higher order births, together with matched twin and singleton controls, were provided by the General Register Offices in Scotland and Northern Ireland.

Before the study began, ethics approval had been obtained from the British Medical

Association and the Cambridge District Ethics Committee. The study was also supported by many relevant organisations including the Royal College of Obstetricians and Gynaecologists, the British Paediatric Association, the Royal College of General Practitioners, the Royal College of Midwives, the British Association of Perinatal Medicine, the National Childbirth Trust, the Twins and Multiple Births Association, the Association for Improvements in the Maternity Services and the Health Visitors Association.

The study design is illustrated as a flow chart in Figure 2.1. The surveys of clinicians were undertaken jointly by OPCS and the National Perinatal Epidemiology Unit (NPEU). Questionnaires in respect of each triplet and higher order birth, and the singleton and twin controls, were sent to medical records officers at each hospital of delivery, with a request for these questionnaires to be forwarded to the consultant obstetrician who had been responsible for the care of the mother.

The questionnaires began by asking for information about the parents and whether the mother had had infertility treatment or in-vitro fertilisation. For singleton births, no further questions were asked. Instead, to make comparisons with our data for multiple births, where possible data about singleton births sampled in the Maternity Hospital In-Patient Enquiry (HIPE) were used, both from published sources[1] and from data tapes for the years 1980 and 1982–85.

For multiple births, obstetricians were asked about how the multiple pregnancy was diagnosed and about the care given during pregnancy and labour. They were also asked to forward to the relevant paediatrician separate questionnaires which sought information about what happened to each baby after birth.

Triplet and higher order births have a higher mortality than singletons and twins. Some families in the study lost one or more of their multiple birth children at or within a few days of birth. Whilst their antenatal and delivery data made a valuable contribution to the study, these families were not included in the next stage of the study which asked questions of GPs and parents about caring for three or more children of the same age. Parents with two or fewer survivors from their multiple birth would be coping with different problems associated with their bereavement. Important as these are, it was decided not to investigate these in our study. Nevertheless, a few parents of quadruplet or higher order births had lost one or more of their multiple birth children but had taken the remaining three or more children home from hospital. These parents had both the problems of bereavement as well as those of caring for three or more children of the same age.

Where the obstetric questionnaire showed that three or more babies were discharged from hospital alive, information about the mother was sent to the National Health Service Central Register (NHSCR) to try to trace her current Family Practitioner Committee (FPC). This is the local body which holds lists of patients registered with general practitioners in its area. Tracing was not possible if the family had moved overseas, joined the armed forces or if the mother had died. It is not possible for NHSCR to identify a person's GP directly, but the FPCs forwarded our questionnaires to the relevant GPs.

This questionnaire asked about care prior to and during the multiple pregnancy, as well as the current health and other problems of the children and other members of their family. Specific questions were asked about whether the children from the multiple birth suffered from any chronic illnesses, disabilities or congenital abnormalities and whether they had ever been under the care of any paediatricians or

Figure 2.1 Study design and response

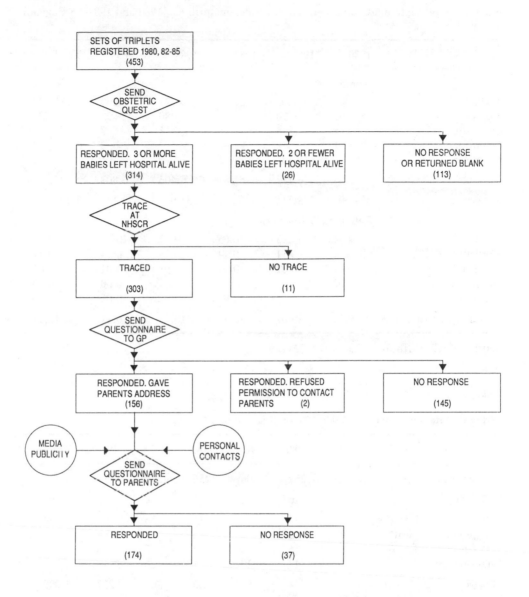

other specialists. If so, a questionnaire was sent to each specialist concerned, asking for details of diagnosis and treatment.

General practitioners were also asked whether they knew of any reason why the family should not be contacted. If there was no such reason they were asked for the mothers' current address so that the parents could be approached in a parallel survey. This survey, which was separately funded by the Department of Health, was under-

Table 2.1

Number of multiple maternities and rate per 1,000 maternities, 1980 and 1982–85 England and Wales

	1980	1982	1983	1984	1985	Total
Number						
Twin	6,308	6,201	6,293	6,321	6,700	31,823
Triplet	91	70	89	80	93	423
Quadruplet	4	6	4	5	7	26
Quintuplet	1	–	–	–	2	3
Sextuplet	–	–	1	–	1	2
All multiple maternities	6,404	6,277	6,387	6,406	6,803	32,277
Total maternities	654,501	623,511	626,277	633,965	653,142	3,191,396
Rate per 1,000 maternities						
Twin	9.64	9.95	10.05	9.97	10.26	9.97
Triplet	0.14	0.11	0.14	0.13	0.14	0.13
Quadruplet	0.01	0.01	0.01	0.01	0.01	0.01
Quintuplet	0.00	–	–	–	0.00	0.00
Sextuplet	–	–	0.00	–	0.00	0.00
All multiple maternities	9.78	10.07	10.20	10.10	10.42	10.11

Source: OPCS Birth Statistics, Series FM1.

Table 2.2

Births and deaths of triplets 1980, 1982–5 England and Wales

	1980	1982	1983	1984	1985	Total
Live births	257	206	256	232	271	1,222
Stillbirths	16	4	11	8	8	47
Early neonatal deaths	34	12	15	16	7	84
Late neonatal deaths	3	5	2	3	4	17
Postneonatal deaths	6	2	4	7	3	22
Infant deaths	43	19	21	26	14	123
Survivors at age 1 year	214	187	235	206	257	1,099
Percentage of live births surviving to age 1 year	83.3	90.8	91.8	88.8	94.8	89.9

Source: OPCS Birth Statistics, Series FM1.
      OPCS linked infant mortality statistics, Series DH3

taken by Frances Price at the Child Care and Development Group (CCDG) at Cambridge University. Our study covered many families where the multiple birth had taken place several years previously and many parents move to larger homes after the multiple birth. Using the home address given at birth registration was therefore considered to be an inadequate way of tracing these families. Hence parents could only be contacted through their GP. This made it impossible to contact the parents first to seek their consent. In an attempt to compensate for this, the survey was given wide media publicity. As a result, some parents approached us directly asking to participate in the study. For many of these families we subsequently obtained a response from the mother's obstetrician and her GP.

Postal questionnaires were sent to parents of children identified through the survey of GPs, and to other parents of triplet and higher order births who came forward after media publicity or personal contacts. Questions were asked about the problems encountered by the parents in bringing up three or more children of the same age and the help they had from health and social services and other sources. Parents were also asked for their perspective on the care they received before, during and after the multiple pregnancy.

A sub-sample of parents was selected and interviewed. There are differences between the north and the south of the country in terms of income, ownership of homes and household equipment, and access to infertility treatment. To allow for these differences two lists of respondents were compiled. One consisted of parents living in, or south of, West Glamorgan, Mid Glamorgan, Gwent, Gloucester, Cheltenham, Oxfordshire, Northampton, Kettering, Peterborough and West Norfolk and Wisbech health districts, and the other of parents living elsewhere. The lists were ordered by the date on which the questionnaire had been completed and every fifth respondent was approached with a request for an interview. In addition, interviews were conducted with those mothers who had requested that the questionnaire be discussed and completed with them in their homes. Agreement was sought and given to tape-record all the interviews. In addition, three interviews were recorded with women with triplet pregnancies whilst they were in hospital and all three were subsequently followed up at home after their multiple birth.

Information was also collected from directors of social services departments and from directors of community nursing services about the support they can provide to parents with multiple births and the problems they perceive. A brief questionnaire was sent to each of the 132 social services departments in the United Kingdom and to each of the 216 district health authorities in England, Wales and Northern Ireland and to all health boards in Scotland.

Population of multiple births covered by the study and their mortality

Tables 2.1 and 2.2 describe the multiple births registered in England and Wales in 1980–85 and covered by our study. Some multiple births are not included in these birth registration data. Under the Births and Deaths Registration Acts in force in the United Kingdom, a baby that is born dead is not registrable as a stillbirth if the birth occurred before 28 completed weeks of gestation. Babies born alive are registrable whatever the gestation. This means that if a multiple birth involves the birth of both live and dead babies before 28 weeks of gestation, only the live births should be registered. As a result we may have missed some triplets and higher order births born before this stage of gestation if some of the babies were born dead.

Table 2.1 shows the total number of maternities resulting in multiple births registered in England and Wales in 1980 and 1982–85, the years covered by the study. The death rates of triplets born in these years are given in Table 2.2. This shows that approximately four per cent of triplets were stillborn and 10 per cent of live born triplets died during their first year of life. Unfortunately, because of the way these statistics are compiled, it is not possible to identify how many of the babies who died were from the same set.

Response rates

The remainder of this chapter looks at the characteristics of the triplet and higher order births for whom completed replies were received. It compares these characteristics with those for all such births registered in the study years. This comparison was made to assess the extent to which our sample may have been typical of all the triplet and higher order births known to have occurred. At the time we closed our main study computer files, however, a considerable proportion of survey forms for Scotland and Northern Ireland had yet to be received. Therefore these responses have not been included in the obstetric and GP data presented in this book.

Table 2.3

Response to questionnaires 1980–85, England and Wales

		1980	1982	1983	1984	1985	Total
Obstetric questionnaires							
Singletons:	sent	96	75	94	85	103	453
	returned complete	71	47	64	64	75	321
	percentage response	74.0	62.7	68.1	75.3	72.8	70.9
Twins:	sent	96	75	94	85	103	453
	returned complete	63	49	68	61	67	308
	percentage response	65.6	65.3	72.3	71.8	65.0	68.0
Triplets and higher order multiple births:	sent	96	75	94	85	103	453
	returned complete	52	61	79	64	84	340
	percentage response	54.2	81.3	84.0	75.3	81.6	75.1
Three or more babies left hospital alive – sent to NHSCR		51	56	66	63	78	314
Traced at NHSCR and GP questionnaire sent		**45**	**54**	**65**	**62**	**77**	**303**
	returned complete	24	27	35	28	42	156
	percentage response	53.3	50.0	53.8	45.2	54.5	51.5
Parents questionnaire							
	sent – contacted	32	29	32	32	45	170
	returned	22	26	27	24	40	139
	sent – volunteered	–	4	11	10	16	41
	returned	–	4	11	10	16	41
	total sent	32	33	43	42	61	211
	returned (number analysed are in brackets)	22(21)	30(28)	38(37)	34(34)	56(54)	180(174)
	percentage response	68.7	90.9	88.3	80.9	91.8	85.3

Some parents from Scotland and Northern Ireland volunteered to complete a parents' questionnaire and these responses have been included in the data from the parents' survey. It is planned that later there will be separate shorter reports for Scotland and for Northern Ireland.

Table 2.3 presents the responses to the various stages of the study, and this is summarised in Figure 2.1. These responses provide the data used in this book. Different problems were encountered at each stage of the study and these had varying effects on response.

Obstetric questionnaire

The response rate to the obstetric questionnaires for triplet and higher order births, with the exception of 1980 (54 per cent), was high, at over 80 per cent for 1982, 1983 and 1985, and 75 per cent for 1984. A few months before the end of the study the response rate to these questionnaires had been much lower, at approximately 60 per cent. Because of this, funds were obtained from the Department of Health to obtain the help of midwives who visited hospitals to complete the outstanding questionnaires. This considerably improved the response rate, but meant that in these cases we were unable to receive answers to questions seeking the obstetricians' opinions about their care of women expecting multiple births. The response to these questions had been unfortunately poor, however, as some earlier replies had been filled in by a successor of the original obstetrician or by a junior doctor.

At an early stage in the study, we had written to the Maternity Services Liaison Committee in each district health authority asking it to nominate a person to liaise with us on this study and many districts did so. The names of the contact persons were given to the midwives, but in many cases the contacts were unable to help.

The midwives also gave insight into possible explanations for the obstetricians' lack of response. One major problem was that the name of the mother's obstetrician is not recorded at birth registration. Since most hospitals have more than one consultant obstetrician, there was no named person to whom we could address the questionnaire. Although medical records officers had been asked to forward the questionnaires to the appropriate consultant, in many cases the questionnaires were just filed with the mother's notes and nothing further was done.

Although Scottish obstetric data are not included in this book, a precedent had been set in Scotland by the Scottish Twins Study[2] in which the forms had been completed by community physicians, not obstetricians. Given this history, the obstetricians did not expect to do the work themselves for the smaller numbers of Scottish births in our study. Subsequently an obstetrician offered to visit Scottish hospitals and complete the forms.

Many of these problems might have been circumvented had the British Paediatric Surveillance Unit (BPSU) been in existence when our study began. The BPSU was set up to monitor rare conditions through a monthly notification system. In 1989 paediatricians were asked to notify triplet and higher order births to BPSU. They then received questionnaires from the British Association for Perinatal Medicine asking about any infertility treatment and obstetric and neonatal care. It will be interesting to see how the response rate and findings of this more recent study compare with our own.

GP questionnaire

The response rate to the questionnaires sent to general practitioners was only 51 per cent, considerably lower than that for the obstetricians' survey. In part this is because many questionnaires could not be sent out until late in the study owing to the slow response to the obstetric questionnaire. This meant that the GPs were given less time to complete their questionnaires. Also it was not possible to follow up the GPs in the same way that the midwives had been able to do with the obstetricians' questionnaires.

Other surveys involving questionnaires to GPs have met also with a poor response. This happened, for example, in a survey of GPs carried out in 1986 in response to an invitation to comment on the Government Green Paper on Primary Health Care. A report given in the Survey Methods Newsletter[3] suggested a number of reasons for the low response. Some of these may also apply to our study. Firstly GPs receive many questionnaires, some of which, such as follow-ups of possible side effects from drug prescriptions, are seen as especially important. Compared with these, our survey may have received low priority. Furthermore, GPs often receive financial or other incentives for taking part in these surveys, but we offered none.

The appearance of our questionnaire was, by GP standards, probably long and complicated. Early in the design of our study, and based on the experience of others who had been involved in questionnaire design, a decision had been made to space out the questions and to make extensive use of multiple choice 'tick' boxes to simplify the completion of questionnaires. This is common practice with questions aimed at the general public. As a result the questionnaire was long, with eight pages relating to the mother, and four pages for each child, and therefore might have appeared daunting to GPs. In any future survey of GPs we recommend that both the number of questions and the space they occupy should be kept to a minimum.

Parents' questionnaire and interviews

From a total of 211 questionnaires sent out for the years 1980 and 1982–85, 180 completed questionnaires were returned, of which 174 were received in time for data entry and analysis, a response rate of 85.3 per cent returned and 82.5 per cent available for analysis. Since families with triplet or higher order births outside the study years also volunteered data, a total of 306 questionnaires were returned, covering families having a triplet or higher order birth between 1979 and 1988, of which 299 were returned in time for data entry and analysis. One hundred and nine (36 per cent) of these 299 completed questionnaires were from the northern survey area and 190 (64 per cent) from the southern survey area.

At the parents' request, 14 questionnaires were completed in their homes and an interview also obtained. In total, 73 first interviews and eight second interviews were obtained with the mothers and sometimes the fathers of triplets, quadruplets and quintuplets born in the years 1979–88. Sixty seven of the first interviews related to births in the years 1979–85. Two mothers who had triplets and one who had quadruplets in 1986 were also interviewed, as were two mothers who had triplets in 1987, one of whom was also interviewed in hospital before delivery. A further two interviews were undertaken in hospital in 1988 with women with triplet pregnancies, both of whom were subsequently followed up.

Data from all sources

For 106 sets of triplets and higher order births we had received a response from the obstetrician, GP and the parents, so for these families we had a very complete picture

Table 2.4

Maternities with triplet and higher order births by mother's age 1980, 1982–85 England and Wales

Mother's age	National		Study – obstetric		Study – GP		Study – parents	
	Number*	Per cent	Number**	Per cent	Number**	Per cent	Number**	Per cent
Under 20	8	2	5	2	2	1	1	1
20–24	91	20	66	20	19	14	25	14
25–29	161	36	110	34	48	36	57	33
30–34	147	32	109	34	47	35	67	39
35–39	43	9	31	10	19	14	23	13
40 and over	4	1	3	1	0	0	1	1
Total stated	454	100	324	100	135	100	174	100
Not stated			16		21			

* Source: OPCS Birth Statistics Series FM1.

** Source: study data.

Table 2.5

Live and stillborn triplets and quadruplet and higher order births by birthweight, 1980, 1982–85, England and Wales

Birthweight g	Liveborn				Stillborn				Not known	
	National*		Study**		National*		Study**		Study	
	Number	Per cent	Number	Per cent	Number	Per cent	Number	Per cent	Number	Per cent
Triplets:										
under 1000	89	7	52	7	19	40	13	5	7	4
1000–1499	210	17	143	20	13	28	11	35	38	20
1500–1999	415	34	256	36	4	9	4	13	71	38
2000–2499	341	28	215	30	3	6	0	0	53	28
2500–2999	75	6	39	5	1	2	1	3	13	7
3000+	7	1	4	1	0	0	0	0	0	0
Not stated	85	7	2	0	7	15	2	6	4	2
Total stated	1,222	100	711	100	47	100	31	100	188	100
Quadruplets+:										
under 1000	24	18	19	18	1	100	1	100	0	0
1000–1499	43	33	36	34	0	0	0	0	1	17
1500–1999	35	27	32	30	0	0	0	0	5	83
2000–2499	15	12	14	13	0	0	0	0	0	0
2500–2999	0	0	1	1	0	0	0	0	0	0
Not stated	13	10	5	5	0	0	0	0	0	0
Total stated	130	100	107	100	1	100	1	100	6	100

* Obstetric survey.
**
Source: OPCS Birth statistics, unpublished tables.

of all stages of pregnancy, delivery and the early days with their multiple birth children. We were also able to make comparisons between the responses given to similar questions from the different questionnaires.

Surveys of health and personal social services provision
A total of 102 completed questionnaires were received from social services departments and 196 replies were received from the health authorities in England and Wales, health departments in Northern Ireland and health boards in Scotland. This represents response rates of 77 per cent and 91 per cent respectively.

Possible biases in the surveys
Any biases in response to the various surveys would mean that findings from them would be unrepresentative of the total population of triplet and higher order births. Separate comparisons were therefore made of the mother's age and the babies' birth weights between all triplet and higher order births born in the study years, and respondents to the obstetricians', GPs' and parents' surveys.

Birth registration and study data for the mother's age presented in Table 2.4 show that the national age distribution and that from the obstetric survey are similar. Almost 70 per cent of registered triplet and higher order births were to women aged between 25 and 34. Comparable data from the GPs' and parents' surveys showed that more of the women were aged 30 or over at the time of their multiple birth, 49 and 52 per cent respectively, compared with 43 and 44 per cent for the national and obstetric survey data respectively. The data from the GPs' and parents' surveys, however, by our study design did not include those mothers who had not taken three or more live children home from hospital. Infant mortality is higher for younger mothers.

Again, the populations from registration and the obstetric survey are very similar in regard to birthweight (Table 2.5). Less than six per cent of singleton births weigh under 2,500 grams at birth compared with almost a half of twins, over 90 per cent of triplets and virtually all quadruplets. Similar proportions of low birthweight triplet and higher order births were found in data from the parents' survey.

Other comparisons were made from the obstetricians' survey data, comparing replies about triplet, and quadruplet or higher order deliveries with the singleton and twin controls. Table 2.6 shows that there was little difference between the family situation for births of different sizes. Over 95 per cent of the mothers were known to be living with the babies' father at the time of delivery. Similarly, in the parents' survey, 95 per cent of households included both the parents of the triplets, quadruplets and quintuplets. Five of these two parent households, all including triplets, also included the mother's relatives. One family had moved out of their own house and into the mother's parents' home to secure round the clock assistance which had proved impossible to obtain elsewhere.

The obstetric survey data showed little difference between the proportion of fathers of singletons who were unemployed and those of twin and higher order multiple births. Table 2.7 shows that eight per cent of fathers of singleton births were known to be unemployed at the time of delivery, compared with six per cent of fathers of children from multiple births. Over 90 per cent of the fathers included in the parents' study were in paid employment at the time of the study.

41

Table 2.6

Mother's family situation

Family situation	Singleton		Twin		Triplet		Quadruplet+	
	Number	Per cent	Number	Per cent	Number	Per cent	Number	Per cent
Living with babies' father	304	96.8	285	95.6	282	95.6	25	100.0
Single parent	9	2.9	10	3.4	9	3.1	0	0.0
Other	1	0.3	3	1.0	4	1.4	0	0.0
Total known	314	100.0	298	100.0	295	100.0	25	100.0
Not known	7		10		18		2	
Total	**321**		**308**		**313**		**27**	

Source: Full obstetric data.

Table 2.7

Fathers' employment

	Singleton		Twin		Triplet		Quadruplet+	
	Number	Per cent	Number	Per cent	Number	Per cent	Number	Per cent
Employed	251	91.6	246	94.3	252	92.6	25	100.0
Unemployed	23	8.4	15	5.7	20	7.4	0	0.0
Total known	274	100.0	261	100.0	272	100.0	25	100.0
Not known	47		47		41		2	
Total	**321**		**308**		**313**		**27**	

Source: Full obstetric data.

Data from the obstetric survey showed similar patterns of social class based on the father's occupation for singleton, twin and higher order multiple births. Approximately one third of these fathers were known to be in occupations classified as 'professional' (for example doctors and lawyers) or 'intermediate' (for example managers). Data from the parents' survey showed a very different pattern. Almost one half of these fathers were in occupations classified as 'professional' or 'intermediate'.

There are several reasons for this difference. First, the parents' survey responses are based on the father's occupation at the time when the questionnaire was completed whereas the obstetric survey data are based on the occupation at the time of delivery. Secondly, there was a true difference in the social class distributions from the two data sources, since the parents' survey drew responses from, not only the formal obstetrician-GP channel, but also from those who heard about the study from the

Table 2.8

Social class* of father

| Social class | Obstetric survey+ | | | | | | Parents survey++ | |
| | Singleton | | Twin | | Triplet | | Triplet | |
	Number	Per cent	Number	Per cent	Number	Per cent	Number	Per cent
I Professional	24	11.4	22	9.8	28	10.0	41	14.1
II Intermediate	47	22.3	58	25.8	53	18.9	105	36.2
IIIN Skilled non-manual	18	8.5	24	10.7	31	11.1	31	10.7
IIIM Skilled manual	64	30.3	65	28.9	82	29.3	87	30.0
IV Partly skilled	14	6.6	16	7.1	25	8.9	19	6.6
V Unskilled	5	2.4	4	1.8	6	2.1	7	2.4
Other	39	18.5	36	16.0	55	19.6	0	0.0
Total stated	211	100.0	225	100.0	280	100.0	290	100.0
Not stated	49		51		48		9	
Total	260		276		328		299	

+ At time of multiple birth
++ At time of enquiry
* Social class classification based on the Registrar General's Classification of Occupations 1980.
Source: Full obstetric data and parents' study.

Table 2.9

Previous pregnancies

| Previous pregnancies | Singleton | | Twin | | Triplet | | Quadruplet† | |
	Number	Per cent	Number	Per cent	Number	Per cent	Number	Per cent
0	86	27.7	112	37.7	99	32.0	8	29.6
1	107	34.5	91	30.6	101	32.7	9	33.3
2	60	19.4	48	16.2	56	18.1	5	18.5
3	29	9.4	23	7.7	29	9.4	3	11.1
4	16	5.2	11	3.7	19	6.1	2	7.4
5+	12	3.9	12	4.0	5	1.6	0	0.0
Total known	310	100.0	297	100.0	309	100.0	27	100.0
Missing	11		11		4		0	
Total	321		308		313		27	
Mean number of previous pregnancies	1.46		1.22		1.31		1.33	

Source: Full obstetric data.

Table 2.10

Living children at time of study pregnancy from the obstetric survey

Living children	Singleton		Twin		Triplet		Quadruplet+	
	Number	Per cent	Number	Per cent	Number	Per cent	Number	Per cent
0	122	42.7	146	52.9	140	47.8	15	55.6
1	93	32.5	75	27.2	83	28.3	11	40.7
2	41	14.3	33	12.0	42	14.3	1	3.7
3	17	5.9	12	4.3	19	6.5	0	0.0
4	9	3.1	4	1.4	8	2.7	0	0.0
5+	4	1.4	6	2.2	1	0.3	0	0.0
Total known	286	100.0	276	100.0	293	100.0	27	100.0
Missing	35		32		20	0		
Total	**321**		**308**		**313**		**27**	
Mean number of living children	0.99		0.83		0.89		0.48	

Source: Full obstetric data.

Twins and Multiple Births Association Newsletter, through the media or from other parents of triplets and quadruplets.

The number of previous pregnancies and the number of previous living children at the time of the delivery for the mothers for whom we have obstetric replies are compared in Tables 2.9 and 2.10. These show that there was little difference in the percentage distribution or mean numbers of previous pregnancies, but that the average number of living children for mothers of quadruplets and higher was half that of mothers who had triplet or fewer babies delivered. Again, these data should be used with caution as they were based on only 19 sets of quadruplets or higher order births.

The sex combinations of the triplet sets in the replies to the obstetricians' survey were compared in Table 2.11 with all registered triplets. In the obstetric survey replies there were fewer all male sets than all female sets but in total the number of boy babies was only slightly lower than the number of girls.

Originally, biases in the responses from obstetricians were expected depending on whether the triplets were delivered in a large teaching hospital or in a smaller local hospital. This problem will have been largely eliminated by the improved response rate achieved by the midwives who completed outstanding questionnaires. There was bias in the control twin and singleton deliveries since more of these, particularly singletons, were born in smaller maternity units which have subsequently closed, making it difficult to find the notes. In addition, a closer examination of singleton questionnaires showed that 18, or six per cent of all singleton questionnaires, were incorrectly completed in that they referred to a more recent singleton birth to the same mother. A further 13, or four per cent, did not state the year of birth.

In the general practitioners' survey, we originally thought that biases in responses may have arisen from differences in quality of the relationship between the triplet

Table 2.11

Sex combinations of triplets, comparing registration with survey data, England and Wales

	Study data	Registration data
3 male	69	100
2 male 1 female	91	95
1 male 2 female	83	118
3 female	81	110
Total	324	423

Source: Full obstetric data.

family and their GP. An analysis showed, however, that there was no difference between the response rates from GPs where the family indicated a good relationship with their GP, and the response rates from GPs where the family did not consider their GP to be supportive.

Parents of triplets were identified through their GP, the media, and other personal contacts. As described earlier, the extensive media coverage in both the medical and the popular press will have introduced social class biases in those identified through this route. It is likely that there are also biases in the response to the parents' survey arising from language problems for mothers who did not speak English. Unfortunately we did not have funds to pay for translators or interpreters to overcome this problem.

In summary, women who were comparatively young at the time of birth, who had left school at the minimum age, who had been employed in manual work before they had their first or higher order birth children or who did not speak English are under-represented in the parents' survey. On all these grounds, it must be assumed that the social, economic and medical problems identified in the study are likely to be an underestimate of their extent in the whole population of families with children from a triplet or higher order birth.

References
1. Department of Health, Office of Population Censuses and Surveys. Hospital In-patient Enquiry, maternity tables, 1982–85, Series MB4 no 28, London: HMSO, 1988.
2. Patel N, Bowie W, Campbell D M, Howat R, Melrose E, Redford D, McIlwaine G, Smalls M. Scottish twins study 1983. Report. Glasgow: Social, Paediatric and Obstetric Research Unit and Greater Glasgow Health Board, 1984.
3. Willmott M. Postal surveys of professional groups, SCPR. Survey Methods Newsletter. Summer 1987.

Chapter 3 – Infertility drugs and procedures

Alison J Macfarlane, Frances V Price, E G Daw

'Semen tests; post coital [tests]; temperature charts; blood samples; hormone levels; laparoscopy; D & C biopsy; X-rays of fallopian tubes and "blowing" thereof; hormone treatment by tablets; ditto by injection. Lots of "Go away and forget it for a while". All for unexplained infertility.'

Mother of triplets

Over the centuries, the distress caused by infertility has been chronicled in literature and song. People turned in desperation to largely ineffective remedies, while fantasising about the existence of cures for infertility. Over the past 20 years, drugs and the other procedures we described earlier have offered hope to the couples concerned.

This chapter compares the use of various forms of investigations and treatments for infertility among women who had had singleton and multiple births. It is based on

Figure 3.1   Infertility investigations and procedures

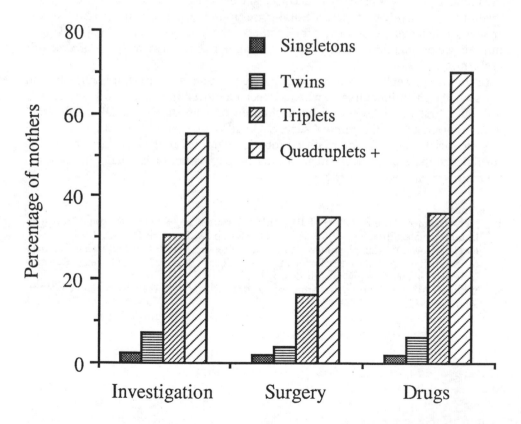

Table 3.1

Investigations and treatment for infertility

	Mothers of			
	Singletons	Twins	Triplets	Quadruplets+
Percentage of women who had				
Investigation	2.5	7.3	30.6	55.0
Surgery	1.8	3.7	16.2	35.0
Drugs	1.8	6.3	35.8	70.0
Combinations of treatments				
Percentage of women who had				
Surgery only	0.7	0.7	1.5	0.0
Drugs only	0.7	3.3	21.0	35.0
Drugs and surgery	1.0	3.0	14.8	35.0
No treatment	97.5	93.0	62.7	30.0
Number responding	285	271	271	20
No information	36	37	42	7

Source: Full obstetric data.

replies from questions to obstetricians, general practitioners and parents asking whether mothers had undergone gynaecological investigations or surgery for infertility and whether they had been prescribed drugs for infertility. Questions were not explicitly asked about investigations and treatment undergone by fathers, as it seemed unlikely that full information would be found in the mothers' notes.

Associations between infertility treatment and multiple birth

As Table 3.1 and Figure 3.1 show, our survey of obstetricians found that 55 per cent of mothers of quadruplets and above and 31 per cent of the mothers of triplets had undergone some form of gynaecological investigation for infertility. In contrast only seven per cent of mothers of twins and under three per cent of mothers of singletons had done so.

Similar differences were found in the use of surgery for infertility, although smaller numbers of women were involved. Just over a third of mothers of quadruplets and above and 16 per cent of mothers of triplets had undergone such surgery, compared with less than four per cent of mothers of twins and under two per cent of mothers of singletons. On the other hand, as Table 3.1 and Figure 3.2 show, over three fifths of mothers of triplets had not had any infertility treatment.

Background of parents who had infertility treatment

Responses to the obstetricians' survey were analysed to compare information about women's previous pregnancies according to whether or not they had infertility treatment. These are summarised in Table 3.2 and the percentages with previous living children are illustrated in Figure 3.3. These show very marked differences in terms of parity, number of living children and total number of previous pregnancies, but not in the number of previous miscarriages.

The social class distributions of parents of triplets are compared in Table 3.3. Among couples who had infertility treatment, 41 per cent of fathers were in non-manual occupations, compared with 29 per cent of fathers in couples who had not used infertility treatment. Less than one per cent of fathers in the group who had received infertility treatment were unemployed, compared with 11 per cent of fathers of spontaneous pregnancies. It would not be surprising if unemployment deterred people from seeking infertility treatment. Amongst the spontaneous pregnancies a much higher proportion of mothers were stated to be housewives and fewer were in professional and other non-manual occupations. As fewer of the spontaneous pregnancies were first births, it is not unexpected that a lower proportion of mothers were in paid employment.

Thus the parents who had had infertility treatment tended to be in higher socio-economic groups than those who had not done so. When considering any comparisons made in the chapters which follow between parents who had had infertility treatment and those who had not done so, it needs to be considered to what extent any differences arise from the consequences of infertility treatment and to what extent they arise from selection and self selection for treatment.

Figure 3.2   Treatment for infertility

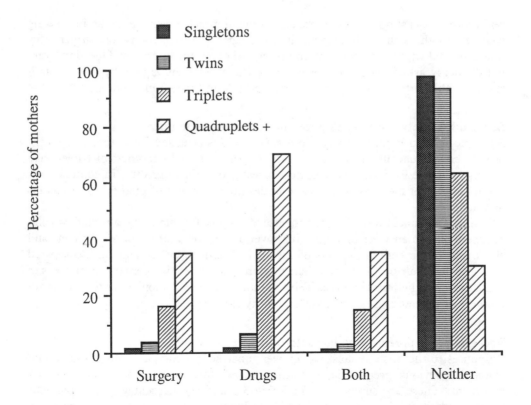

Table 3.2

Demographic characteristics and infertility treatment for mothers of triplets

	Percentage of women						Number of women
	Previous pregnancies						
	0	1	2	3	4+	Total	
No treatment	21.8	30.0	21.8	12.9	13.5	100.0	170
Treatment	45.5	35.0	12.2	4.1	3.2	100.0	123
	Previous miscarriages						
	0	1	2	3	4+	Total	
No treatment	82.4	14.1	2.4	0.6	0.6	100.0	170
Treatment	80.5	13.8	3.2	0.8	1.6	100.0	123
	Previous live and stillbirths						
	0	1	2	3	4+	Total	
No treatment	29.4	34.1	17.1	12.4	7.1	100.0	170
Treatment	65.8	26.0	8.1	0.0	0.0	100.0	123
	Previous living children						
	0	1	2	3	4+	Total	
No treatment	32.4	31.2	20.0	11.2	5.3	100.0	170
Treatment	69.1	24.4	6.5	0.0	0.0	100.0	123

Note: The treatment group in this table includes women who were stated to have had either drugs or surgery irrespective of whether both questions were answered. It therefore includes 22 women excluded from Tables 3.1 and 3.4–3.7.
Source: Full obstetric data.

Figure 3.3 Number of living children at the time of birth of triplets and use of infertility drugs and procedures

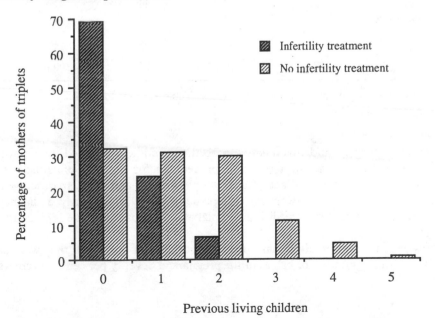

49

Table 3.3

Infertility treatment and social class of parents of triplets

| a) Fathers's social class | Infertility treatment | | | |
| | Treatment | | No treatment | |
	Number	Percentage	Number	Percentage
I Professional	10	8.1	16	9.4
II Intermediate	26	21.1	20	11.8
IIIn Skilled non-manual	15	12.2	14	8.2
IIIm Skilled manual	38	30.9	39	22.9
IV Partly skilled	8	6.5	14	8.2
V Unskilled	1	0.8	5	2.9
Unemployed	1	0.8	19	11.2
Other, including armed forces	7	5.7	15	8.8
Not stated	17	13.8	28	16.5
Total	123	100.0	170	100.0

| b) Mother's social class | Infertility treatment | | | |
| | Treatment | | No treatment | |
	Number	Percentage	Number	Percentage
I Professional	2	1.6	2	1.2
II Intermediate	35	28.5	30	17.6
IIIn Skilled non-manual	21	17.1	22	12.9
IIIm Skilled manual	6	4.9	6	3.5
IV Partly skilled	7	5.7	4	2.4
V Unskilled	1	0.8	0	0.0
Housewife	22	17.9	54	31.8
Other, including armed forces	4	3.2	8	4.7
Not stated	25	20.3	44	25.9
Total	123	100.0	170	100.0

Note: This table was compiled on the same basis as Table 3.2. See footnote.
Source: Full obstetric data.

Patterns of infertility care

The remedial surgery and investigative procedures mothers received are shown in Tables 3.1 and 3.4. The most common procedures for mothers of triplets were 'Laparoscopic hydrotubation' and 'Laparoscopy with D and C'. Laparoscopy is a technique used to assess a woman's fallopian tubes. It is primarily a diagnostic procedure, but can also be remedial. An explanation of this technique is given in the glossary.

Drugs were used more often than surgery, but the extent to which they were used increased with the number of babies in the pregnancy. Seventy per cent of mothers of

Table 3.4

Types of surgery for investigation and treatment of infertility

Procedure	Number of mothers of			
	Singletons	Twins	Triplets	Quadruplets+
Procedure				
Laparoscopic hydrotubation	1	3	11	1
Laparoscopy and D and C	–	1	7	2
Hysterosalpingography, tubal insufflation	1	3	1	1
Dye perturbations	–	1	4	–
In-vitro fertilisation	1	1	11	1
Tubal reconstruction				1
Other surgery	–	–	4	1
No information about type of surgical treatment	2	2	9	1
Total women having surgery	5	10	44	7
No surgery	280	261	227	13
No information	36	37	42	7

Note: As some women had more than one type of surgery, numbers of procedures do not add up to totals.
Source: Full obstetric data.

quadruplets and above and 36 per cent of mothers of triplets had been prescribed drugs for infertility, compared with six per cent of mothers of twins and just under two per cent of mothers of singleton babies.

The types of medication used are shown in Table 3.5. Some women had more than one course of treatment, undergoing repeated cycles of treatment until they conceived. Clomiphene citrate was the most common and was prescribed in 58 per cent of first courses of treatment but in only 28 per cent of second courses of treatment for mothers who had triplets. The next most commonly used set of drugs were the group of follicle stimulating hormones and gonadotrophins. They were prescribed in the first course of treatment to about a quarter of women who had triplets, but accounted for nearly three fifths of second courses of treatment to these women.

Obstetricians were asked where the treatment had been initiated. As Table 3.6 shows, this happened mainly in hospital clinics. Treatment for about a fifth of the mothers of triplets and above was stated to have been in endocrinology clinics although this percentage was slightly higher for second courses of treatment. Only four per cent of first courses of treatment for mothers of triplets and none of those for mothers of higher order births were said to have been initiated in GPs' surgeries.

It is difficult to draw conclusions from Table 3.6 as the information is missing for a significant proportion of the women who had drug treatment. Comparison was therefore made with the GPs' survey in which almost identical questions were asked and reporting was fuller. Of the 58 women in the GPs survey who had been prescribed

Table 3.5

Drugs prescribed for infertility

	Number of mothers of			
	Singleton	Twins	Triplets	Quadruplets+
First occasion				
Clomiphene citrate	4	13	56	6
Follicle stimulating hormones and gonadotrophins	1	1	23	8
Other	0	1	6	0
Not stated	0	2	12	0
Number of women having at least one course of drugs	5	17	97	14
Second occasion				
Clomiphene citrate	1	0	9	0
Follicle stimulating hormones and gonadotrophins	0	1	19	4
Other	0	2	4	0
Number of women having second course	1	3	32	4
All occasions				
Clomiphene citrate	5	13	66	6
Other anti-oestrogen	0	0	2	0
Follicle stimulating hormones and other gonadotrophins	3	3	47	13
Inhibitor of gonadotrophin	0	1	2	0
Iron tablets	0	0	1	0
Dopamine agonists	0	1	4	0
Oestrogen	0	1	1	0
Total women prescribed drugs	5	17	97	14

Source: Full obstetric data.

drugs for infertility, information about the first course of treatment was missing for only 10 per cent of women reported as receiving such treatment. Sixteen per cent of first courses of treatment were initiated in an endocrinology clinic, 74 per cent in another hospital clinic and none was initiated by a GP. This, taken together with the replies from obstetricians suggests that GPs did not have a major role in deciding on the type of treatment to be prescribed although they may have prescribed drugs selected by hospital consultants.

Table 3.7 shows a difference between treatment in endocrinology clinics and other hospital clinics. In endocrinology clinics, treatment was almost equally divided between

Table 3.6

Where drug treatment for infertility was initiated

Percentage of women whose treatment was initiated in	Mothers of			
	Singletons	Twins	Triplets	Quadruplets+
Endocrinology clinic	20	6	18	21
Other hospital clinic	40	70	52	64
GP's surgery	20	12	4	0
Not stated	20	12	25	14
All	100	100	100	100
Number of women	5	17	97	14

Source: Full obstetric data.

clomiphene citrate and follicle stimulating hormones. In other clinics, there was a much greater use of clomiphene citrate.

As many women started with investigations for infertility and then moved on to either surgery or drugs, it is not surprising that there was some considerable overlap between the women concerned. As Table 3.1 and Figure 3.4 show, nearly all the women who had surgery were also prescribed drugs.

This position did not change greatly through the study period. There were small increases between 1980 and 1985 in the extent to which women who had triplet and higher order births had had investigations and surgery, but the percentage who had

Figure 3.4   Trends in infertility treatment among mothers of triplets

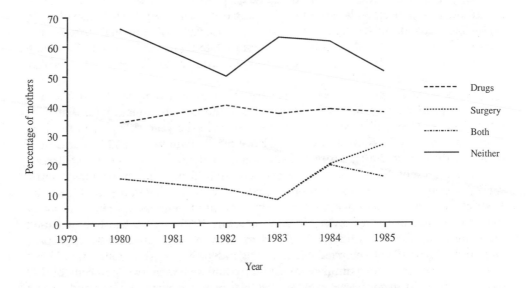

Table 3.7

Type of drug treatment for mothers of triplets and above (first course of treatment only)

Place where treatment was initiated	Percentage of women having					Number of women
	Clomiphene citrate	Follicle stimulating hormones and gonadotrophins	Other	Not stated	Total	
Endocrinology clinic	48	43	5	5	100	21
Other hospital clinic	60	27	5	8	100	60
GP's surgery	25	0	50	25	100	4
Not stated	58	23	0	19	100	26
All	56	28	5	11	100	
Number of women	62	31	6	12		111

Source: Full obstetric data.

used drugs did not change markedly over time. Nor was there any decrease in the percentage of women who did not have any treatment, as Figure 3.4 shows.

It was not possible to use information from our survey to estimate risks of multiple births associated with different types of infertility treatment, as there is no information about the numbers of couples in the population receiving them, nor about the types of treatment they receive. Infertility treatment can involve both in-patient and out-patient care, often in more than one hospital department. Although general practitioners do not play a large part in initiating treatment, they are often involved in prescribing and administering treatment initiated elsewhere. Although statistics about prescriptions are collected, it is not possible to relate them to the people for whom they are prescribed. In addition, even fewer statistics are available about infertility treatment outside the NHS.

What is possible, however, is to compare information from the obstetric survey about the proportion of births which arise from infertility treatment with that from other studies. Data collected about multiple births in the years 1978–85 in the East Flanders region of Belgium showed that 11 per cent of twin births and 74 per cent of triplet births occurred after artificial induction of ovulation.[1] This is high, compared with the corresponding figures of six per cent and 36 per cent from our obstetric survey. Unpublished data about multiple births to women living in the Aberdeen City District showed, on the other hand, that six per cent of mothers of twins and one of the two mothers of higher order births in the years 1986 to 1989 had had ovulation induction.[2] Similarly, a study of 111 mothers of twins born alive between January 1981 and August 1982 to married parents living in Nottinghamshire found that 11 per cent had used drugs to stimulate ovulation, compared with two per cent of 102 mothers of singleton controls.[3] Most studies of triplets are hospital-based and cover a very long time span and others use volunteer samples. As a result they cannot be compared directly with our obstetric survey.

In-vitro fertilisation

In-vitro fertilisation (IVF) was the subject of a separate question. At first sight, it seemed unexpected to find that only one mother of quadruplets, 11 mothers of triplets, one mother of twins and one mother of a singleton baby had had IVF. It should be remembered, however, that the first successful IVF birth took place as recently as 1978 and the technique did not start to become more widely used until the mid 1980s. Of the 14 women with IVF pregnancies in obstetric survey, four delivered in 1984 and 10 in 1985. Thus, known IVF pregnancies accounted for an estimated nine per cent of sets of triplets born in 1985.

IVF was not, and at the time of writing still is not, widely available under the NHS. The obstetricians' replies showed that two of the 14 mothers had IVF under the NHS and six had it privately. There was no information about the other six women.

The end of our study period coincided with the beginning of a period of rapid change, and the appearance of a second, less expensive technique, Gamete Intra-Fallopian Transfer (GIFT). The fourth report of the Voluntary (later Interim) Licensing Authority shows that treatments given in licensed clinics in 1987 led to 55 triplet pregnancies among women who had IVF and 22 among women who had GIFT.[4] Many of these women would have delivered in 1988 and so contributed to the upsurge in triplet births in that year, although some women came from abroad and returned to their home countries before their babies were born. Also not all pregnancies resulted in registrable births, as some women will have miscarried.

Discussion between parents and doctors about the possibility of a multiple birth

'The subject [the possibility of a multiple birth] was touched on in a light hearted way as the Walton sextuplets had just been born when initial treatment started.'

In the parents' survey, 71 per cent of women who had been prescribed a pituitary hormone or fertility drug or who had undergone IVF or GIFT, reported that there had been some discussion concerning the possibility of a multiple birth. Fifty three per cent of them understood that a multiple birth was a possibility or, particularly in relation to assisted conception, that it was difficult to predict how many embryos might implant and how many fetuses might result. Only one woman reported that she been told that there was no risk of a multiple pregnancy. On the other hand, a very small proportion of women, the majority of whom were prescribed clomiphene, were given reassuring advice, with one per cent being told that the treatment would be controlled and four per cent that twins were unlikely. Nine per cent reported that only twins were mentioned as a possibility.

A woman prescribed clomiphene citrate because she was not ovulating commented:

'My consultant simply said that there was no risk of a multiple pregnancy.'

A mother of triplets who had been prescribed clomiphene as an infertility drug wrote:

'Told it would never be more than twins!!'

Another commented that:

'After I had the babies I was told clomiphene was not a fertility drug.'

A woman who had triplets after taking a follicle stimulating hormone (Pergonal) wrote:

'I was told that there was a very small possibility of a multiple birth and that the consultant had never had more than twin results.'

Although few obstetricians and no GPs reported that infertility treatment started in general practice, six mothers who responded to the parents' survey reported that they had been prescribed clomiphene by their GP. Only one of them indicated that the possibility of a multiple pregnancy had been discussed:

'I was told that Clomid would not cause a multiple birth but very rarely can cause twins.'

Three of the five mothers whose GPs had not discussed the possibility of a multiple birth with them added the following comments:

'I was told there was a very slight association with twins and I was advised by my GP that the dosage of Clomid I was taking was so low that I would be lucky to fall for one baby!!'

'It was mentioned that twins were a possibility but we did not expect it after a single baby was conceived in 1983.'

'I asked [about this] when Clomid was first prescribed and was told: "At the most the drug could cause twins but this is highly unlikely." '

The fourth mother commented that she was simply told that the drug would help her ovulate. There was no added comment on the questionnaire from the fifth mother, who had quadruplets after taking clomiphene citrate prescribed by her GP with no discussion of the possibility of a multiple birth. Thus, although GPs' role in initiating treatment is relatively small, they may be doing so with less knowledge and caution than hospital consultants, and unwittingly giving parents inaccurate or inadequate advice.

Seven of the 21 women in the parents' survey who had had IVF reported that the possibility of a multiple birth had not been discussed with them. Sometimes this appeared to be because the emphasis had been on establishing a pregnancy. Thus one father of quadruplets said:

'They said that they would fertilise four eggs to implant and that didn't even give us a 50–50 chance of one [baby].'

All the four women who delivered triplets after the GIFT procedure said that the possibility of a multiple birth had been discussed:

'The possibility of a multiple pregnancy was discussed with my husband and I, because that was one of [the] risks we took with test-tube GIFT method.'

'We were told that with the fertility treatment there was a possible chance of a multiple birth. We were given counselling on this.'

Attention also needs to be given to monitoring the consequences for parents of infertility treatment. Two deaths from anaesthetic accidents to women undergoing IVF have been reported from Australia.[5,6] In addition it has been hypothesised that drugs to stimulate ovulation may carry a risk of ovarian cancer. Although this is very tentative and based on only three cases, there are reasons to monitor and study trends in ovarian cancer amongst women using these drugs.[7] It follows that there is a need to look more widely at other possible adverse effects.

Conclusions

Drugs and procedures for infertility, including assisted induction of ovulation, contributed substantially to the numbers of triplet and higher order births in our study. Only 30 per cent of couples having quadruplets or more and 63 per cent of parents of triplets had not had any infertility treatment compared with 93 per cent of parents of twins and 98 per cent of parents of singletons. The proportion did not change substantially between 1980 and 1985. Before 1985, few couples had undergone IVF, but it is likely that IVF and GIFT have accounted for the considerable increase in the numbers of triplet and higher order births since our main study years. It is essential that all methods of assisted reproduction are developed in a way which will reduce the risk of having a triplet or higher order birth.

In its report on human fertilisation and embryology, the Warnock Committee recommended, among other things that 'funding should be made available for the collection of adequate statistics on infertility and infertility services'.[8] As far as IVF is concerned, considerable efforts have been made to collect statistics[9] and the decision to establish a national IVF register is welcomed. Where both GIFT and newer procedures and the longer established surgical and drug treatments are involved, the picture is a less happy one. Few data are collected routinely[10] and little is known about the long term consequences of these treatments for mothers and their babies.

Although there are no routinely collected national data about the pattern of infertility services,[10] ad hoc surveys show that they are not universally available under the NHS.[11, 12] This leads to problems of access and to fragmentation. Our survey showed that employed people in non-manual occupations were over-represented among the people who used these services. Although it is difficult to draw a firm conclusion without better data about the prevalence of infertility, it is likely that the over-representation of middle class people among users of infertility treatment arises from financial constraints. In other words, many people may not be able to afford to pay privately for treatment when it is not available under the NHS. Even where they can, the NHS usually has to reap the consequences in caring for the mother and her babies conceived in the private sector.[13] This makes it very difficult to plan the relevant NHS services.

Although treatment for infertility contributed substantially to the numbers of multiple births in our survey, some of the parents who had this treatment were not fully prepared for this consequence. Perhaps this is not surprising given the lack of information needed to quantify the risks. This is particularly true where IVF or GIFT is not involved, as was the case with most of the parents in our main survey years.

There is also cause for concern about the quality of the services, both in terms of minimising the risks of multiple pregnancy and in terms of giving information to and discussing treatment with prospective parents. Although their role did not appear to be large, general practitioners seemed to be particularly unsatisfactory in this respect. Even if their role is largely that of dispensing treatment initiated elsewhere, they need access to better information to share with their patients.

References

1. Derom C, Vlietinck R, Derom R, Van den Berghe H, Thiery M. Increased monozygotic twinning rate after ovulation induction. Lancet 1987; i: 1236–1238.
2. Campbell D M, Lemon J S. Unpublished data from Aberdeen Maternity Data Bank.
3. Webster F, Elwood J M. A study of the influence of ovulation stimulants and oral contraception on twin births in England. Acta Genetica Medica Gemellogica 1985; 34: 105–108.
4. Voluntary Licensing Authority for Human In-vitro Fertilisation and Embryology. Fourth report. London: VLA, 1989.
5. Lang B. IVF clinic set to get guidelines. Daily News, Perth, Western Australia April 24 1988.
6. Lenton C. Doctor failure led to 'op' death. Daily News, Perth, Western Australia November 28, 1988.
7. Fishel S, Jackson P. Follicular stimulation for high tech pregnancies: are we playing it safe? British Medical Journal 1989; 289: 309–311.
8. Department of Health and Social Security. Report of the Committee of Enquiry into human fertilisation and embryology. Cmnd 9314. London: HMS0, 1984.
9. MRC Working Party on Children Conceived by In Vitro Fertilisation. Births in Great Britain resulting from assisted conception, 1978–87. British Medical Journal 1990; 300: 1229–33.
10. Written parliamentary replies, Hansard, July 28 1989, cols 969–970, 986, July 29 1989, col 1111.
11. Mathieson D. Infertility services in the NHS: what's going on? London: Frank Dobson MP, 1986.
12. Pfeffer N, Quick A. Infertility services—a desperate case. London: Greater London Association of Community Health Councils, 1988.
13. Galloway G. The future of research in medicine. Nature 1989; 341: 683–685.

Chapter 4 – Antenatal care

Alison J Macfarlane, Frances V Price, E G Daw

'The rarity of a plural birth in women and the increased danger to both mother and offspring in these circumstances, render such an event, in a certain limited sense, an abnormity.'

J Matthews Duncan, 1866[1]

It has long been recognised that a multiple pregnancy places a greater physical strain on the mother than a singleton pregnancy. Complications are more common and can arise earlier in pregnancy. This makes it important to diagnose multiple pregnancy as early as possible, to make an accurate assessment of gestational age and establish the exact number of fetuses. Parents need time to adjust to the news that they are likely to have three or more babies to care for and start to plan for the changes that are likely to

Table 4.1

Method of diagnosis of multiple birth

a) **More than one baby**

	Mothers of		
	Twins	Triplets	Quadruplets+
Percentage detected by			
Ultrasound	90.6	96.8	100.0
X-Ray	2.4	1.5	
At delivery	5.2	0.0	
Clinically	1.7	1.5	
Number of replies	287	253	21
No reply given	21	60	6

b) **Correct number of babies**

	Mothers of	
	Triplets	Quadruplets+
Percentage detected by		
Ultrasound	87.3	64.0
X-Ray	6.6	20.0
At delivery	5.5	16.0
Clinically	0.4	0.0
Number of replies	256	25
No reply given	57	2

Source: Full obstetric data.

occur in their lives. Obstetricians and paediatricians have to anticipate clinical problems which may arise for the mother and the babies, both during pregnancy and at delivery. In particular, serious difficulties can occur if arrangements have not been made for the babies to be born in a hospital which is equipped to deal with the complications which can happen in multiple pregnancies and which has the capacity to admit the babies to intensive care, if necessary.

Diagnosis of multiple pregnancy

Ultrasonic scanning techniques now enable a multiple pregnancy to be confirmed much earlier than was possible in the past using only clinical observations and x-rays. Routine ultrasound scanning at booking may not detect all multiple pregnancies, however, as booking is likely to occur before the best time for detecting multiple pregnancies.[2] It has been suggested that a base line scan at 18 to 20 weeks is the optimum for the diagnosis of multiple pregnancies, and that this should be followed by further scans until the exact number of fetuses is determined.[3] In any case, it is important to look for other clinical signs of multiple pregnancies.[2]

Not surprisingly, most of the multiple births in our survey were diagnosed by ultrasound, as Table 4.1 shows. While five per cent of parents of twins did not discover until delivery that they had a multiple birth, this did not happen with triplets or higher order births. On the other hand, for six per cent of triplets and 16 per cent of quadruplets and above, the correct number of babies was not known until they were delivered.

X-rays did not play much part in the initial diagnosis, but were used to establish the correct number of babies in seven per cent of triplet pregnancies and in 20 per cent of quadruplet and higher order pregnancies. In the 1970s and early 1980s, it was recommended that whenever a multiple pregnancy was diagnosed, the mother's abdomen should be x-rayed in the late second or third trimester[4] or before 33 weeks

Table 4.2

Serum alpha-fetoprotein tests

	Mothers of		
	Twins	Triplets	Quadruplets+
Number of tests done	82	58	5
Percentage of results described as			
High	29.3	44.8	80.0
Medium	31.7	17.2	–
Low	13.4	8.6	–
Not known	25.6	29.3	20.0
Numbers of women not tested	177	165	17
Not stated	49	90	5
Total	308	313	27

Source: Full obstetric data

Table 4.3

Soures of information about gestational age

	Mothers of		
	Twins	Triplets	Quadruplets+
Percentage estimated by			
Date of last menstrual period	83.3	85.3	79.0
Best estimate	16.7	14.7	21.0
Total	100.0	100.0	100.0
Number of replies	281	259	19
Number not stated	27	54	8
Total numbers in sample	308	313	27

Source: Full obstetric data

of gestation[5] to check whether or not there were more than two babies. The difference between this suggestion and the use of x-rays in our survey may reflect the more widespread use of ultrasound techniques by the mid 1980s.

Another way of diagnosing multiple pregnancy is through serum alpha fetoprotein tests. These are done on the mother's blood as part of the process of screening for abnormalities in the fetus. High levels of alpha fetoprotein are likely if there are abnormalities but they can also arise if the pregnancy is a multiple one.[2] In our survey of obstetricians, 22 per cent of notes recorded that women had these tests done. Where the tests were done, results tended to be described as high, as Table 4.2 shows.

If done early enough in pregnancy, the first ultrasound scan is routinely used to estimate the duration of the pregnancy. In the obstetric survey, 83 per cent of mothers of twins, 85 per cent of mothers of triplets and 79 per cent of the mothers of quadruplets and above were sure of the dates of their last menstrual period. This meant that for only a minority of women was the duration of pregnancy based on a 'best estimate' using ultrasound, as Table 4.3 shows.

Very few of the multiple pregnancies in our survey were not detected by the first scan. On the other hand, for a quarter of mothers this first scan did not ascertain the correct number of babies, as can be seen in Table 4.4. The ability of a first scan to detect that the mother was carrying more than twins and to detect the correct number of fetuses was better later in pregnancy as Table 4.5 shows. Table 4.6 summarises how, with more scans, diagnosis improved. Over half the triplet pregnancies had been diagnosed as multiple before 16 weeks and three quarters before 20 weeks. In just half of the triplet pregnancies the correct number of babies had been diagnosed before 16 weeks.

As well as being used to diagnose multiple pregnancy, serial ultrasound scans are the most commonly used method of assessing growth rates, both of individual babies and of the set as a whole. A quarter of mothers of triplets in the obstetric survey were scanned more than six times, compared with seven per cent of twins, as Figure 4.1 shows. The average number of scans reported was 3.2 for mothers of twins, 4.8 for mothers of triplets and 5.2 for mothers of quadruplets and above.

Table 4.4

Detection of multiple birth at first scan

	Twins	Triplets	Quadruplets+
Percentage of first scans which detected			
Multiple birth	94.5	93.3	95.2
More than two babies		77.4	81.0
Correct number of babies		73.7	78.8
Number of replies	253	239	21
No reply given	55	74	6

Source: Full obstetric data

Parents were also asked about the number of scans they had. Tables 4.7 and 4.8 compare numbers of scans reported in the parents' survey with those reported in the obstetric survey. Forty two per cent of parents reported more scans than obstetricians and 28 per cent of parents reported fewer. Identical numbers were reported in only 29 per cent of cases.

Parents' experiences of diagnosis

Of the parents who commented on their experience of scans, half the mothers of triplets and a quarter of mothers of quadruplets were positive about their experience. Half reported that they had been given a photograph of at least one of the scans and a few had been given a video. Comments included:

'It positively confirms (by your own eyes) that there is more than one baby. It allows for easier adjustment to the reality.'

Table 4.5

Detection of triplet and higher order births detected at first scan by gestational age

Gestational age at first scan, weeks	Percentage of first scans which detected		
	Multiple birth	More than two babies	Correct number of babies
Under 12	96.1	73.2	64.3
12–15	98.7	78.4	76.1
16–19	96.4	86.0	81.2
20–23	100.0	88.9	88.2
24 or more	94.1	85.7	85.7
All	93.9	74.6	75.0
Number of replies	242	227	220

Source: Full obstetric data

Table 4.6

Gestational age at diagnosis of multiple birth

a)   **More than one baby**

	Twins	Triplets	Quadruplets+
Percentage detected			
before 12 weeks	10.0	26.0	38.1
12–15 weeks	20.1	30.2	42.1
16–19 weeks	34.4	26.8	4.8
20–23 weeks	14.7	8.9	–
24–27 weeks	6.2	6.4	9.5
28–31 weeks	5.0	0.4	4.8
32 weeks or later	9.7	1.3	–
Number stated	259	235	21
Not known	49	78	6

b) **Correct number of babies**

	Triplets	Quadruplets+
Percentage detected		
before 12 weeks	26.9	20.0
12–15 weeks	24.1	25.0
16–19 weeks	18.6	10.0
20–23 weeks	9.1	10.0
24–27 weeks	8.7	15.0
28–31 weeks	5.1	20.0
32 weeks or later	7.5	–
Number stated	253	20
Not known	60	7

Source: Full obstetric data

'Reassuring to see heartbeats and babies moving.'

'We were very lucky to be scanned by a doctor doing research into scanning and therefore were given long and very informative sessions – including video recordings. Everything was explained in detail and measurements shown. Now find scans very easy to read. We were also told the probable sexes when we asked.'

This contrasted with the experience of some other parents who had inadequate explanations of scans, or delays in being told the diagnosis. Some of these problems can arise from the division of responsibility between radiographers and doctors. In the United Kingdom, radiographers' professional code of ethics does not allow them to convey a diagnosis to a patient, as this is considered to be the role of the consultant or general practitioner who makes the referral.[6] Yet it is recognised that this presents

Figure 4.1 Numbers of ultrasound scans in multiple pregnancies

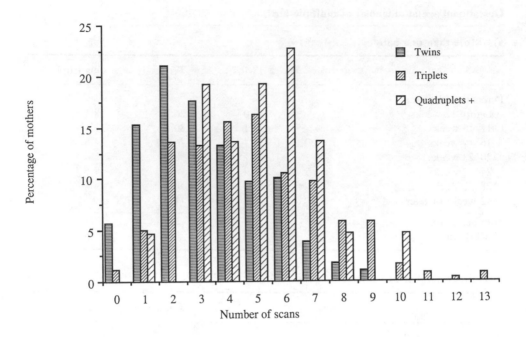

Table 4.7

Numbers of scans reported by parents and obstetricians

Number of scans	Parents		Obstetricians	
	Number	Per cent	Number	Per cent
0	0	0	2	1.9
1	3	2.8	4	3.8
2	12	11.3	9	8.5
3	13	12.3	7	6.6
4	12	11.3	16	15.1
5	13	12.3	15	14.2
6	17	16.0	14	13.2
7–10	20	18.9	23	21.7
Over 10	9	8.4	2	1.9
'Many'	4	3.8	–	–
At least one, exact number not known	–	–	8	7.6
Not known	3	2.8	6	5.7
Total	106	100.0	106	100.0

Source: Linked obstetric and parents data

Table 4.8

Comparison of parents' and obstetricians' replies about numbers of scans

Parents who reported	Number	Per cent
More than two more scans than obstetricians	17	20.0
Two more scans	3	3.5
One more scan	16	18.8
Same number of scans as obstetricians	25	29.4
One fewer scan	13	15.3
Two fewer scans	7	8.2
Less than two fewer scans	4	4.7
Total	85	100.0
Missing information	18	

Source: Linked obstetric and parent data

radiographers with difficult dilemmas in reconciling the needs and expectations of pregnant women with the constraints on them not to divulge the results of the examination.[7] Several women were very dissatisfied by the consequences of this. One woman described her experience of a scan at 15 weeks:

'The scan operator was totally unappreciative of my feelings – in fact she practically ignored me whilst doing the scan. She called her colleague (or a doctor or it could have been a porter – he wasn't introduced to me!). Anyway she called him to check, that "there were only three babies not four". Once they confirmed three babies they asked why I was having a scan – I told them "to confirm the obstetrician's diagnosis of twins" – they then spoke to me and told me it was definitely three babies.'

Another woman wrote:

'Scan was done by two or three people – nothing mentioned that they had found three. Told to go back to see hospital doctor after blood test. Sat waiting thinking they had found something abnormal with *the baby*. Felt worried. Doctor eventually came in, flicked open my file and said "It's triplets". No gentle lead in to prepare me. Biggest shock of my life.'

A woman who had a scan at 20 weeks wrote:

'I was told by the radiographer I was having triplets. She sent me to my GP with a letter. On reading the letter my GP said the contents said only that I had an enlarged uterus. So I was confused and my doctor not interested in my predicament.'

A mother of quintuplets described a radiographer's attempt to convey the news of her multiple pregnancy through what was intended to be a joke.

'The first comment I was given during the scan was very insensitive, i.e. "Are you good at knitting". The scan was inconclusive. I was told "a lot of arms and legs, two babies or possibly three".'

There were other problems, such as being an 'interesting case'. One woman commented on the way she had been scanned for research purposes:

'When I was in hospital [a consultant] used me for research – and I am afraid simply treated me like a body with no name!'

Other women mentioned the shock when a triplet or higher order birth was diagnosed late in pregnancy. The most disturbing instances were when the correct number was not diagnosed before delivery. Those who had been scanned several times without any hint of more than two babies were shocked to then deliver triplets rather than the twins that they had been led to expect:

'During all three scans only two babies were ever detected. Up until I gave birth everyone thought I was having twins. It still amazes me how no-one ever noticed the third baby. I had my last scan at about 30 weeks and was told I was "extra large" for the small twins I was carrying. But no-one queried it.'

'At the five and half week scan it was confirmed that I was carrying three babies, however, I began to bleed at seven weeks and a further scan at nine weeks showed a blighted ovum so we were told that we were now down to twins. We were transferred from the [teaching hospital] to the [local district hospital] and continued to believe we were expecting two babies. At the actual birth when the "twins'" placenta would not come out, further examination revealed a third baby.'

These problems were magnified when four or more babies were involved. In the parents' survey 46 per cent of the women with quadruplet pregnancies knew by or during the sixteenth week of their pregnancy that four babies were diagnosed and over 30 per cent knew of this diagnosis by or during the tenth week. On the other hand 54 per cent of the women with quadruplet or quintuplet pregnancies did not know that they were carrying four or five babies until or after the twentieth week. Five did not discover until they gave birth:

'I was told throughout my pregnancy that I was expecting triplets. Right up until the previous day to delivery no-one mentioned the possibility of more. When I went into hospital (on that day) they took an x-ray – but still couldn't decide, but I gave birth the next morning and therefore settled the argument!'

'I was told about my fourth in the labour ward when the first three were born which was very shocking. I only wish they had known before.'

Infertility treatment and the diagnosis of multiple pregnancy
Not surprisingly, there were marked differences in the patterns of diagnosis according to whether parents had or had not used infertility treatment. Figure 4.2 compares the gestational ages at first scan for mothers of triplets. Half of those who had used

Figure 4.2 Gestational age at first scan and infertility treatment, triplets

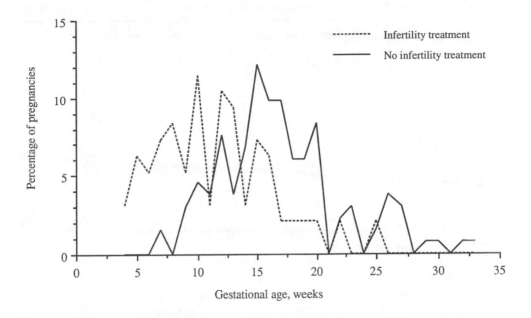

Figure 4.3 Ultrasound scans for triplet pregnancies and infertility treatment

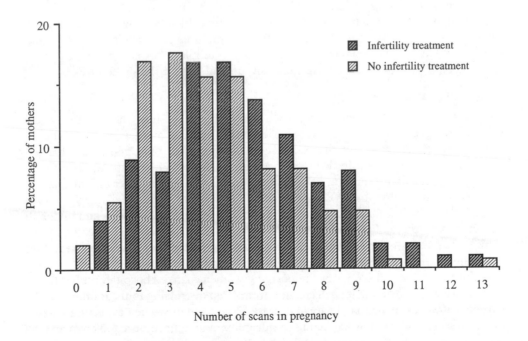

Table 4.9

Correct diagnosis of triplets and infertility treatment

Gestational age	Percentage of triplet sets correctly diagnosed			
	Treatment	No treatment	Not stated	All
Under 12 weeks	41.6	16.3	27.3	26.9
12–15 weeks	26.7	22.7	18.2	24.1
16–19 weeks	11.9	24.8	0.0	18.6
20–23 weeks	5.0	10.6	27.3	9.1
24–27 weeks	3.0	13.5	0.0	8.7
28–31 weeks	4.0	5.7	9.1	5.1
32 weeks or later	7.9	6.4	18.2	7.5
Number stated	101	141	11	253
Not known	22	29	9	60

Source: Full obstetric data

infertility treatment had their first scan before 12 weeks of gestation compared with only 13 per cent of those who had not had infertility treatment.

Having had their first scans earlier, the women who had had infertility treatment then went on to have more, as Figure 4.3 shows. Forty six per cent of mothers who had had infertility treatment had six or more scans compared with 27 per cent of the untreated women.

As a consequence of all this activity, the correct number of babies tended to be diagnosed at an earlier stage. This is summarised in Table 4.9. It was also clear from the parents' survey data for years after 1985 that multiple pregnancies after IVF and GIFT tended to be diagnosed earlier than multiple pregnancies which were spontaneous. This is because scanning is an integral part of the procedures.

Booking for delivery and changes in booking

Replies to the obstetricians' survey shown in Table 4.10 show that relatively few women changed their initial booking for delivery. Only 21 mothers of twins and 10 mothers of triplets were initially booked to deliver in a GP unit, and these changed their booking after the multiple pregnancy was diagnosed. Others already booked to deliver in a consultant unit may have changed to one which was larger or had space in its special care baby unit. These reasons probably lay behind changes later in pregnancy or during labour, but under four per cent of mothers of twins and under 10 per cent of mothers of triplets and above changed during labour. The reasons most commonly cited for the change at this later stage were preterm labour or premature spontaneous rupture of membranes without labour.

Although only a relatively small minority of women changed hospital, replies to the parents' survey showed that such changes were often distressing to the mother. In the parents' survey, the antenatal care of at least 12 per cent of women expecting triplets and a quarter of women expecting quadruplets and quintuplets took place in a hospital other than the one into which they booked originally.

The main reason for transfer was that the first hospital had insufficient provision or no provision at all for preterm infants. In some cases the immediate reason for transfer of antenatal care was that there was no high resolution ultrasound scanner in the original hospital. Only two women, one now the mother of triplets and the other now the mother of quintuplets had moved house to a different area in the antenatal period. Clearly all such transfers, at the very least, caused additional complications and usually involved longer travelling times from home to hospital for the woman herself.

For a few women, however, what was of far greater impact was being placed under a new consultant at the hospital to which they had been transferred and confronting completely different plans for their care during pregnancy and delivery. One woman commented that:

'I was placed under a new consultant gynaecologist whom I did not get on with very well. He disagreed with my previous treatment.'

Special help for parents with multiple pregnancies

Once multiple pregnancy was diagnosed, women wanted information, not only about the birth but about the help available afterwards. As one woman put it:

'An additional strain through the pregnancy was the lack of information about what help we would be given, eg: home help, night nurse. Nothing definite was offered until after I came home with the babies. Then we did get help, but it would have been a weight off our minds to have known we could rely on this.'

Only a tiny number of obstetricians reported that they had run special clinics or

Table 4.10

Reasons for change in booking

	Mothers of					
	Twins		Triplets		Quadruplets+	
	Number	Per cent	Number	Per cent	Number	Per cent
Percentage of women changing because of:						
Change of address during pregnancy	3	1.0	1	0.3	0	0.0
Diagnosis of multiple pregnancy	20	6.5	13	4.2	1	3.7
Other reasons during pregnancy	4	1.3	11	3.5	1	3.7
Clinical reasons during labour	9	2.9	24	7.7	1	3.7
Other reasons during labour	2	0.6	6	1.9	0	0.0
Not known	4	1.3	7	2.2	1	3.7
Total women changing	41	13.3	58	18.5	4	14.8
Total women	308	100.0	313	100.0	27	100.0

Note: Some women changed for more than one reason
Source: Full obstetric data

facilities for women with multiple pregnancies at the time of the births, or had since set up such clinics. About a third of all obstetricians reported special policies for women with multiple pregnancies. In about two thirds of cases the special policy was admission for bed rest. Other policies mentioned more than twice were more frequent antenatal attendance, serial scans, and use of cervical cerclage and beta-mimetics. Cervical cerclage is a stitch placed round the cervix during pregnancy with the object of preventing preterm labour. There is, however, no evidence that it does so in twin pregnancies[8] and it may even have the opposite effect.[2] Beta-mimetics are drugs which are sometimes used prophylactically to try to prevent preterm labour. So far, there is no clear evidence that they are effective in prolonging multiple pregnancies.[2, 9] Even in singletons, where they may prolong pregnancy, there is no evidence that this prevents death or morbidity in the babies.[9]

Many questionnaires were filled in by people such as midwives and obstetricians other than the consultant obstetricians concerned. As a result, these policies may have been under-reported. This may also apply to responses to the questions about subjects discussed with parents and referral to other sources of help.

Obstetric problems during multiple pregnancy

As expected, a considerable proportion of women in our survey experienced problems such as high blood pressure during their multiple pregnancy. Table 4.11 shows few reported differences in the obstetric survey between women expecting triplets and those expecting twins. Some complications, including moderate/severe pre-eclamptic toxaemia, threatened miscarriage, anaemia and polyhydramnios, were much higher among women expecting four or more babies, however.

Women expecting more than one baby are more likely to experience threatened miscarriage than those expecting singletons.[2] Table 4.11 shows this was slightly more common with triplets than with twins, and occurred in nearly a quarter of quadruplet pregnancies. Within mothers of triplets, Table 4.12 shows that threatened miscarriage was twice as common among those who had infertility treatment compared with mothers whose pregnancies were spontaneous. It may be that women who have a long history of infertility and have undergone treatment have a heightened awareness of problems and are more likely to report symptoms.

Blood loss later in pregnancy, known as ante-partum haemorrhage, is more likely to occur in multiple pregnancies than with singletons.[2] This is because raised blood pressure, often now referred to as pregnancy-induced hypertension, or pre-eclampsia, is more common and this may be accompanied by placental abruption, which means that the placenta becomes detached from the wall of the uterus.

Comparisons of the extent to which women have pre-eclampsia are often problematic because basic definitions and criteria for reporting can vary between hospitals and doctors. Despite this, it is generally agreed that pre-eclampsia is more common among women in their first pregnancy (primagravidae).[2] It has been suggested that this is likely to be the case among women with a long history of infertility, so if they have a multiple pregnancy they may be even more likely to develop pre-eclampsia.

In our survey, there were no marked differences detected between twins and triplets, possibly because women expecting triplets had shorter pregnancies and there was less time for pre-eclampsia to develop. Table 4.11 shows, however, that women expecting quadruplets and above were more likely to develop moderate or severe

Table 4.11

Women with obstetric problems during pregnancy

Complications	Mothers of					
	Twins		Triplets		Quadruplets+	
	Number	Per cent	Number	Per cent	Number	Per cent
Threatened miscarriage	23	7.5	35	11.2	6	22.2
Antepartum haemorrhage	13	4.2	19	6.1	1	3.7
Essential hypertension	5	1.6	3	1.0	0	0.0
Mild pre-eclamptic toxaemia	54	17.5	47	15.0	4	14.8
Moderate/Severe pre-eclamptic toxaemia	10	3.2	16	5.1	5	18.5
Urinary complications	13	4.2	14	4.5	2	7.3
Anaemia (haemoglobin below 9.5g)	12	3.9	19	6.1	6	22.2
Polyhydramnios	14	4.6	17	5.4	4	14.8
Spontaneous labour at under 37 weeks, followed by delivery	76	24.7	161	51.4	15	55.6
Other problems	30	9.7	44	14.1	4	14.8
Number of women with specific problems mentioned*	148	48.1	160	51.1	20	74.1
Total women	308	100.0	313	100.0	27	100.0

* Excluding women whose only problem mentioned was spontaneous labour before 37 weeks.

Note: Some women had more than one problem mentioned

Source: Full obstetric data

Table 4.12

Obstetric problems among women expecting triplets and higher order births according to infertility treatment and previous pregnancies

	Infertility treatment			No infertility treatment		
	First pregnancy	Second or later pregnancy	Total	First pregnancy	Second or later pregnancy	Total
Percentage of women having:						
Threatened miscarriage	20	15	17	3	9	8
Ante-partum haemorrhage	2	11	6	5	7	6
Essential hypertension	0	2	1	3	0	1
Mild pre-eclampsic toxaemia	21	11	16	14	8	9
Moderate/severe pre-eclampsic toxaemia	7	8	7	8	4	3
Urinary complications	2	8	5	3	5	5
Anaemia (haemoglobin below 9.5g)	9	8	8	0	5	5
Polyhydramnios	2	6	4	5	7	6
Spontaneous labour less than 37 weeks leading to delivery	43	42	43	65	58	60
Other	12	20	16	16	11	12
Total women giving information	56	66	122	37	132	169

Source: Full obstetric data

Table 4.13

Numbers of antenatal admissions to hospital

Number of admissions	Mothers of					
	Twins		Triplets		Quadruplets+	
	Number	Per cent	Number	Per cent	Number	Per cent
0	47	15.3	17	5.4	0	0.0
1	167	54.2	171	54.6	15	55.6
2	67	21.8	84	26.8	3	11.1
3	10	3.2	18	5.8	3	11.1
4	6	2.0	6	1.9	1	3.7
5 or more	2	0.6	3	1.0	0	0.0
Not known	9	2.9	14	4.5	5	18.5
Total women	308	100.0	313	100.0	27	100.0

Source: Full obstetric data

Figure 4.4   Antenatal admissions, length of stay

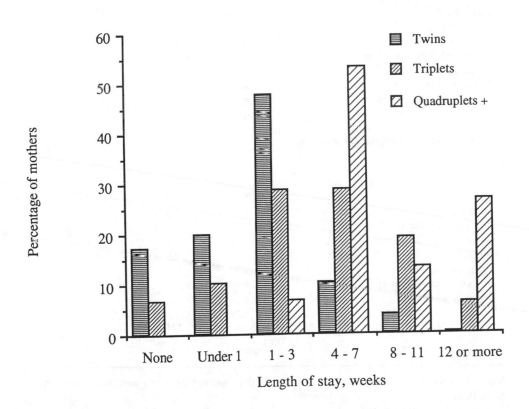

73

pre-eclampsia. With mothers of triplets, there was a much higher rate of mild pre-eclampsia among those who had had infertility treatment but the differences were far less marked for moderate and severe pre-eclampsia and there was no difference for women in their first pregnancy.

Tables 4.11 and 4.12 show relatively high proportions of mothers of triplet and higher order births and, to a lesser extent, mothers of twins going into labour and delivering before 37 weeks of pregnancy. This is not surprising in the light of data about the gestational ages at delivery for multiple births which will be discussed in the next chapter. In retrospect, perhaps the question about complications, which was taken from the Scottish Twins Study[10] should have been modified, with a gestational age below 28 weeks being used as a cut-off point.

Table 4.14

Reasons for antenatal admissions to hospital

	Mothers of		
	Twins	Triplets	Quadruplets+
First admission			
Percentage of women admitted for:			
Bed rest only	29.8	48.2	72.7
Mild PET	17.9	11.4	4.6
Severe/moderate PET	2.4	1.8	9.1
Suspected preterm labour	21.0	21.6	18.2
Bleeding	6.8	7.4	9.1
Hyperemesis	0.8	1.4	0
Suspected poor growth	5.6	3.2	0
Other reasons	27.4	20.6	36.4
Number of women admitted at least once:	252	282	22
Second admission			
Percentage of women admitted for:			
Bed rest only	16.5	35.1	71.4
Mild PET	16.5	17.1	0
Severe/moderate PET	7.1	2.5	0
Suspected preterm labour	17.1	26.1	0
Bleeding	7.1	9.0	14.3
Hyperemesis	8.4	0.9	0
Suspected poor growth	5.9	1.8	0
Other reasons	35.3	36.2	0
Number of women admitted at least twice:	85	111	7
Total number of women	308	313	27

Note: As some women were admitted with more than one problem, the percentages add up to more than 100.
Source: Full obstetric data

Table 4.15

Length of antenatal stay in hospital

a) **Mean length of stay, days**

Mothers of			
Singletons	Twins	Triplets	Quadruplets+
1.36	9.51	29.5	54.4

b) **Distribution of length of stay**

	Mothers of					
	Twins		Triplets		Quadruplets+	
	Number	Per cent	Number	Per cent	Number	Per cent
Not admitted	47	17.5	17	6.6	0	0.0
Admitted for						
Under 1 week	120	44.6	62	24.2	0	0.0
1–3 weeks	76	28.2	62	24.2	4	21.0
4–7 weeks	22	8.2	67	26.2	10	52.6
8–11 weeks	3	1.1	40	15.6	2	10.5
12 or more weeks	1	0.4	8	3.1	3	15.8
Total	269	100.0	256	100.0	19	100.0
No information	39		57		8	

Source: Maternity Hospital In-patient Enquiry. Full obstetric data.

Admission to hospital during pregnancy

Women with multiple pregnancies are usually admitted to hospital when there are specific complications such as pre-eclampsia, antepartum haemorrhage or pre-term labour. Most of the women in the obstetric survey were admitted at least once, as Tables 4.13 to 4.15 show. Table 4.14 summarises the reasons given for the first two admissions, while Figure 4.4 and Table 4.15 compare the total time spent in hospital before delivery for twins, for triplets and for higher order births.

Table 4.15 includes an attempt to compare obstetric survey data about antenatal hospital stays with those for mothers of singletons, taken from the Hospital In-Patient Enquiry for the survey years. These latter data did not link successive stays by the same women and from 1982–85 covered hospital stays in England only. It does show, however, a much greater use of antenatal beds by women expecting multiple births.

Not surprisingly, the numbers of hospital admissions and the overall length of stay tended to be longer for mothers of triplets than twins, and mothers of quadruplets and above tended to spend even more time in hospital. A considerable proportion of admissions were reported to be for bed rest only.

A number of articles on obstetric care for mothers of triplets recommend routine admission to hospital for bed rest,[3, 5, 11, 12] while others have concluded that it makes no difference to outcome.[13, 14] One of these articles suggested that the differences in outcome reflected the stage in the pregnancy at which diagnosis was made.[12] This could well be the case, as none of the articles were based on any attempt to make a formal assessment of the effectiveness of the policy through a randomised trial. Only one such trial has been done, and it is, in fact, the only known randomised trial of care for triplets, at the time of writing.[15] In this trial, 16 women with triplet pregnancies were allocated randomly either to hospitalisation from 26 weeks onward or to a policy of selective admission to hospital. The author concluded that 'although the comparisons between the hospitalised and the control groups tended to suggest beneficial effects of routine hospitalisation, the differences observed could easily reflect the play of chance and they do not provide a basis for widespread adoption of the policy'[15]. The same article reviewed research on routine hospitalisation for bed rest in twin pregnancy. It concluded that routine hospitalisation did not improve outcome in terms of birthweight, gestational age, perinatal mortality and Apgar score and could possibly have adverse effects.

Despite this lack of evidence that it was beneficial, many respondents to the parents' survey found consultants had a policy of routinely admitting women for bedrest at 24, 26 or 28 weeks of gestation. The reason given was that the mothers would already be at the hospital if they should go into preterm labour and prompt action could therefore be taken if the babies needed to go into intensive care. Although no specific question about antenatal hospital admission was asked in the parents' survey, a number of women described their experiences. Some felt reassured to be in hospital. For example, one woman who went into hospital at 28 weeks for bed rest said:

'As we had been trying for a family for a number of years, my consultant had me admitted to hospital at 28 weeks as there was a chance of premature births. I didn't really mind being in, except I felt a little lonely at the weekends.'

Others felt that they became institutionalised. This mother, who was admitted to hospital at 25 weeks, felt that it caused more problems than it solved:

'With my toddler. We worried about the separation. I grieved and fretted. My husband needed a constant stream of babysitters in order to visit me each night. We paid a nanny to look after our son in his own home to minimise the upheaval he suffered. The only advice we were given was where to get a list of childminders and that he could always be taken into care if necessary, which horrified us. He was less than two years old when I went away and I was away three months and came home with three new babies – a lot for a small boy to cope with but we felt that we did ensure that he suffered as little as possible by paying a nanny. My husband took a lot of time off work in order to give him his breakfast and tea – was unable to work full days. I had a very healthy pregnancy with no problems. When admitted to hospital for "rest", I found I had a worse diet – the hospital food was very poor, low in fresh fruit, protein etc. and my husband supplemented my diet with supplies of fruit, milk, wholemeal bread, cheese, yoghurts etc. I slept much worse and was often woken when I could sleep in order to fit in with the hospital routine. I worried and fretted about my husband and child. The strain on our family life of my three-month hospitalisation was considerable. My husband lost weight and was run-down and ill towards the end from the strain, worry, and sheer hard work of being, to all

Figure 4.5   Infertility treatment and antenatal stay, mothers of triplets

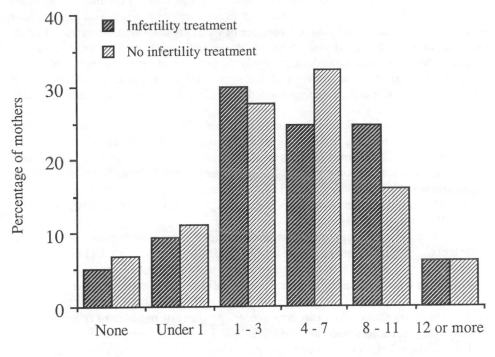

Length of antenatal stay, weeks

intents and purposes, a wage-earning single parent. We frequently wondered why I had to go into hospital. Why couldn't a midwife have visited me at home for blood pressure checks and fetal heart monitoring, at least until later in the pregnancy?'

There was no difference between the mean length of hospital stay of mothers of triplets depending on whether they had used infertility treatment. As Figure 4.5 shows, however, there was a difference in the upper end of the distribution representing longer stays, with a tendency for longer stays by women who had had infertility treatment.

Not only do women vary in their responses to long hospital stays, but also the pattern of hospital 'bed rest' and its implications varies between hospitals. Furthermore the social and cultural implications of bed rest vary, not only from country to country, but also from family to family within a given society. As well as a larger trial of bed rest there is also a need for closer studies of women's and their partners' views about it. Also the alternatives to hospital admission for 'bed rest' should include giving help and support to the mother while resting at home, rather than simply a policy of not admitting her to hospital unless there are specific indications.

Conclusions

Problems were encountered with diagnosis of multiple pregnancy. For 91 per cent of mothers of twins, 97 per cent of mothers of triplets and all mothers of quadruplets and above, the multiple pregnancy was diagnosed by ultrasound. In the majority of cases this diagnosis was made before 20 weeks of pregnancy. For triplet and higher order pregnancies, diagnosing the correct number of babies was more problematic. For six per cent of sets of triplets and 16 per cent of quadruplets and above, the correct diagnosis was not made until delivery. Only 70 per cent of sets of triplets and 55 per cent of quadruplets and above had been correctly diagnosed by 20 weeks of pregnancy. On the whole, diagnosis tended to be earlier for women who had infertility treatment.

Parents reported problems in obtaining diagnosis of multiple pregnancy from medical staff. Sometimes diagnoses were communicated in an insensitive way and in others professional demarcation lines created barriers to communication. Efforts need to be made to improve communication and to give parents help with dealing with the implications of the diagnosis. There is clearly a need to give prospective parents more help in the antenatal period to help them plan how to cope when their babies are eventually born and go home.

Even though only a minority of women changed their bookings in pregnancy or early labour, these changes can cause problems for the parents. If such changes cannot be avoided, care needs to be taken to ensure as smooth a transition as possible.

Many women experienced obstetric complications in the antenatal period. These were reported for a third of mothers of twins and triplets and half of mothers of quadruplets and above. As a consequence, 95 per cent of mothers of triplets and all mothers of quadruplets were admitted to hospital at least once in the antenatal period and the average length of stay was very much higher than for singleton pregnancies. In addition women without complications were admitted routinely to hospital around the end of the second trimester.

Although some women were relieved to be admitted to hospital for 'bed rest', these admissions caused stress to other women. Given the lack of evidence of the effectiveness of the policy of routine admission to hospital for 'bed rest' and the demand it makes on NHS resources, there should be larger scale randomised trials to compare this policy with any possible alternatives, coupled with a full study of the women's and their partners' views in relation to their domestic circumstances.

References

1. Duncan J M Fecundity, fertility, sterility and allied topics. Edinburgh: Adam and Charles Black, 1866.

2. MacGillivray I, Campbell D M, Thompson B, eds. Twinning and twins. Chichester: John Wiley, 1988.

3. Daw E. Triplet pregnancy. In: Studd J, ed. Progress in obstetric and gynaecolcgy, Volume 6. London: Churchill Livingstone, 1987; 119–131.

4. Itzkowic D. A survey of 59 triplet pregnancies. British Journal of Obstetrics and Gynaecoloqy 1979; 86: 23–28.

5. Holcberg G, Biale Y, Lewenthal H, Insler V. Outcome of pregnancy in 31 triplet gestations. Obstetrics and Gynaecology 1982; 59: 472–476.

6. Witcombe J B, Radford A. Obstetric ultrasonography: a wider role for radiographers? British Medical Journal 1986; 292: 113–115.

7. Furness M E. Reporting obstetric ultrasound. Lancet 1987; i; 675–676.

8. Grant A. Cervical cerclage to prolong pregnancy. In: Chalmers I, Enkin M, Keirse M N C eds, Effective care in pregnancy and childbirth. Oxford: Oxford University Press, 1989.

9. Keirse M N C, Grant A, King J F. Preterm labour. In: Chalmers I, Enkin M, Keirse M N C eds, Effective care in pregnancy and childbirth. Oxford: Oxford University Press, 1989.

10. Patel N, Bowie W, Campbell D M, Howat R, Melrose E, Redford D, McIlwaine G, Smalls M. Scottish twin study 1983. Report. Glasgow: Social Paediatric and Obstetric Research Unit, University of Glasgow and Greater Glasgow Health Board, 1984.

11. Micklewitz H, Kennedy J, Kawada C, Kennison R. Triplet pregnancies. Journal of Reproductive Medicine 1981; 26: 243–246.

12. Loucopoulos A, Jewelewicz R, Van de Wiele R L. Multiple gestations: management of pregnancy and delivery. Acta Genetica Medica Gemellologica 1982; 31: 263–266.

13. Ron-el R, Caspi E, Schreyer P, Weinrubz Z, Arieli S, Goldberg M. Triplet and quadruplet pregnancies and management. Obstetrics and Gynaecology 1981; 7: 458–463.

14. Syrop C H, Varner M W. Triplet gestation: maternal and neonatal implications. Acta Genetica Medica Gemellologica 1985; 34: 81–88.

15. Crowther C A, Chalmers C. Bed rest and hospitalisation during pregnancy. In: Chalmers I I, Enkin M, Keirse M N C, eds. Effective care in pregnancy and childbirth. Oxford: Oxford University Press, 1989.

Chapter 5 – The delivery

Alison J Macfarlane, Frances V Price, E G Daw

'A very good experience, with a lot of humour and excitement.'

'I received very good care. I was asked if I had any questions to ask every time I saw a gynaecologist. However I was too frightened [of what he might tell me] to ask. I could never think of any questions about birth. I wish he would have just explained everything that would happen as a matter of course.'

Labour and delivery pose greater problems for multiple than for singleton births. These arise both because of the numbers of babies and because they are born at earlier gestational ages. These problems are a source of anxiety, not only to the parents but also to the staff involved, who may have little previous experience of these births. This chapter describes when and how the babies were born and the parents' experience of the event. Before this, it describes parents' views of preparation for the birth and discussions about how it would be.

Discussions with hospital staff about the birth

In the parents' survey, 74 per cent of women with triplet pregnancies reported that during pregnancy there had been at least some discussions with hospital staff about the birth. These were either about what was being planned or about what options were available. Some discussions were fuller than others. An open discussion of all the possibilities for delivery was reported by 28 per cent of mothers of triplets but only two mothers of quadruplets. Two mothers described what was covered in these terms:

'Method of delivery; types of anaesthetic; use of machinery; who would be involved and why; observers; where the babies would be after the birth and what would happen to them; who would look after them; sterilisation; what I would be like after.'

'The consultant discussed the whole pregnancy and birth with me. When I stressed my desire to have as natural a delivery as possible he accepted this but explained that obviously there could be problems.'

By contrast, others regretted that there had not been enough attention given to such details:

'I feel that more thought should have been given to our feelings about the type of birth intended. Having had three at once it's unlikely that we shall have more.'

Most discussions centred on the likelihood of a caesarean section. This was the focus of discussion about delivery with 42 per cent of parents of triplets and two thirds of parents of quadruplets:

'I was told it would be caesarean. I was told exactly what would happen to me and the babies.'

'I was told I would have a caesarean.'

'As I'd lost babies in the past my consultant thought it best to have a caesarean (and I was glad of it).'

'As I'd had a caesarean to have my first child, the consultant thought it advisable to have a caesarean once more in case one of the triplets tore the old scar – I was quite happy.'

'My consultant discussed whether the birth should be a normal delivery or an elective caesarean and whether by general anaesthetic or by local epidural. In the end, however, another consultant delivered me and he was heavily in favour of a caesarean by general. I was guided by him.'

'Caesarean section and special care [were discussed]. The nurses were more informative about details than the consultant who shared few of his decisions with us.'

'The strong possibility of a caesarean – high risk of neonatal fatality – lack of available "beds" in NICU, some of the minor problems of prems.'

A particular issue which arose with caesareans was whether they were to be done under general or epidural anaesthesia. Recent studies have suggested that after a general anaesthetic, mothers are more tired and are less able to care for their newborn babies than after an epidural.[1,2] The possibility of using an epidural either for normal delivery or as an alternative to general anaesthesia for caesareans was discussed with just over a quarter of women in the parents' study. One reported discussions about:

'Whether I would need a caesarean, whether I would have an epidural if normal labour – extent of monitoring etc and the need for planned induction.'

In another instance, obstetric staff had agreed:

'That we would try for a normal vaginal delivery (with epidural anaesthesia as one baby was lying feet first). Nothing else was discussed with the doctors/ consultants ("let's wait and see" was the attitude). The physiotherapist gave me a quick lesson on breathing but assumed it would be caesarean and so didn't mention anything else!).'

In another instance, where the triplets were not diagnosed until delivery, the consultant:

'Told me twins would be small and would be taken straight to the SCBU and it would benefit babies if I had an epidural, in case they got into any difficulty.'

Some women who requested epidurals found opposition from obstetricians:

'I wanted an epidural caesarean instead of a general but was not allowed to. They said it was in case of complications. They could deal with the situation better.'

'I wanted a natural birth if possible but was advised against it by the consultant (because of the cutting off of oxygen during each part of labour which stresses the last child). I then elected to have an "epidural" section and stressed I only wanted a "bikini line" incision. I had to be very firm about the section when it came to the births as they still wanted a) to do it by general anaesthetic' and b) using a vertical incision. I did, however, have it done as I wanted in the end.'

As many as a quarter of women with triplet pregnancies and four women with quadruplet pregnancies reported no discussions with hospital staff about the method of delivery. One woman commented that:

'I was not told about having to have a caesarean section. I was not allowed to have an epidural. My consultant never explained anything and never discussed anything about the birth or pregnancy.'

A mother of triplets commented:

'I did however ask several times as I then weighed 15 stone 10lb and couldn't sit, stand, bath or wash my hair. I couldn't even bend my knees. The hospital staff said that I'd be surprised what I could do when the time came! I normally weigh 9½ stone.'

Even where communication was good, problems were likely to arise because of the need for staff to try to anticipate medical problems, particularly if the mother went into labour at a very early stage.

Table 5.1

Gestational age at delivery, cumulative distribution

	Mothers of		
	Twins	Triplets	Quadruplets+
Percentage of mothers who had delivered before			
24 weeks	0.0	0.7	0.0
28 weeks	1.4	4.0	16.0
32 weeks	8.6	24.5	48.0
36 weeks	27.7	76.6	92.0
40 weeks	86.3	98.2	96.0
Number with known gestational age	278	273	25
Not known	30	40	2
Total	308	313	27

Source: Full obstetric data.

Figure 5.1 Gestational age at delivery

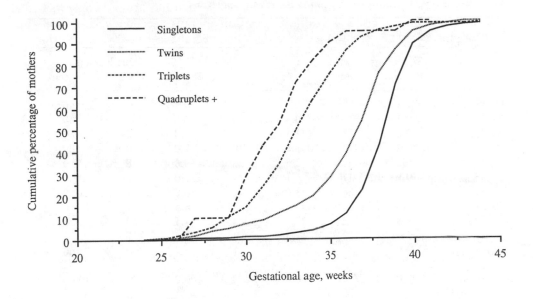

Figure 5.2 Infertility treatment and gestational age at delivery, mothers of triplets

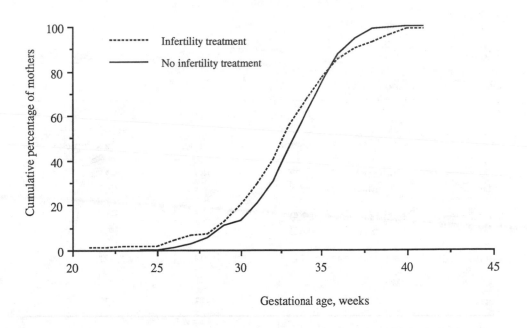

Table 5.2

Gestational age by multiplicity, comparison with singletons

Gestational age, weeks	Mothers of							
	Singletons Per cent	Twins Number	Per cent	Triplets Number	Per cent	Quadruplets+ Number	Per cent
Under 24	0.1	0	0.0	2	0.7	0	0.0
24–25	0.1	1	0.4	0	0.0	2	8.0
26–27	0.2	3	1.1	9	3.3	2	8.0
28–29	0.2	10	3.6	19	7.0	0	0.0
30–31	0.5	10	3.6	37	13.6	8	32.0
32–33	0.9	17	6.1	71	26.0	7	28.0
34–35	2.2	36	13.0	71	26.0	4	10.0
36–37	7.0	71	25.5	45	16.5	1	4.0
38–39	31.8	92	33.1	14	5.1	0	0.0
40–41	46.4	32	11.5	4	1.5	1	4.0
42+	9.9	6	2.2	1	0.4	0	0.0
Total stated	100.0	278	100.0	273	100.0	25	100.0
Not stated		30		40		2	

Source: Full obstetric data, Maternity Hospital In-patient Enquiry.

Table 5.3

Did spontaneous labour occur?

		Mothers of		
		Twins	Triplets	Quadruplets+
No spontaneous labour	Number	102	109	11
	Percentage	33.8	35.4	40.7
Spontaneous labour	Number	200	199	16
	Percentage	66.2	64.6	59.3
Total stated		302	308	27
Not stated		6	5	0
Total		308	313	27

Source: Full obstetric data.

Table 5.4

Estimated gestational age at first onset of spontaneous labour

Estimated gestational age at first onset of spontaneous labour, weeks	Mothers of		
	Twins	Triplets	Quadruplets+
Percentage			
Before 20		0.5	7.1
20–23		1.1	7.1
24–27	1.1	5.4	28.6
28–31	13.1	32.1	42.9
32–35	24.0	48.9	7.1
36+	61.8	12.0	7.1
Total stated	183	184	14
Not stated	17	15	2
Total women with spontaneous labours	200	199	16
Total women with no spontaneous labour	102	109	11
No information	6	5	0
Total	308	313	27

Source: Full obstetric data

Gestational age at birth

Triplet and higher order births tend to be born at even lower gestational ages than twins who, in their turn, tend to be born earlier than singletons. This can be seen in Table 5.1 and in Figure 5.1 where obstetric survey data are compared with those from the Maternity Hospital In-Patient Enquiry. They show cumulative frequencies (the percentages of babies born before and at a given gestational age), whereas the numbers and proportions of survey babies born at individual gestational ages are shown in Table 5.2 where they are compared with data for singletons from the Maternity Hospital In-patient Enquiry.

On average, women who had had infertility treatment tended to have shorter pregnancies than those who had not, as Figure 5.2 shows. There was also a wider variation in gestational ages among women who had had infertility treatment.

Table 5.3 shows that two thirds of mothers of twins, triplets and higher order multiple births went into spontaneous labour at some stage, although mothers of twins tended to do so at higher gestational ages. The gestational ages at which women expecting triplet and higher order births first went into spontaneous labour are shown in Table 5.4.

Women with triplet and higher order pregnancies tended to go into spontaneous labour earlier so it is not surprising that attempts to stop preterm labour in order to delay the birth were more common than for mothers of twins. Attempts were made to suppress the first spontaneous labour among about 10 per cent of women expecting twins, a third of those expecting triplets and nearly half of those expecting quadruplets or more. The most common method was to use the drugs ritodrine (yutopar) followed by salbutomol (ventolin). Attempts were made to suppress about a half of second or subsequent spontaneous labours, but these involved relatively small numbers of women.

Labour and delivery

Despite the tendency for women expecting multiple births to go into labour early, some of them had their labours induced for various reasons. Not surprisingly, this was less common among women expecting triplet and higher order births than among those expecting twins. Just over a quarter of twins were induced compared with nine per cent of triplet and higher order births, as Table 5.5 shows. By comparison, the induction rate for all births in the Maternity Hospital In-Patient Enquiry in the study years was 18 per cent. Among mothers of twins, induction rates were higher for women who had undergone infertility treatment, but there was no difference in the very low induction rates for mothers of triplets and above.

The low induction rates for triplets and above are hardly surprising given the likelihood of spontaneous preterm labour and their high elective caesarean rates. Table 5.6 and Figure 5.3 show that 28 per cent of twins, 65 per cent of triplets and 74 per cent of quadruplets and above were born by caesarean. In the Maternity Hospital

Table 5.5

Induction rates

a) **Percentage of labours induced**

	Mothers of		
	Twins	Triplets	Quadruplets+
Percentage of women induced			
After infertility treatment	41.7	8.6	4.8
No infertility treatment	24.8	9.9	16.7
All	26.8	9.4	7.4

b) **Methods of induction**

	Mothers of		
	Twins	Triplets	Quadruplets+
Percentage by			
Artificial rupture of membrances	92.1	92.0	50.0
Oxytocics	84.2	88.0	–
Prostaglandins	56.1	33.3	–

Source: Full obstetric data.

Figure 5.3   Method of delivery of singleton and multiple births

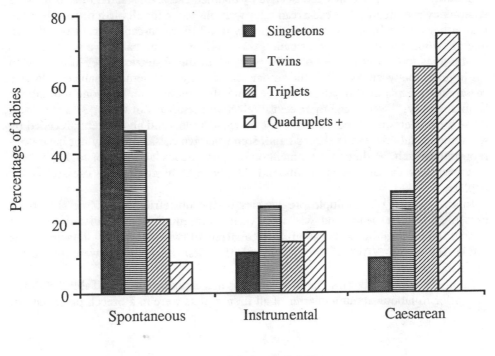

Table 5.6

Method of delivery of multiple births

	Twins	Triplets	Quadruplets+
Percentage of births which were			
Spontaneous	46.8	20.9	8.9
Instrumental	24.7	14.3	17.0
Caesarean	28.4	64.8	74.1
Total babies	589	903	112
Not known	19	33	3

Source: Full obstetric baby data.

In-patient Enquiry, 10 per cent of singleton babies born during our study years were delivered by caesarean.

Table 5.7 gives more details of the triplet deliveries included in the obstetric survey and shows that 29 per cent were elective or planned caesareans and 35 per cent were emergency caesareans. The caesarean rates were the same for all birth orders showing that either all the babies were born vaginally or all by caesareans, except possibly in one or two instances where information was missing for one baby in a set.

The question about method of delivery asked in the obstetric survey attempted to distinguish between elective and other caesareans. In some instances elective caesareans are planned in advance to be done after the woman has gone into labour spontaneously. Twenty eight per cent of elective caesareans of twins, 31 per cent of those for triplets and 25 per cent of those for quadruplets and above were preceded by spontaneous labour. On the other hand, some elective caesareans may not have been reported as such, as there was no mention of spontaneous labour prior to 47 per cent of emergency caesareans for twins and 23 per cent of emergency caesareans for triplets.

In the majority of multiple pregnancies in the obstetric survey, the first baby presented by the head, and was in a vertex presentation, immediately prior to delivery. This was the case in about three quarters of twin and triplet pregnancies, as Table 5.8 shows. About three fifths of the first quadruplets were in vertex presentations.

In most vaginal deliveries, the first baby was in a cephalic position. Table 5.8 shows that prior to labour about a quarter of all first triplets were in a breech presentation,

Table 5.7

Method of delivery within triplet sets

	Triplet 1	Triplet 2	Triplet 3	Total
Percentage of births which were				
Spontaneous vertex	22.7	12.7	11.7	15.7
Spontaneous other cephalic	1.0	1.0	1.0	1.0
Low forceps (not breech)	7.0	2.7	3.0	4.2
Other forceps (not breech)	1.6	2.3	1.0	1.7
Vacuum extraction	0.0	0.0	0.0	0.0
Breech spontaneous	1.3	7.0	4.4	4.2
Breech extraction	2.0	9.7	13.7	8.4
Elective caesarean	29.9	29.0	29.1	29.4
Emergency caesarean	34.5	35.7	36.1	35.4
Total babies	304	300	299	903
Not known	8	12	13	33

Note: The slight anomalies in caesarean section rates arose from instances where one or two sets of baby notes were missing from within triplet sets.

Source: Full obstetric baby data.

Table 5.8

Presentation prior to delivery

Twins	First	Second
Percentage which were		
Vertex OA	70.9	47.4
Vertex OP	5.4	10.2
Face	–	0.4
Brow	0.7	0.8
Breech	22.2	40.2
Other	0.7	1.1
Total stated	279	266
Not stated	23	35

Triplets	First	Second	Third
Vertex OA	71.2	40.6	34.4
Vertex OP	2.3	3.5	2.9
Face		0.4	
Brow			
Breech	24.5	52.3	59.8
Other	2.0	3.1	2.9
Total stated	257	256	244
Not stated	53	53	65

Quadruplets	First	Second	Third	Fourth
Vertex OA	53.8	23.5	28.6	25.0
Vertex OP	7.7			
Face				
Brow				
Breech	38.5	70.6	50.0	75.0
Other		5.9	21.4	
Total stated	13	17	14	16
Not stated	9	5	8	6

Source: Full obstetric baby data.

but this was true of only three per cent of sets of triplets delivered vaginally.

For second babies there was much more variation between twins and triplets. Just over half of second triplets and around 40 per cent of second twins were in a breech position. Just over a third of third triplets presented by the head, whereas 60 per cent were in the breech position.

Women having triplet and higher order births would be expected to have higher caesarean rates than those having singletons or twins, given that they tend to have more complications. Also, even though the majority of first babies in the set were in cephalic presentations, slightly over half of the subsequent babies were breech. The next section examines the extent to which these factors are responsible for the very high caesarean rates seen in our survey.

Policies about methods of delivery

While decisions to do caesareans are taken with the safety of the babies and their mother in mind, a high proportion of women who embark on the hard task of caring for three or more babies do so after what is a major operation. As we have already shown, some parents mentioned that consultants had not discussed their decisions about delivery with them. Women who changed hospitals during their pregnancies sometimes found that quite different plans were made for their deliveries at the new hospital. Some reported that they were upset by the lack of communication about these altered plans for the birth. One woman commented:

> 'In the [hospital of transfer] they were unwilling to discuss a natural birth but said it was policy to deliver by caesarean. In the [original hospital] the consultant discussed delivering normally if everything was OK and explained it would have to be in the theatre. He insisted on a spinal block.'

This woman was so upset by the change of hospital that she was eventually transferred back to the hospital where she had originally booked.

Articles published by obstetricians about care in labour for women with triplet and higher order pregnancies reflect similar differences of opinion.[3-12] A survey of 367 triplet pregnancies in South Africa and Namibia recommended caesareans for all triplets.[3] This was despite the fact that, in this African population, 45 per cent of triplets were undiagnosed before labour! Other articles were based on reports of small numbers of triplet births, some over a long period of time. One study of 15 triplet deliveries over a period of 23 years suggests that 'based on a handful of cases where triplets were delivered by caesarean section and on the literature on twin gestation, caesarean section seems to be the most appropriate method of delivery to improve fetal survival'.[4] Another study of 14 triplet pregnancies suggested that 'the poor prognosis of triplets delivered breech first suggests that most triplets should perhaps be delivered by caesarean section'.[5]

Two articles based on data presented in 1986 at the International Society for Twin Studies' Conference in Amsterdam showed diametrically opposed approaches to practice. One came from a major hospital in Paris where all triplets were delivered by elective caesarean section[6] and the other came from Gent in Belgium where a considerable proportion of triplets were delivered vaginally.[7] Despite these differences the outcome for the babies was very similar.

Two studies of 31[8] and 59[9] sets of triplets found that all the stillbirths and neonatal deaths occurred among babies born vaginally. They pointed out that vaginal deliveries took place at lower gestational ages and would therefore be expected to carry a higher risk of death. The author of the second of these studies suggested that, 'After 34 weeks it is reasonable to allow vaginal delivery of uncomplicated triplets'.[9] A study of 19 sets of triplets and six sets of quadruplets born in Tel Aviv, Israel found no difference in death rates for caesarean and vaginal deliveries.[10] The report commented, 'Nevertheless, the author's indications for caesarean section are as follows: malpresentation of the first fetus regardless of the gestational age, prolonged premature rupture of the membranes, dysfunctional labour, and all other medical and obstetric complications as in singletons'.[10] In contrast to one of the articles quoted above, they went on to suggest that, 'Approaching term, there is a place for elective caesarean section for optimum management of neonatal problems'.[10]

Perhaps the most telling comment from the Tel Aviv study was that, 'Clear-cut indications as to the management of multiple gestations are lacking in spite of increased frequency'.[10] This was echoed in an article reporting on 20 triplet births between the years 1946 and 1983 in Iowa, USA which concluded that' ... because our case numbers are small, we cannot conclude that abdominal delivery is advantageous per se. Only a prospective randomised study could adequately answer this question'.[11]

A review of articles about higher order multiple pregnancies, including most, but not all, of those mentioned in this chapter showed wide differences in practice. It also showed differences in mortality rates which were not directly related to practice about method of delivery. The authors commented that, 'The lack of randomised prospective trials of different therapeutic regimens and delivery modes does not allow any solid conclusions regarding the optimal approach in terms of antepartum and intrapartum management'.[12]

Figure 5.4 Caesarean rates and infertility treatment

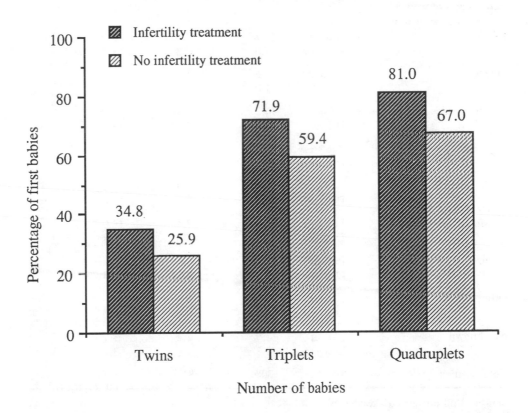

Given the weak basis for conclusions which are drawn from non-randomised studies it is not unreasonable for parents to question them. The rise in the numbers of multiple births opens up the possibility of randomised trials to test whether caesareans should be recommended in the many cases where the indications for doing them are not clear cut, particularly in younger women who have not experienced major difficulties during their pregnancy.

Women who had infertility treatment had a higher caesarean rate as Figure 5.4 shows. It has been suggested that this arises not from clinical complications but from the desperate concern of the parents and their obstetricians to deliver a 'precious' baby successfully. Any trials which are done should investigate and take appropriate account of this hypothesis.

Instrumental delivery rates were also high compared with singletons, as Figure 5.3 shows. Including forceps and breech extraction, instrumental delivery rates were 14 per cent for triplets and 17 per cent for quadruplets and above, as Table 5.6 shows.

Table 5.9
The use of anaesthesia in labour and delivery

		Mothers of		
		Twins	Triplets	Quadruplets+
Percentages of women using each method at some stage				
Pethidine	Labour	22.7	7.4	0.0
	Delivery	1.0	0.3	3.7
Opiates	Labour	1.6	1.0	3.7
	Delivery	1.0	0.3	0.0
Nitrous oxides and oxygen	Labour	16.2	7.7	0.0
	Delivery	9.1	7.7	3.7
Epidural	Labour	32.8	15.0	7.4
	Delivery	22.4	19.5	13.0
Local (including spinal)	Labour	1.0	1.3	0.0
	Delivery	11.7	8.0	13.0
General anaesthesia	Labour	2.6	7.4	13.0
	Delivery	23.7	47.3	51.8
None	Labour	13.6	8.6	11.1
	Delivery	10.4	3.5	7.4
Other	Labour	0.0	0.6	0.0
	Delivery	0.3	0.0	0.0
Not known	Labour	2.9	2.2	3.7
	Delivery	2.3	1.6	3.7
Total women		308	313	27

Source: Full obstetric data.

Within triplet sets, instrumental delivery rates rose from 11 per cent for first triplets to 15 per cent for second triplets and 18 per cent for third triplets.

The high caesarean and operative delivery rates influence, in their turn, the extent to which different types of anaesthesia and analgesia are used. The obstetric questionnaire asked separately about the anaesthesia and analgesia used in labour and for the delivery of each baby. In women with triplet and higher order births, Table 5.9 shows a pronounced tendency towards epidurals and general anaesthesia for delivery, as a consequence of the high operative delivery rates. On the other hand, if information in this table is compared with the caesarean rates given in Table 5.6 it would appear that about two thirds of caesareans for triplets and above were done under general anaesthesia. This suggests that there was widespread use of epidurals.

Examination of placentas and assessment of zygosity
Questions were asked about whether the placentas had been examined and if attempts had been made to determine zygosity. Although the placentas were said to have been examined in about 90 per cent of cases, in about 10 per cent of these cases the results of the examination were not recorded.

Table 5.10 describes the placentas which were examined, while Table 5.11 shows the available information about zygosity. These data were very incomplete, but it is possible that zygosity may have been assessed at a later stage through blood tests, but not recorded in the obstetric notes. An attempt to relate the form of the placenta to zygosity among triplets is made in Table 5.12. Because of their small numbers a similar analysis was not done for quadruplets.

Parents' experience of the birth
A multiple birth is not only a momentous event for the parents. Despite their increasing numbers these births tend also to be unusual events for most hospital staff.

Table 5.10

Description of placenta

Twins			Triplets		
Type	Number	Per cent	Type	Number	Per cent
Separate	79	33.1	3 Separate	57	23.5
Fused	96	40.2	2 fused and 1 separate	101	41.6
Single	64	26.8	3 fused	80	32.9
			Other	5	2.1
Total reported 239		100.0	Total reported 243		100.0
Not known 69			Not known 70		

Source: Full obstetric data.

Table 5.11

Determination of zygosity

	Twins		Triplets		Quadruplets+	
	Number	Per cent	Number	Per cent	Number	Per cent
Zygosity determined	138	44.8	90	28.8	7	25.9
Monochorionic placenta	75	24.3	40	12.8	3	11.1
Blood groups	5	1.6	12	3.8	2	7.4
Other method	38	12.3	27	8.6	1	3.7
Method not stated	20	6.5	11	3.5	1	3.7
Zygosity not determined	93	30.2	96	30.7	10	37.0
Not known	77	25.0	127	40.6	10	37.0
Total	308		313		27	

Source: Full obstetric baby data.

Table 5.12

Relationship between placenta and zygosity

a) **Twins**

	Zygosity		
Placenta	Monozygous	Dizygous	Total
Separate	0	40	40
Fused	19	31	50
Single	37	0	37
Total	56	71	127

b) **Triplets**

	Zygosity			
Placenta	Monozygous	Monozygous pair and one different	Trizygous	Total
3 separate	4	1	15	20
2 fused and 1 separate	3	31	15	49
3 fused	12	6	7	25
Other	1	1	0	2
Total	20	39	37	96

Source: Full obstetric data.

For some women, who had well-established relationships with hospital staff, this was a positive asset. One satisfied mother commented that:

> 'There was tremendous air of "camaraderie" and excitement amongst theatre staff. I knew most of them and felt very safe and relaxed. They were all "rooting" so hard for me and the babies.'

For others the unusualness of the occasion was a disadvantage:

> 'The hospital staff at delivery did not know what to expect as none of them had delivered triplets before.'

Some parents felt eclipsed by the large audience 'their' event attracted:

> 'I understand that approximately 36 students and doctors were at the birth (it was a teaching hospital).'

> 'I've never seen a labour ward quite so full of people. My husband and I were lost in the middle of it!'

> 'I would have preferred not to have the large audience of nurses and doctors if I had been given the chance to choose.'

Some mothers conveyed their sense of fear and of need for information, reassurance and sensitivity. One said that the consultant:

> 'Decided on an emergency caesarean. All rather frightening. Asked if it could be done under local anaesthetic so that I could see the births. Was told there were "enough problems already". Would have liked more information – some reassurance.'

Another was unaware of arrangements to transfer her to another hospital:

> 'I was offered an epidural when my waters went – which I accepted. But the labour was so short. It didn't have time to work. I should have been more informed before I came into labour. Also there was an ambulance waiting to take me to [another hospital] but the labour was too short. None of this was discussed with me.'

One woman reported that labour became frightening after an unsuccessful epidural:

> 'After four attempts including one by the "top" anaesthetist the epidural was unsuccessful. The dural membrane was pierced and I had to have a dural tap and had to lie on my back for the next 24 hours. (I had many headaches as a result of this – up to six months after the birth.) The seven hours of labour were very frightening as a result. I was unable to use the gas and air properly when the forceps were used and was very relieved when the consultant decided on an emergency caesarean. (They were finding it difficult to monitor the third baby whilst they were trying to deliver the first).'

Despite the enormous significance of the delivery to all those involved, the companion of the women giving birth was, in some cases, excluded from the large audience, some of whom were passive observers. When so many people were present, either because they were part of the paediatric team which had to be there for each baby delivered or because they had permission to watch, there was a degree of hurt indignation expressed by some women when their husband or some other companion was not also allowed to be there:

'My husband was not allowed into theatre although every member of hospital seemed to be there. He was very worried, waiting alone.'

'Because it was an "emergency" there was not time for my husband to be there, and I did feel very alone and scared. The staff were all too busy rushing about to sit with me or explain what was going on. I was very concerned that all of them [the babies] would not make it.'

Sometimes no rational explanation for denying a woman a companion during the delivery was offered. One who was a nurse herself commented:

'Throughout the labour hospital staff said they were going to stop me from going into labour because I was only 28 weeks. Although I had labour pains which were monitored, at no time did anyone say at what stage of labour I was in or suggest that my husband should be contacted so he could be present at the birth. Consequently I couldn't believe it when we were on our way to the delivery room. My husband arrived just as the third child was born so missed everything.'

In other instances no effort had been made to include a partner:

'My babies were delivered by the registrar of the other consultant obstetrician. She did not inform my consultant. My husband was away on holiday with my other children and the hospital would not allow my friend (who was a nurse) to stay with me during the delivery.'

The presence, when possible, of partners and also of familiar and trusted hospital staff during the delivery was often a calming influence:

'My husband was allowed into the theatre with me, and staff that I had built up relationships with during my stay in the hospital were with me, and a wonderful gynaecologist with a sense of humour all helped to make the birth a most wonderful experience.'

'The consultant I had from the beginning, including the fertility treatments, carried out the section, and I was allowed to have two of the midwives who had worked on the ward I had been on for two months and whom I trusted, to be two of the midwives taking the babies at birth. These two midwives met me before I went into theatre and calmed me down – I was, I admit, very frightened. The anaesthetist and the consultant both talked to me to reassure me before the operation. My husband was not allowed in the theatre, and was in a waiting room outside. The consultant came to give him the news as soon as he had finished the operation – and took him to the SCBU to see the quads.'

Several mothers made it clear that the presence of their husband, relative or friend, if only in a gallery above, was extremely comforting, especially when problems arose and they became distressed:

> 'I was induced and had an epidural – as a result labour did not proceed beyond 4cm dilation and I needed a caesar. This was done by epidural which failed to work adequately and was very distressing. My husband was allowed to watch from the gallery which was great.'

> 'I was totally informed of the circumstances/risks. The staff were all keen to involve my husband who was with me. They were keen to show me the babies as soon as they were able to (when ventilated) – when still in theatre. Polaroids given to me immediately.'

Replies to the parents' survey revealed that in 70 per cent of cases, photographs were taken by hospital staff of the higher order multiple birth babies at the time of their birth, or shortly after, and given to their mothers. This thoughtful and increasingly standard hospital practice was much valued, particularly when the mother was not able to see her babies for some time, or if one or more baby subsequently died. Photographs can help to bridge the long interval between the birth and a mother's first sight of her children:

> 'Babies born on Tuesday afternoon 4.00 pm, I did not see them until Thursday when a nurse took me in wheelchair. A photo would have been nice to have as I couldn't see them straight away.'

In total, 69 per cent of triplet sets and 79 per cent of quadruplet sets and quintuplet sets included in the parents' survey were photographed by staff at the time of delivery. Cases where this was not done included one instance where the neonatal unit camera was reported as broken and another where there was no film.

When the birth was under general anaesthetic, photographs and the presence of a companion both tended to help mothers compensate for experiences they had missed.

Conclusions

Not surprisingly, there were marked differences between the gestational age at delivery of triplet and higher order births and those of twins and singletons. Almost half of the quadruplet or higher order births covered by the obstetric survey were born before 32 weeks of gestation, compared with a quarter of triplets and less than a tenth of twins. Only one per cent of singletons in the Maternity Hospital In-Patient Enquiry samples for the survey years were born before 32 weeks.

There is a considerable shortage of valid information on which to base decisions about the relative advantages and disadvantages of caesareans and vaginal deliveries in different circumstances. There is a need for more research to answer these questions to enable more informed decisions to be made and to restrict caesareans to circumstances where they offer clear advantages. There is also a need to make similar comparative assessments of the use of epidural and general anaesthetics when caesareans are considered to be necessary.

Many parents did not receive the information and reassurance they needed before the delivery. Events, such as visiting the neonatal facilities, seeing small babies, and taking part in discussions anticipating the birth were not always encouraged. Yet these were mentioned by mothers as practices that they welcomed. Given the associations between preterm delivery, low birthweight babies and higher order multiple births[5], it is surprising that more women were not prepared for what might happen. Women wanted to discuss what options were available to them for the delivery, what choices there were to make, and if, when, and why a caesarean was the consultant's recommended mode of delivery. The anticipated birth was of momentous significance to the woman concerned and all who were close to her. This is a time when familiar faces and voices are comforting. Women recounted in interviews how important it was to them, not only to have participated in some anticipatory discussion about delivery and about anaesthesia and analgesics but to have available to them after the delivery a 'good enough' account of the delivery to be able to reflect on it.

References

1. Garel M, Lelong N, Kaminski M. Psychological consequences of caesarean childbirth in primaparas. Journal of Psychosomatic Obstetrics and Gynaecology 1987; 6: 197–209.
2. Morgan B M, Anlak J M, Barker J P, Reginald P W, Goroszeniuk T, Trojanowski A. Anaesthetic morbidity following caesarean section under epidural or general anaesthesia. Lancet 1984; i: 328–330.
3. Deale C J C, Cronjé H S. A review of 367 triplet pregnancies. South African Medical Journal 1984; 66: 92–94.
4. Michelwitz H, Kennedy J, Kawada C, Kennison R. Triplet pregnancies. Journal of Reproductive Medicine 1981; 26: 243–246.
5. Daw E. Triplet pregnancy. British Journal of Obstetrics and Gynaecology 1978; 85: 505–509.
6. Pons J C, Mayenga J M, Plu G, Forman R G, Papiernik E. Management of triplet pregnancy. Acta Genetica Medica Gemellologica 1988; 37: 99–103.
7. Thiery M, Kermans G, Derom R. Triplet and higher order births: what is the optimal delivery route? Acta Genetica Medica Gemellologica 1988; 37: 89–98.
8. Holcberg G, Biale Y, Lewenthal H, Insler V. Outcome of pregnancy in 31 triplet gestations. Obstetrics and Gynaecology 1982; 59: 472–476.
9. Itzkowic D. A survey of 59 triplet pregnancies. British Journal of Obstetrics and Gynaecology 1979; 86: 23–28.
10. Ron-el R, Caspi E, Schreyer P, Weinraub Z, Arieli S, Goldberg M. Triplet and quadruplet pregnancies and management. Obstetrics and Gynaecology 1981; 57: 458–463.
11. Syrop C H, Varner M W. Triplet gestation; maternal and neonatal implications. Acta Genetica Medica Gemellologica 1985; 34: 81–88.
12. Pemkovsky B M, Vintzileos A M. Management and outcome of multiple pregnancy of high fetal order: literature review. Obstetrical and Gynecological Survey 1989; 44: 578–584.

Chapter 6 – Early days

Alison J Macfarlane, Frances V Price, Elizabeth Bryan, Beverley J Botting

'I used to get very upset because I could not care for all of my children *on my own*. I used to almost resent the staff feeding, changing them etc, and would not ask them for help – even when it was perfectly clear to me [that] I would not be able to manage to feed, wash and change four tiny people.'

After the birth – the early days and weeks

The first few days of any child's life are momentous enough for the parents but they are even more so if there is more than one baby. The outcome in terms of mortality and birthweight has already been touched upon in Chapter 2. In this chapter, we describe the extent to which the babies who were born alive had problems which may have led to admission to special care and how this affected their parents. Before doing so, we discuss the consequences of the delivery for the mother. These are, perhaps, less well known but can also have implications for the children.

Mothers' medical problems in the neonatal period

According to the replies to the obstetricians' survey, just under a fifth of mothers of twins, just over a quarter of mothers of triplets and just over a third of mothers of quadruplets and above experienced medical problems in the early days and weeks after birth. More precise information is given in Table 6.1 which shows the major groups of problems. The first group of problems centred round haemorrhage or blood loss and included mentions of post partum haemorrhage or anaemia. Three per cent of mothers of twins, five per cent of mothers of triplets and nearly a quarter of women who had four or more babies had blood transfusions. The next was conditions related to infection, notably wound infection, and included mentions of sepsis or fever. Three per cent of mothers of twins, four per cent of mothers of triplets and 13 per cent of mothers of four or more babies had wound infections recorded on the questionnaire. These were mainly caesarean wounds, but one or two were wounds in the perineum. Infections or pyrexia were recorded for two per cent of mothers of twins and three per cent of mothers of triplets. Another major group related to high blood pressure. Usually hypertension was mentioned and a few women were diagnosed as having eclampsia or oedema. In a few cases it was mentioned that the woman's blood pressure was raised after delivery but soon went down. On the other hand, two mothers of triplets had severe heart problems and one of them spent 18 hours on a ventilator.

In the obstetricians' survey, no problems were recorded for just under three quarters of mothers of triplets and two thirds of mothers of quadruplets and above. On the other hand, in the parents' survey only half of the mothers of quadruplets and 55 per cent of mothers of triplets reported that they were all right, in response to the question, 'After the birth, were you all right or was anything the matter with you?' Their comments included:

'Normal post operative "disabilities" but other than that I was fine.'

Table 6.1

Obstetricians' reports of mothers' problems after the birth

	Twins		Triplets		Quadruplets+	
	Number	Per cent	Number	Per cent	Number	Per cent
Mothers with problems recorded	56	19.2	80	27.6	8	34.8
Blood loss or anaemia	29	9.9	22	7.6	4	17.4
Wound infection sepsis or pyrexia	16	5.5	24	8.3	4	17.4
Hypertension or eclampsia	7	2.4	19	6.6	0	0
Other problems	15	5.1	20	6.9	1	4.4
No problems recorded	236	80.8	210	72.4	15	65.2
Total	292	100.0	290	100.0	23	100.0
No information	16		23		4	

Source: Full obstetric data.

'I felt pretty grim for a couple of days – partly effect of general anaesthetic, partly pain and soreness, partly all the tubes and drips attached, partly unhappiness.'

The problems that were reported varied in their severity:

'Lost two pints of blood, in intensive care for 24 hours.'

'An infection in the scar which needed two different antibiotics to clear it.'

'Wound infection and subsequent abscess.'

'I bled heavily and needed three units blood transfusion, and was sedated for 12 hours. My caesarean incision was infected and took six months to heal.'

A small group of women, five per cent of those who responded to the parents' study, reported that they had faced a major debilitating or life threatening event. For example, of these 15 women, three mentioned post partum eclampsia, three acute renal (kidney) failure and two had very severe blood loss followed by a hysterectomy. Another was not sure what had happened to her:

'I had a fit approximately two hours after delivery and was unconscious for approximately four hours following the fit. I was in a single room and apparently only discovered fitting by the special care sister who had come to tell me about the babies and was rather neglected by the ward staff. I am eternally grateful for that nurse's prompt action. No-one explained the cause of the fit except that they stated my blood pressure was normal and that it wasn't an eclamptic fit. I had never had a fit before or since in life.'

Table 6.2

Comparison of obstetricians' and parents' replies about mothers' problems after the birth

Mothers' problems reported on obstetric questionnaire	Mother's state after birth according to parents' questionnaire				
	All right/just post-operative effects	Not all right, transfusion, depression and shock, infection	Major debilitating event	No reply	Total
Problems reported	14	12	6	3	35
None	55	34	1	12	102
Not known	11	1			12
Total	80	47	7	15	149

Source: Linked obstetric and parents' data.

Figure 6.1   Birthweight distributions of singleton and multiple births

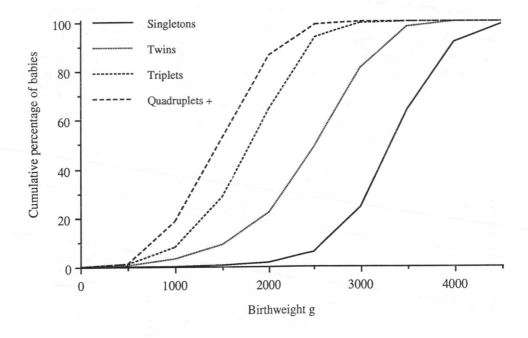

Table 6.2 links replies by obstetricians to replies from mothers for 149 women for whom both were available. Some problems reported by the mothers in the parents' study, in particular caesarean wound infections, may not have occurred until after they were discharged. Other problems may not have been considered by obstetricians to be serious enough to record. On the other hand, 14 women who felt they had no problems or simply the usual after effects of caesareans were reported by obstetricians as having had obstetric problems.

While considerable differences exist in the way problems and their severity are perceived, perhaps the most important point to emerge is that a considerable proportion of mothers are far from well when they begin to care for their three or more babies.

The babies

Differences between birthweight distributions are tabulated in Table 6.3 and illustrated in Figure 6.1. Both of these are presented in terms of the proportions of babies weighing less than a given weight at birth. Just over half of quadruplets and above weighed under 1500g, compared with a little over a quarter of triplets, nine per cent of twins and under one per cent of singletons.

Differences within triplet sets are illustrated in Table 6.4 and Figure 6.2. These show that third-born triplets tend to be lighter than second-born triplets and these, in their turn, tend to be lighter than first-born triplets. Only a quarter of first-born triplets weighed under 1500 grams, compared with almost a third of third-born triplets. A similar effect was found in a much smaller study of 31 sets of triplets conceived by IVF.[1] In contrast, no marked differences were seen between the birthweight distributions of first and second twins. This is consistent with analyses of twins born in Aberdeen. These show no difference between birthweights of twins born in the 1970s and early 1980s, although second twins tended to be lighter in the

Figure 6.2 Birthweight of triplets by birth order

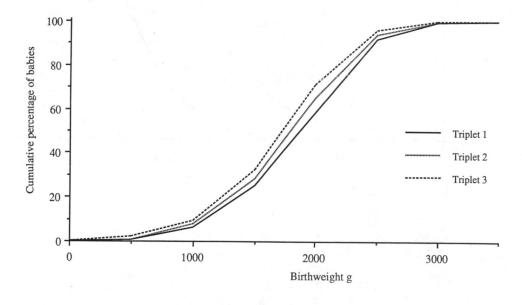

Table 6.3

Comparisons of birthweights of triplet and higher order births with singletons and twins

Percentage of babies weighing under	Singletons	Twins	Triplets	Quadruplets+
500 g	0.0	0.5	0.9	0.9
1,000 g	0.2	3.3	7.9	18.4
1,500 g	0.7	9.0	28.4	52.3
2,000 g	1.7	21.7	66.4	86.2
2,500 g	5.7	48.6	93.8	99.1
3,000 g	24.1	81.0	99.6	100.0
3,500 g	63.7	97.8	100.0	
4,000 g	91.4	100.0		
4,500 g	98.9			

Source: Full obstetric data and Maternity Hospital In-patient Enquiry.

1950s and 1960s.[2] This difference was also seen in twins in the 1958 British Births Survey.[3]

The analyses in Table 6.4 and Figure 6.2 include all babies, regardless of whether they were born vaginally or by caesarean section. Birth order may not have the same significance for caesareans, however, as the birth order may be different than if the mother had delivered vaginally. In Figure 6.3 the birthweight distributions are shown separately for vaginal and caesarean deliveries. The mean birthweight of first triplets

Figure 6.3   Birthweight distribution of triplets by method of delivery

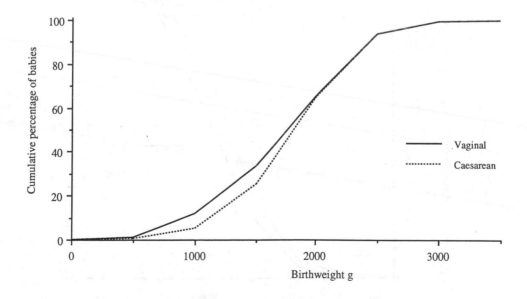

103

Figure 6.4   a) Birthweight by birth order, triplets born vaginally

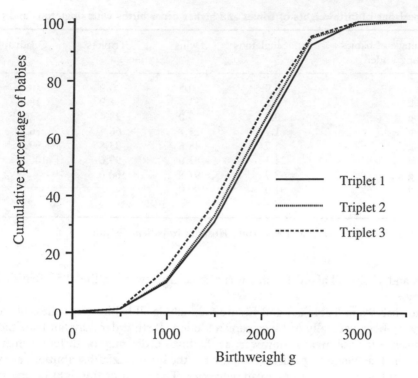

Figure 6.4   b) Birthweight by birth order, triplets born by caesarean

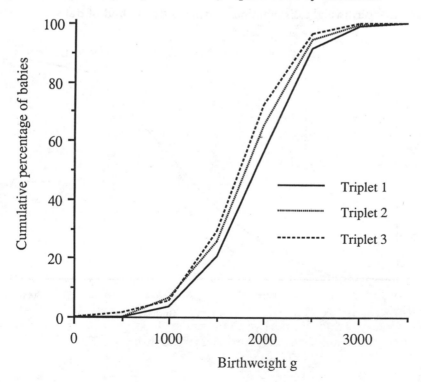

Table 6.4

Comparison of birthweights of triplets by order of birth within each set

Percentage of babies weighing under	Triplet 1	Triplet 2	Triplet 3
500 g	0.3	0.3	2.0
1,000 g	6.2	7.9	9.4
1,500 g	25.0	28.5	32.6
2,000 g	58.1	64.9	71.0
2,500 g	91.6	93.8	96.1
3,000 g	99.4	99.3	100.0
3,500 g	100.0	100.0	100.0

Source: Full obstetric data

born vaginally was 1730 grams, 140 grams higher than that of third-born triplets. Somewhat unexpectedly, birth order differences in birthweight distribution are possibly larger for triplets born by caesarean.

Figure 6.3 compares the birthweight distributions of all triplets by mode of delivery. It shows that a higher percentage of vaginally born triplets weighed under 1500g. As Figure 6.4 shows, this difference between babies born vaginally and by caesarean was seen in the birthweights of first, second and third-born babies. These differences could have arisen either from hospital policies about delivery of triplets or from the speed with which very preterm triplets were born. The birthweight distributions are summarised in Table 6.5.

Although these analyses are based on all births, the picture was unchanged when stillbirths were excluded and analyses were confined to live births.

Mortality rates

Survival rates for triplets up to the age of one year are tabulated by birth order in Table 6.6. This shows that first-born triplets had a better chance of surviving than second-born children who, in turn, had a better chance than third-born children. Stillbirth rates were also higher for the later born children. The overall pattern of mortality is similar to that shown in Table 2.2. For twins there was little difference in the stillbirth and infant mortality rates of first and second twins. Overall stillbirth rates for triplets were lower than those for twins, but infant mortality rates were considerably higher for triplets.

In many cases the outcome was not recorded on babies' questionnaires as this item was missing from the hospital notes. It was thought that the hospital would be more likely to record a death than whether the baby was still alive. To check this, a cross-check was done with the general practitioners' survey. Babies with an unknown outcome, who were discharged from hospital alive, were all still alive when their general practitioner completed our questionnaire, apart from one whose status was unknown. For this reason, babies discharged from hospital alive were grouped with those explicitly stated to be still alive in Table 6.7, which analyses mortality by birthweight.

This shows that for babies weighing under 1500 grams and those weighing 1500–2499 grams, stillbirth rates were higher for twins than triplets. Under 1500

Table 6.5

Birthweights of triplets by birth order and method of delivery

Birthweight, g	Percentage of babies in each group									
	Born vaginally				Born by caesarean					
	Triplet 1	Triplet 2	Triplet 3	Total	Triplet 1	Triplet 2	Triplet 3	Total		
Under 500	0.9	0.9	1.0	0.9	0.0	0.0	1.5	0.5		
500–999	9.3	9.4	13.5	10.7	3.6	6.7	4.1	4.8		
1,000–1,499	20.4	22.6	23.1	22.0	16.9	19.2	23.6	19.9		
1,500–1,999	30.6	31.1	31.7	31.1	35.4	39.4	43.1	39.3		
2,000–2,499	30.6	30.2	26.0	28.9	35.4	29.0	24.1	29.5		
2,500–2,999	8.3	4.7	4.8	6.0	7.7	5.2	3.6	5.5		
3,000–3,499	0.0	0.9	0.0	0.3	1.0	0.5	0.0	0.5		
Number of babies	108	106	104	318	195	193	195	583		

Source: Full obstetric data.

grams, infant mortality rates were similar, but for babies weighing 1500–2499 grams, they were higher for triplets. It is difficult to look at differences by birth order or compare babies weighing 2500 grams or over because of the small numbers involved.

Information about the survival of individual triplet sets is shown in Table 6.8. Although Table 2.2 showed that 90 per cent of liveborn triplets survived to one year of age, because of the problems described earlier, only 60 per cent of triplet sets were positively known to be still alive on their first birthday. On the other hand, many of those whose outcome was not known were discharged alive from hospital and were almost definitely still alive on their first birthday.

Babies' problems immediately after birth

Not surprisingly, many of the babies needed to be resuscitated after birth. As Table 6.9 shows, the proportion resuscitated ranged from just under a third of twins to three fifths of quadruplets and higher order births. Babies born first in sets of twins, triplets and quadruplets were less likely to need resuscitation than subsequent babies. As Figure 6.6 shows, the difference was much more marked for babies born vaginally than for those born by caesarean. Despite the higher proportions of very low birthweight babies among the vaginal deliveries, the proportion of first-born babies needing resuscitation was lower than for babies born by caesarean. For second and third-born triplets the proportions were similar.

Table 6.6

Outcome at one year for twins and triplets by birth order

a) **Twins**

	Twin 1		Twin 2		Total	
	Number	Per cent	Number	Per cent	Number	Per cent
Stillbirths						
Ante-partum	13	4.2	17	5.5	30	4.9
Intra-partum	6	2.0	5	1.6	11	1.8
Born alive but died in first year						
Under 24 hours	1	0.3	4	1.3	5	0.8
1–6 days	1	0.3	1	0.3	2	0.3
7–27 days	1	0.3	1	0.3	2	0.3
28 days–1 year	2	0.6	0	–	2	0.3
Age at death not known	2	0.6	1	0.3	3	0.5
Total	7	2.3	7	2.3	14	2.3
Live born and surviving to age 1	197	64.0	191	62.0	388	63.0
Not known						
Discharged alive	61	19.8	61	19.8	122	19.8
No information	24	7.8	27	8.8	51	8.3
Total	308	100.0	308	100.0	616	100.0

Table 6.6 (continued)

b) Triplets

	Triplet 1		Triplet 2		Triplet 3		Total	
	Number	Per cent	Number	Per cent	Number	Per cent	Number	Per cent
Stillbirths								
Ante-partum	2	0.6	9	2.9	15	4.8	26	2.8
Intra-partum	0	0.0	2	0.6	3	1.0	5	0.5
Born alive but died in first year								
Under 24 hours	7	2.2	8	2.6	5	1.6	20	2.1
1–6 days	6	1.9	7	2.2	8	2.6	21	2.2
7–27 days	4	1.3	4	1.3	2	0.6	10	1.1
28 days – 1 year	2	0.6	3	1.0	4	1.3	9	1.0
Age at death not known	0	0.0	3	1.0	2	0.6	5	5.3
Total	19	6.1	25	8.0	21	6.7	65	6.9
Liveborn and surviving to age 1	227	72.5	212	67.7	205	65.5	644	68.6
Not known								
Discharged alive	38	12.1	38	12.1	40	12.8	116	12.4
No information	27	8.6	27	8.6	29	9.3	83	8.8
Total	313	100.0	313	100.0	313	100.0	934	100.0

Source: Full obstetric data.

Table 6.7

Mortality by birthweight

Under 1500g

	Twins			Triplets			
	1	2	All	1	2	3	All
Stillbirths							
Antepartum	8	8	16	1	8	13	22
Intrapartum	4	1	5	0	1	3	4
Stillbirth rate†	387	321	356	15	114	176	111
Infant deaths							
Neonatal	2	4	6	15	17	12	44
Postneonatal	2	0	2	1	1	2	4
Time unknown	1	0	1	0	2	2	0
Infant mortality rate*	263	210	237	239	286	213	231
Discharged alive or still alive	14	15	29	51	50	59	160
No information	8	8	16	14	13	12	39

1500–2499g

	Twins			Triplets			
	1	2	All	1	2	3	All
Stillbirths							
Antepartum	3	6	9	1	1	2	4
Intrapartum	1	3	4	0	0	0	0
Stillbirth rate†	37	78	59	5	5	11	7
Infant deaths							
Neonatal	0	2	2	2	2	3	7
Postneonatal	0	0	0	1	2	2	5
Time unknown	0	0	0	0	1	0	1
Infant mortality rate*	0	19	10	16	27	28	23
Discharged alive or still alive	103	104	207	189	183	174	546
No information	3	5	8	12	10	14	36

	Twins			Triplets			
	1	2	All	1	2	3	All
Stillbirths							
Antepartum	2	3	5	0	0	0	0
Intrapartum	1	1	2	0	1	0	1
Stillbirth rate†	20	29	25	0	56	0	18
Infant deaths							
Neonatal	1	0	1	0	0	0	0
Postneonatal	0	0	0	0	0	0	0
Time unknown	1	1	2	0	0	0	0
Infant mortality rate*	14	8	11	0	0	0	0
Discharged alive or still alive	141	133	274	25	17	12	54
No information	7	7	14	1	1	0	2

† Rate per thousand total births, excluding those with no information.
* Rate per thousand live births, excluding those with no information.
Source: Full obstetric data.

The methods of resuscitation used for triplets are shown in Table 6.10. It was disappointing that the details were not given in a high proportion of instances. About half of the babies for whom information was available were resuscitated using Intermittent Positive Pressure Ventilation (IPPV) by mask and a further fifth using IPPV by tube. For a further nine per cent both methods were recorded. As Table 6.10 shows, drugs were used for only a small percentage of babies. For a further 16 per cent who were resuscitated, no information about methods was given. The main difference according to birth order was that second and third triplets were less likely than first triplets to have IPPV by mask and more likely to have it by endotracheal tube.

Apgar scores

Apgar scores are a way of assessing a baby's state at birth. They relate particularly to the extent to which the baby is asphyxiated.[4] Scores are made at one and five minutes after birth. Most babies score between 7 and 10. Babies scoring between 3 and 6 require some form of resuscitation. Severely asphyxiated babies score 0, 1 or 2.

There was a considerable difference between the Apgar scores at one minute within sets of triplets born vaginally and a smaller difference for those born by caesarean. In both cases, smaller proportions of first-born babies had low Apgar scores, as Figure 6.7 shows. This would agree with earlier studies which found a higher proportion of low Apgar scores in second twins as well as higher perinatal mortality rates.[5, 6]

Table 6.8

Outcome of triplet sets at one year, obstetric survey data

	Number of sets	Percentage
All survived to age 1	176	56.2
2 survived 1 went home alive	6	
1 survived 2 went home alive	2	12.5
3 went home alive	31	
2 survived 1 stillborn	16	
2 survived 1 neonatal death	14	12.1
2 survived 1 postneonatal death	5	
2 survived 1 died age unknown	3	
2 survived 1 not known	4	
1 survived 1 went home alive 1 not known	1	
1 survived 1 went home alive 1 postneonatal death	1	3.2
2 went home alive 1 neonatal death	1	
2 went home alive 1 postneonatal death	1	
2 went home alive 1 not known	2	
1 survived 2 stillborn	3	
1 survived 1 stillborn 1 neonatal death	1	
1 survived 1 neonatal death 1 postneonatal death	1	3.8
1 survived 2 neonatal deaths	6	
1 survived 2 died age unknown	1	
1 survived 2 not known	1	
1 went home alive 1 stillborn 1 postneonatal death	2	1.6
1 went home alive 2 neonatal deaths	2	
3 stillborn	1	
2 stillborn 1 neonatal death	1	2.2
3 neonatal deaths	5	
2 stillborn 1 not known	1	
2 neonatal death 1 not known	1	
1 stillborn 2 not known	1	8.3
1 neonatal death 2 not known	1	
3 not known	22	
Total	313	100.0

Source: Full obstetric data.

For the five minute Apgar scores however, Figure 6.8 shows that the difference between Apgar scores of first, second and third triplets had all but disappeared. In both cases, there was a slight tendency for there to be more low Apgar scores among babies born by caesarean than among those born vaginally, as Figure 6.9 shows.

Figure 6.5   Very low birthweight triplets by method of delivery

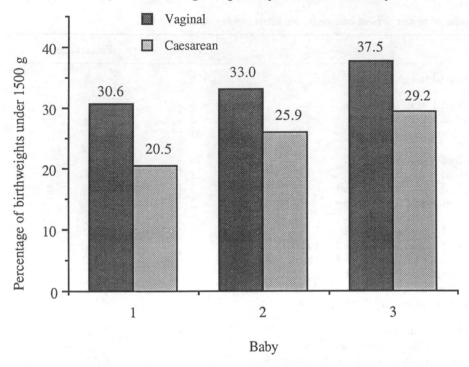

Figure 6.6   Resuscitation by method of delivery, triplets

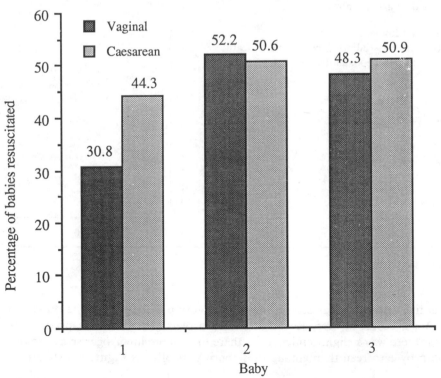

Table 6.9

Percentage of babies resuscitated after birth

	Twins	Triplets	Quadruplets+
Percentage resuscitated	31.6	47.4	60.8
Number of babies	526	801	107
No information or stillborn	36	96	6

Source: Full obstetric data.

Table 6.10

Method of resuscitation of triplets

Method	Triplet 1	Triplet 2	Triplet 3	All
Percentage of babies resuscitated				
IPPV by mask only	56.1	48.2	42.2	48.6
IPPV by tube only	12.2	22.2	24.4	20.0
IPPV by mask and tube	7.3	11.1	8.9	9.3
Drugs only	2.4	1.8	2.2	2.1
Drugs and IPPV by mask	0.0	0.0	2.2	0.7
Drugs and IPPV by tube	2.4	0.0	6.7	2.9
All these methods	2.4	0.0	0.0	0.7
No method stated	17.1	16.7	13.3	15.7
Total babies with information	41	54	45	140
No information	70	87	83	240
Total babies resuscitated	111	141	128	380

Source: Full obstetric data.

Babies' problems in the neonatal period

On the baby forms of the obstetricians' questionnaire, a general question was asked about whether babies had medical problems in the neonatal period. This led into a further question asking for details about the nature of the problem. Obstetricians were asked to pass these forms on to paediatricians. Medical problems were reported in 32 per cent of twins, 53 per cent of triplets, 68 per cent of quadruplets and all quintuplets and sextuplets. These problems were less common for first twins and triplets than for subsequent babies in the set.

113

Figure 6.7 a) Apgar score at 1 minute, triplets born vaginally

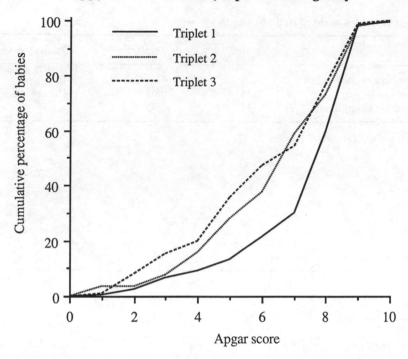

Figure 6.7 b) Apgar score at 1 minute, triplets born by caesarean

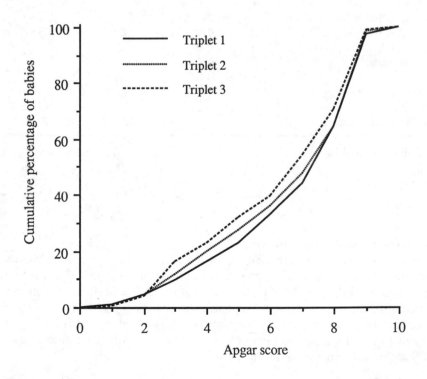

Figure 6.8 a) Apgar score at 5 minutes, triplets born vaginally

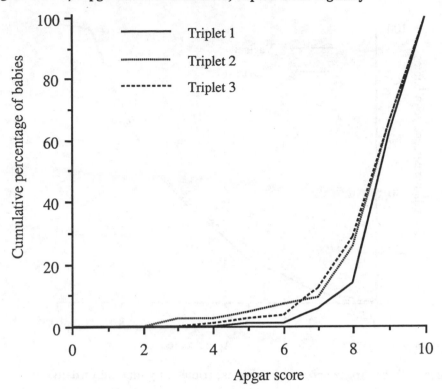

Figure 6.8 b) Apgar score at 5 minutes, triplets born by caesarean

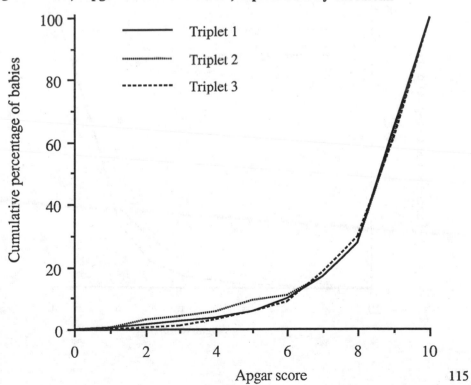

Figure 6.9 a) **Apgar score at 1 minute, triplets, by method of delivery**

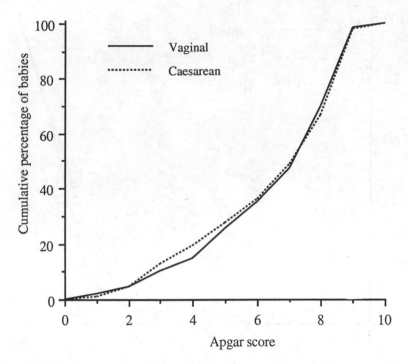

Figure 6.9 b) **Apgar score at 5 minutes, triplets, by method of delivery**

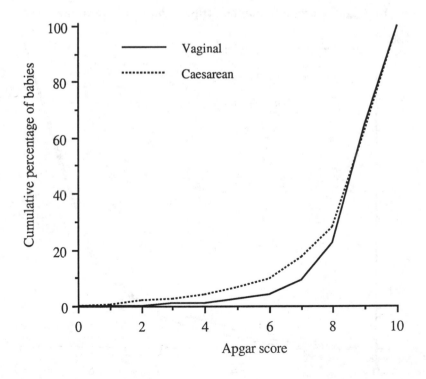

Table 6.11

Medical problems in the neonatal period

	Twins		Triplets		Quadruplets+	
	Number	Per cent	Number	Per cent	Number	Per cent
Problems mentioned						
Respiratory problems including hyaline membrane disease, respiratory distress syndrome, apnoeic attacks	58	11.9	240	31.4	44	47.8
Feeding problems, poor suckling reflexes, vomiting	28	5.7	82	10.7	17	18.5
Congenital malformations	16	3.3	47	6.1	10	10.9
Prematurity, low birthweight, poor temperature control	34	7.0	119	15.6	28	30.4
Anaemia, jaundice, hyper-bilirubinaemia, fetofetal transfusion	74	15.2	170	22.2	36	39.1
Other problems	51	10.4	229	29.9	36	39.1
Any mention of problems	156	32.0	406	53.1	69	75.0
Total babies	488	100.0	765	100.0	92	100.0
No information	74		132		21	

Note: As up to 5 problems could be listed for each baby, percentages total more than 100.
Source: Full obstetric data.

The nature of the problems is summarised in Table 6.11. The quality of the description of the problems given on the obstetric questionnaire was somewhat variable suggesting that many forms did not find their way to paediatricians.

Where forms were filled in by midwives, they were not always able to find the babies' case notes. These problems were more likely if the babies had been transferred to another hospital. Also, it might have been preferable to use a checklist for the problems.

Particularly with quadruplets and higher order births, the problems tended to be given simply as 'prematurity' or 'low birthweight'. Nearly a third of triplets and nearly two thirds of quadruplets and above were described as having respiratory or lung problems. Just under a quarter of triplets and over a half of quadruplets and above had problems which included anaemia, jaundice or hyperbilirubinaemia, or fetus to fetus transfusion between two of the babies. Feeding problems were mentioned for just over 10 per cent of triplets and nearly a quarter of quadruplets and above.

Congenital malformations
In the obstetric survey, a specific question was also asked about congenital malformations. Table 6.12 shows the numbers of triplets and twins in whom malformations were recorded in the obstetric survey. Unfortunately it is difficult to

117

make any comparisons with the national notification system because the methods of ascertainment are different.

Talipes, or club foot, can be caused by pressures in an overcrowded uterus,[7] and naevi, or 'strawberry stains', are thought to occur more frequently in preterm infants. The high incidence of these malformations may, therefore, be less significant than the figures suggest. Previous studies have shown that some congenital malformations are more common amongst triplets than singletons, however. There have been many instances in which one or more babies from the higher multiple birth was malformed. Conjoined or 'siamese' twins occur with unexpected frequency in triplet sets[7] and this is shown in these data. A higher than expected incidence of acardia has been reported among identical twins[7] but was not seen in our data.

Table 6.13 looks at the prevalence of malformations according to the birth order within the set, separating the babies into those born vaginally and those born by caesarean. For twins, malformations tended to appear in only one baby. In only two sets of twins were both children affected, but in triplets there were usually two or more babies affected in each set. Only 11 babies were the only affected baby from their set, while in eight cases two babies from a set were malformed, including two pairs of conjoined or 'siamese' twins. In five cases, all three babies were malformed. Of these, three sets all had patent ductus arteriosus and one set all had genito-urinary malformations. In view of other findings about birth order, it is particularly interesting to note that there were no malformations recorded for the first child of a triplet set delivered vaginally.

Table 6.12

Recorded malformations in multiple births

Malformation	Twins	Triplets
Central nervous system	3	3
Ear and eye	2	1
Alimentary	3	3
Cardiovascular (heart and circulatory system)	5	23
Respiratory system	1	0
Urogenital	3	11
Talipes (club foot)	8	1
Other limb malformations	10	2
Musculoskeletal	5	0
Haemangioma and other skin anomalies	3	0
Chromosomal anomalies	1	0
Conjoined twins	0	4
Total malformations	44	48
Total babies with malformations	35	42
Total babies	616	939
Malformed babies per 1,000 total births	54.8	44.7

Source: Full obstetric data.

Table 6.13

Numbers of malformed multiple births by birth order and type of delivery

	Twin		Triplet		
Type of delivery	1	2	1	2	3
Vaginal	11	12	0	6	2
Caesarean	4	5	7	17	7
Not known	2	1	1	1	1
Total	17	18	8	24	10

Source: Full obstetric data.

Of course not all malformations are diagnosed at birth. Congenital malformations diagnosed later and reported to us by general practitioners are discussed later in Chapter 8.

It has been suggested that infertility treatment and, more recently, assisted conception may have contributed to the upturn in the multiple birth rate and that these procedures may carry an increased risk of malformations.[8–12] In contrast, our survey found that very few of the women who had babies with malformations had undergone any form of infertility treatment. Only three of these women, two of whom had triplets, had been taking drugs and in each case this drug was clomiphene. In one case the second and third-born babies had urino-genital malformations and in the other, the second-born baby, although not malformed, had a systolic heart murmur at birth. In the third case, the mother had twins, and the second of these had alimentary and limb malformations. There is much discussion concerning the prevalence of malformations after IVF and other forms of assisted conception. It was not possible to investigate this in the years covered by our study. The MRC study of IVF and GIFT pregnancies did not contain enough pregnancies to detect a difference in prevalence.[13]

Admission to special care

Given the extent to which they were immature and had medical problems of various sorts, it was not surprising to find that many babies from triplet and higher order births were admitted to special or intensive care, often for long periods. As Table 6.14 and Figure 6.10 show, only a fifth of triplets and under five per cent of quadruplets were not admitted to special or intensive care. This is probably an underestimate as many data were missing as a consequence of the extent to which babies were transferred to other hospitals and details of their neonatal care were not available at their hospital of birth. Even so, the available data showed over a quarter of triplets and three fifths of quadruplets stayed for four or more weeks in intensive care.

The separation of the babies from their mother created difficulties at various stages. Particularly after a caesarean, or if the mother herself was confined to bed with other problems, it could be difficult for the mother to see the babies. One commented that:

> 'I felt very upset after the birth that various members of the staff kept telling me how lovely my babies were but no-one was prepared to take me to SCBU to see them for nine hours. I felt the babies belonged to the hospital and not to me.'

119

Figure 6.10   Admission to special care and length of stay

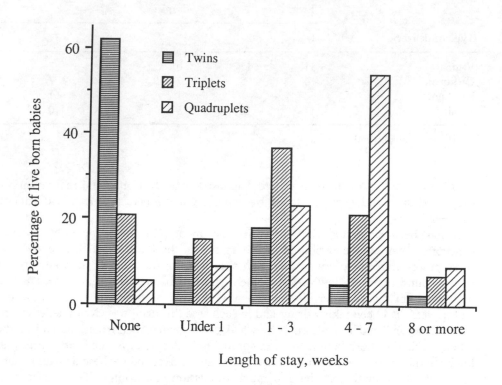

Only 29 per cent of the mothers of triplets and 13 per cent of the mothers of quadruplets and quintuplets who responded to the parents' survey saw their babies immediately at birth. Half of the mothers of quadruplets and over a quarter of mothers of triplets did not see their babies for the first time for between 12 and 24 hours. This was usually when the babies had been transferred to a neonatal unit while the mother was recovering from surgery or was otherwise debilitated after the delivery. A small proportion did not see their babies for much longer still.

One woman, who had had quadruplets by planned caesarean section under a general anaesthetic, and was then given oxygen for several hours after the delivery, wrote of the circumstances in which she first saw her children, more than 12 hours after they were born:

'My husband saw the babies as soon as they were in SCBU and in the incubators. My son was allowed to see them that afternoon, as were my parents. I was taken down by the registrar I had seen throughout the months in hospital and by a private midwife. I was not supposed to see them until the next day as I was poorly after the section but was so pleased to go down with the doctor, drip attached, to

Table 6.14

Length of stay in special care

	Twins	Triplets	Quadruplets+
Percentage			
Not admitted	61.8	20.6	4.3
Staying			
Under 24 hours	1.8	0.5	4.3
1–2 days	8.1	6.8	7.1
3–6 days	3.2	7.8	2.9
1 week	7.7	11.5	7.1
2 weeks	5.9	9.7	7.1
3 weeks	4.3	15.2	5.7
4–7 weeks	4.8	20.9	44.3
Over 8 weeks	2.5	7.0	17.1
Total	100.0	100.0	100.0
Number of babies	442	617	70
No information	120	280	43

Source: Full obstetric data.

see my little mites at long last. That kindly, human touch by the doctor and midwife meant so much.'

Even after a vaginal birth, a few mothers had difficulties seeing their newborn babies. One mother of triplets wrote that she 'very briefly saw a glimpse' of her babies within a few minutes of a straightforward vaginal birth after a 34-week pregnancy. The triplets were taken immediately to incubators in the neonatal unit. She added that she then did not see them for two days:

'I had a drip in my arm for Valium and glucose, for very high blood pressure. The *physiotherapist* came to see me two days after the birth and asked if I had seen my babies. When I said no she immediately got a wheelchair and took me to SCBU to see them drips and all. Otherwise I don't know when I would have seen them.'

Another mother also recounted how her physical condition after a vaginal birth prevented her from seeing her triplet girls for some time, other than fleetingly as they were taken to incubators in the special care unit.

'Births fine. But real problems following births. According to consultant – massive post-partum haemorrhage for 17 hours necessitating hysterectomy and 36 pints of blood. I was very lucky. [Second-born triplet] was in an incubator for 10 days; [first-born triplet] and [third-born triplet] for one or two days. I was too ill to move for four or five days so could not visit the special care unit. Nevertheless the staff did everything possible, including bringing the incubators to the delivery room and showing the babies to me.'

Despite an emergency caesarean with an epidural one mother described how she was taken immediately to see her triplets:

'The staff were *very very* good. I was taken to special care to see my babies once I had been tidied up. I was still on a trolley but they allowed me to hold the first two even though by rights I should not have been there.'

These accounts again emphasise the unusual circumstances in which these mothers, the majority of whom were delivered by caesarean section, began their relationships with their three or more babies.

Mothers' discharge from hospital

In the obstetric survey, the average length of postnatal stay was 7.6 days for mothers of twins, 9.1 days for mothers of triplets and 11.6 days for mothers of quadruplets and more. On average, women with previous living children had a shorter length of stay than those without any other children at home. Twenty two per cent of the mothers in the parents' study reported that they had been discharged home without their babies within a week of delivery. Just over half of the women who had delivered their babies vaginally, and just under a fifth of those who had had caesareans were home within a week. In a few instances, the babies were cared for in hospital until their mothers' condition improved.

In some hospitals, mothers were allowed to remain in hospital until their children were 'ready to go home'. In some places, this was interpreted in terms of weight gain, and usually meant reaching five pounds or over. In others, the criterion was that the babies be on four-hourly feeds. A mother who was discharged with her triplets 14 days after delivery said:

'All the girls were of good birth weight and could have gone home straight away. But they offered the extra time in hospital to get feeding routines etc settled before we left.

Another who was discharged after six days, but whose triplets were discharged together after 24 days said:

'The care they received was marvellous and they weren't allowed home until *all* of them were sucking properly and feeding four-hourly.'

Prolonged postnatal hospitalisation was seldom a desired option for women with other children at home. In general, the mothers who stayed in hospital the longest were those who did not have other children at home and some women made it clear that their relatively early discharge from hospital was because they were distressed about remaining in hospital and anxious to get home.

One mother wrote about the pressure she felt was put on her by some of the midwives to remain with her triplets in hospital:

'. . . at 10 days [after the delivery of her triplets] I wanted to go home, having a two year old daughter that had not really had or seen a mother for 12 weeks. They [the midwives] felt my duty was to my new babies. This was, as you would expect, a very emotional time. It was my consultant who stepped in, in the end, [and] told me to go home as I had been there long enough.'

On the other hand, if the mother was discharged and the babies remained in hospital, there could be problems with visiting. Distance from the hospital and transport difficulties were the main difficulties to be overcome in relation to visiting children in hospital. Sometimes two or three hospitals were involved. When some, but not all of the babies were discharged from hospital, there were sometimes stressful consequences as the mother attempted to care for one or more babies at home and visit the others who were still in hospital.

Just over half of the mothers who left hospital to go home without their triplets or quadruplets, subsequently visited them in hospital at least once a day. Twenty-nine mothers did not visit daily for various reasons. Seven, all mothers of triplets, were able to visit only once a week or less.

'I *did* visit but only once a week because of my health and the distance to [the hospital].'

'It was very difficult to visit when I had one baby at home to look after who was so small and he had tummy upsets. I cannot drive so it was impossible to go and see the girls during the day.'

One mother, who did visit daily but who could not drive, explained why she usually could not visit her quadruplets, except in the evenings and at weekends when her husband could take her and their older son aged only two years and eight months to the hospital by car:

'Public transport would have entailed two buses and I was not physically fit enough to manage this with [her older son] and his pushchair. I was quite debilitated after the birth, suffered a burst blood vessel in the caesarean section scar which resulted in large haematoma under the scar. This bled for six weeks after the operation and had to be dressed by a district nurse daily at home until healed. I was not able to visit [second-born quadruplet] and [fourth-born quadruplet] for the weeks they were still in hospital and when [first-born quaruplet] and [third-born quadruplet] had been discharged. My husband visited them daily after work.'

A few of the mothers who were interviewed explained that they did not feel strong enough to drive to the hospital. Arranging to visit the hospital compounded the pressures on mothers, especially when they had other children at home.

Feeding

'I expressed milk all the time I was in hospital. I could not stay in special care long enough to feed them myself as I had a rash and the heat aggravated it.'

'I tried to express milk, spent hours trying to do it. But very little milk produced. Gave up after 10 days.'

The difficulties described earlier in this chapter obviously impinged on decisions about feeding the babies, particularly if the mother was discharged in advance of the babies. Eighty-seven per cent of the infants in the parents' survey were tube-fed after birth. On average, this feeding arrangement continued for about a fortnight, although the average for quadruplets was a few days longer. All the babies in over three quarters of the triplet sets and in all but one set of quadruplets had been tube-fed, although the period varied from a few days to six months. In some instances, the milk used was expressed by the mother, in others by a donor, and in others the mother's expressed milk was supplemented by milk from the hospital's milk bank.

Almost half of the mothers did not attempt to express milk for or to breast-feed their higher order multiple birth children. Three of these mothers provided explanations. One had been very ill with kidney failure and eclampsia after the delivery of her triplets at 28 weeks of gestation. She wrote, 'My milk did not come in'. Another mother of triplets commented, 'I was told that I would be too tired to breast-feed and not to bother'. It is possible that other mothers who did not attempt to express milk or to breast-feed were also given this advice. A mother of quadruplets who could not drive and lived some considerable distance from the hospital made it clear, however, that she had discussed the matter fully with her midwife. She felt completely comfortable about the decision she reached:

'I considered breast-feeding prior to my having the babies but after much discussion with my midwife decided against it. My midwife felt I would not be physically strong enough to take on breast-feeding and pointed out I would have difficulties bringing into hospital expressed milk and that the babies would probably need special milk to help them put on weight quickly. Once I decided against it, I felt one worry lifted off me and have never regretted it.'

Eighty-nine women reported that they expressed milk for their babies and a few of these also breast-fed briefly. At the very least, this meant expressing some milk for three or four days. This was fed to the babies either by tube or by bottle. Some of these mothers reported that after this time they 'dried up' or decided not to continue expressing breast milk. In some cases, however, mothers were expressing milk for five or six weeks for their babies, often going into hospital daily to use a pump, so that the milk could be stored for the baby, or babies, remaining in hospital, or hiring a pump and taking the milk into the hospital regularly.

Undoubtedly, some of these mothers who expressed milk, or attempted to breast-feed, did experience distress:

'I expressed milk for about two weeks. I found it most distressing trying to express, and travelling to hospital to visit the babies.

'Expressed milk for first four weeks. This was difficult, tried hand pump but not much success. In end expressed by hand. One nurse in special care unit told me the amount was very poor for three babies. This depressed me. I did breast-feed for a while – four weeks at home but was not very successful – lack of help and advice.'

Other mothers reported that they became too exhausted to continue:

'Tried to breast-feed in rotation, and took pump-expressed milk to hospital to feed those in SCBU. Stopped after three weeks – too exhausting.'

'I hired an electric pump from the National Childbirth Trust. I expressed milk for six weeks until I found that with three babies at home and one more due home any minute I was too tired and hadn't any milk much anyhow – when the (caesarean) wound broke down I was advised to stop.

One mother provided an account of what she did without comment:

'I expressed milk – hand pump for six weeks. Attended hospital from 8.30 am–6.30 pm every day for next three weeks to try and breast-feed one baby at each feed.'

She added the comment:

'Would have liked an electric breast pump but none available.'

Forty-six mothers managed to continue breast-feeding for more than two weeks and a further 17 for an unspecified period of time. One mother wrote an article describing her experience of breast-feeding her triplets and also the rewards:

'It gave me a special time with each baby as an individual'[14]

In total, 25 mothers breast-fed one or more of their babies for more than two months. One breast-fed two of her triplets for nine months and one for 10 months. She noted on her questionnaire that she had found it helpful during her pregnancy to meet mothers of triplets who had successfully breast-fed all their infants.
Another mother wrote:

'It would have been very easy to abandon any hope of feeding the babies myself, especially as the SCBU nurses thought I was quite mad to try (the unit had had triplets 10 weeks earlier – all bottle-fed). However, it was worth persevering as I fed two at each feed (bottle-fed third) in rotation for four and a half months and then just one at each feed for eight months.'

For the breast-fed triplet babies, the commonest method for feeding involved establishing a rota for the babies. Either one baby was breast-fed while the other two were given bottles or two babies were breast-fed, one on each breast, while the third had a bottle:

'I breast-fed all three for about four months, expressing milk in between feeds to give to the third baby while breast-feeding the other two. They did this on a rota system.'

Parents' views about hospital care
Parents were asked for their views about the care and information they received while their babies were still in hospital. Most who responded to the question wrote about their satisfaction:

'SCBU kept us fully informed of their progress and any question, however small or silly, was answered.'

'Whilst at the [London teaching hospital] the doctors and nurses in the neonatal unit were marvellous. They always told you exactly what was happening to the babies and gave us a great deal of support and where possible involved us in their care.'

'The staff were excellent! [They kept us] fully informed as to every detail of my own and the babies progression. We were made to feel very involved in the care of the babies. The doctors told us everything two or more times as the first time details tended to be forgotten. Only found night agency staff disinterested.'

Some also forged long-term relationships with the nursing staff who became 'aunties' or godparents.

Mothers made clear that what they did not want was just to be left 'to get on with things':

'[The hospital] were very caring re the babies and provided me with a [closed circuit] TV to see them when it was difficult to get down to SCBU. Being diabetic presented problems especially to the night staff who woke me every hour throughout the night to make me do my own blood tests. The last thing you want when you are exhausted! They also appeared not to understand the contraptions I was wired up to which made me feel very insecure and upset. Generally you were well looked after but left very much to get on with things. Nobody suggested I use the breast pump until about the fourth day and then I was just shown how it worked and left to get on with it. I feel that if this had been started sooner and more helpfully I might have been more successful in trying to give breast milk.'

Several mothers qualified their praise with comments about their confused feelings about their babies or their personal sense of isolation from the care their infants received whilst in hospital. One mother described how she felt as though I was a stranger looking in'. Another wrote:

'I felt that the staff treated the babies as if they belonged to the hospital rather than to me and I had to 'earn' the right to them by showing I could cope.'

Several mothers were also physically isolated after the birth and this greatly contributed to their feelings of loneliness and isolation:

'I was in a side room on my own and the babies were all in special care. I felt very lonely and isolated and had few visitors, as I was in hospital over 20 miles from home. I was also feeling ill and low and worried about how I would cope yet nobody talked to me about this. The paediatricians at no point came to see me to talk about the babies' progress. Everything seemed to depend entirely on me and I felt totally inadequate.'

Others felt 'in the dark' or 'a little lost' because they lacked information, advice and encouragement:

'Staff in SCBU were obviously dedicated and very hardworking. Would have liked more information about babies' medical condition – weights, jaundice, feeding, breathing, etc – but realise staff very busy. Would have liked some information and possible advice about likely problems and developments as well. Felt a bit "in the dark", rather overwhelmed at what had happened and not knowing how we would cope – or what the future would hold.'

'Sisters and nurses in baby-care unit very good, but they did not encourage me to do anything with my babies. Most help and advice given to me by the baby doctor who told me to see them in the unit as often as I wanted to during the days, to touch them in the incubator, to talk to them. I felt a little lost as I had hardly any contact with them for the first week.'

One mother described how she had been helped by the staff in special care to overcome her fears about handling and feeding her very small babies:

'The SCBU staff were wonderful with the babies and gave me confidence to handle and feed them, although I was frightened to do this at first as they seemed so small.'

Nevertheless a few mothers admitted that, despite all the efforts of the hospital staff, they had only felt comfortable about caring for their babies when they were home from hospital:

'The paediatrician saw the babies daily and I was able to see him to hear the reports of their condition. [First-born quadruplet] developed a virus after three days, as did [third-born quadruplet] a little later. They carried out tests every few hours until they could isolate the problem and antibiotics soon cleared them. Despite the fine efforts of the SCBU staff to involve me in the babies' care, I did not really feel that they were my babies until they were home.'

Preparation for discharge of babies
Parents' views of the preparation for the discharge of the babies were rather less positive than their views about intensive care. There were negative comments such as:

'I felt that not enough time was taken with mother. Comments like, "How will you cope?" were given, but not much practical help.'

'Doctors and hospital staff just asked me, "How will you cope?" but had no suggestions – hence no discussion.'

Well over a third of the mothers of triplets and a quarter of mothers of quadruplets and quintuplets reported that none of the hospital staff nor any of the primary health care team in their area had discussed details of how they would manage practically after the babies were born and were discharged home from hospital. One mother of quadruplets wrote, 'They just asked me how I was going to manage'. In contrast to this, a third of the mothers reported that as well as discussion of their situation with such people there had been some form of positive assistance, rather than just suggestions of what the mother might do herself. In 36 per cent of cases the people who initiated these discussions with mothers in the antenatal period were health visitors:

> 'Health visitor contacted voluntary services and arranged some volunteer helpers for after the birth.'

A range of other people were also mentioned, but less frequently:

> 'The only practical help I received was from my midwife who arranged a trainee nanny to come from a local college.'

Contact with a health visitor was welcomed at this time. In several instances it was the health visitor who suggested and arranged a nursery place for an older child, well before the babies were delivered, so that the child should not feel pushed out at the time of the homecoming. Arrangements for providing a home help predominated in reports of practical help which had been given, as Chapter 7 shows.

Discharge of the babies

Although the discharge of the babies was touched on briefly in the obstetric questionnaires, fuller information about the babies' homecoming was collected through the parents' survey. In more than half of the triplet sets and in seven intact quadruplet sets, all the infants were discharged from hospital together. In at least one instance, the infants were discharged together because it was clear that there would be difficulties in visiting the infants who remained in hospital. One mother who lived 12 miles away from the hospital, on the opposite side of a big city, wrote:

> 'Born at 31 weeks. Came home five weeks later. [First-born triplet] still only weighed four and a half pounds. Had them all home at once because could not see how would cope with two home and one still in hospital many miles away.

> 'It was agreed that it would help me if all the babies came home at the same time, even though second baby could have come home within two weeks. In the event they all came home after three weeks although the third was a little underweight for normal discharge.'

There is considerable discussion amongst paediatricians about whether all the babies should be discharged home together and evidence of a divergence of views on the matter. Mothers who were interviewed echoed paediatricians' concerns that it was difficult once at least one baby was discharged home to visit those remaining in hospital, and that there was a tendency to refer to the last discharged baby as 'the hospital's baby'. In interview, a few mothers related differences in their feelings for their children to the timing of their discharge from hospital.

Conclusions

Although many mothers appeared to have no major clinical problems themselves after birth, about a quarter of mothers of triplets and third of mothers of quadruplets experienced high blood pressure, blood loss or anaemia, wound infection or other problems. This meant that they were not in the best condition to start caring for three or more babies. A handful of mothers experienced very severe problems.

Just over half of the quadruplets and above, and a little more than a quarter of triplets weighed under 1500 grams at birth. Because of this, many had problems which led to long periods in intensive care. Although complication rates as measured by low Apgar scores were lower among first babies in sets of triplets born vaginally, overall the complication rates were lower than in those sets where the babies had been born by caesarean section. This is despite the higher percentage of babies weighing under 1500 grams among those born vaginally.

Survival rates were higher for first-born triplets than for second-born triplets, who in their turn had higher survival rates than third-born triplets. In at least 58 per cent of triplet sets, all were still alive at the age of one year. This is likely to be a considerable under-estimate.

Although congenital malformation rates in our study cannot be directly compared with national statistics, the proportions of twins and triplets affected were relatively high. Very few women whose babies were affected had infertility treatment, but the numbers of babies with malformations were too small to reach a definite conclusion. In general babies from a multiple birth are more likely to have problems which require medical attention after birth than are singletons.

The post-delivery process of emotional, psychological and physical readjustment for the woman who has just delivered three or more babies is likely to be uncomfortable. She may take some time to feel well and mobile and the first few days after the birth may prove very stressful indeed. If she has post-delivery complications, these may make it difficult for her to be able to get to see her babies in a neonatal unit which may be some distance away. Most mothers found some difficulty in relating to all of their babies, and initially some felt anxious and overwhelmed. Many women reported that they would have liked help and advice, at an early stage, especially about feeding their babies, so that they could feel adequate to meet the demands of the situation. Knowing what was happening and feeling comfortable about asking questions were clearly uppermost in the positive accounts of hospital care.

Where there is uncertainty about how parents will manage once their children come home, the postnatal period can be anxious and uneasy. At each stage there is a need, not only for reassurance about the condition of the babies and adequate explanation if difficulties have arisen, but also for opportunities to make practical plans for when they are discharged home from hospital. Where children have received neonatal care, there needs to be discussion with parents about the appropriate time for discharge and, if the weight and condition of individual babies is not too disparate, whether or not it is desirable for all the children to come home together. In about two thirds of cases in this study, no positive plans had been made in advance to ensure that the mother had help and support when her babies came home. Both parents and professionals reported that discharging the babies home from hospital without any anticipatory planning with their parents for practical assistance often had very costly long-term consequences in terms of the effects of heightened stress and anxiety and possible later crisis management. There is clearly increased scope here for liaison between the hospital and the primary care team, which will involve hospital social workers or liaison health visitors, and the mother's own health visitor and general practitioner.

References
1. Kingsland C R, Steer, C V, Pampilglione J S, Mason B A, Edwards R G, Campbell S. Outcome of triplet pregnancies: a contemporary review. Abstract for British Conference of Obstetrics and Gynaecology: London, 1989.

2. MacGillivray I, Campbell D M, Thompson B, eds. Twinning and twins. Chichester: John Wiley and Sons, 1988.

3. Butler N R, Alberman E D. Perinatal problems. Edinburgh and London: ES Livingstone, 1969.

4. Apgar V, Holaday D A, James L S, Weisbrot I M, Berrien C. Evaluation of the newborn infant – second report. Journal of the American Medical Association 1958; 168: 1985–1988.

5. Macdonald R R. Management of second twin. British Medical Journal 1962; 1: 518–522.

6. MacGillivray I. Twins and other multiple deliveries. Clinics in Obstetrics and Gynaecology 1980; 7: 581–600.

7. Schinzel A A G L, Smith D W, Miller J R. Monozygotic twinning and structural defects. Journal of Paediatrics 1979; 9S: 921–930.

8. Lancaster P. Congenital malformations after in-vitro fertilisation. Lancet 1987; 2: 1392–1393.

9. Cornel M C, Ten Kate L P, Dubes M N G, Berg L T W de J, Heyboom R H B, Garbis H, Peters P W J. Ovulation indication and neural tube defects. Lancet 1989; 1: 1386.

10. Czeizel A. Ovulation induction and neural tube defects. Lancet 1989; 2: 167.

11. Cuckle H, Wald N. Ovulation induction and neural tube defects. Lancet 1989; 2: 1281.

12. Cornel M C, Ten Kate L P, Te Meermas G J. Ovulation induction, in-vitro fertilisation and neural tube defects. Lancet 1989; 2: 1530.

13. MRC Working Party on Children Conceived by In Vitro Fertilisation. Births in Great Britain resulting from assisted conception; 1978–87. British Medical Journal 1990; 300: 1229–33.

14. Rushworth F. Supply and demand, demand, demand. New Generation 1988; March: 33–34.

Chapter 7 – Who helps?

Frances V Price

'There are four different demands being made on you, constantly and relentlessly. You begin to feel you can't take it any longer. You just have to have somebody here to take over.'

'. . . a triplet family cannot survive without additional help with the babies. Out of the possible 168 hours in a week (7 x 24) the mother of six month old triplets expended 197.5 hours (between herself and the paid voluntary help) in just caring for the babies and the household chores. . .'[1]

'This family has quadruplets and the sheer physical task of caring for them is more than one person's work. The HS [Home-Start] volunteer is part of a team of helpers who enable the mother to function. In my opinion, the mother needs full time help – her health is at risk through the unending chores. Even coping with an army of different helpers is tiring.' (Home-Start organiser)

Parents who had experienced the continuous charge of triplets, quadruplets and quintuplets described the juxtaposition of time-consuming tasks and the effects on them of insufficient sleep. There was seldom enough time, space, hands or authoritative advice. Often others misunderstood their situation. With or without the children, it was sometimes a struggle to get out. This chapter draws on data from the parents' study, and from the surveys of community nursing and social services provision, to describe and assess the contributions made towards the care and welfare of households which include higher order multiple birth children.

It is far from obvious in such circumstances who can, regularly and reliably, provide help when it is most needed at night, at the babies' feed-time, at their bath and bed time and at the times one parent or other wanted to go out of the house or be released from complete responsibility for the children. Parents wanted helpers with whom they felt comfortable and who would not let them down. The dynamics of the relations between carers, and the continuity of care, are of crucial importance for the quality of the child care and the well-being of all concerned.

Parents requested help to enable them to get some sleep, to feed their babies, to complete practical tasks and to claim some time, rest and respite for themselves. This chapter looks at who provided such night time and day time help and discusses which professionals could and did facilitate such assistance, as well as contributing general support and reassurance.

The chapter opens by looking at data from the parents' study to see what help and support was provided by relatives, friends and neighbours and what was provided by the statutory health and social services. Sections of the chapter focus on the provision of night nurses or night sitters, on home help or other home care assistance, on the care provided by GPs and health visitors, and finally on the help and support which was provided by various trainees, volunteer schemes and self-help groups.

Help and support from relatives

'My family were magnificent and but for them I don't think I would have survived as I had no help *whatsoever* from official sources and [local] social services showed no interest in trying to help'.

'Usually the family will rally round'. This expectation was often voiced by managers in the health and personal social services when approached about the level of help and support they could provide for households including triplets, quadruplets, quintuplets and more. It was presumed, without reference to the intensity of support required, that there would be some 'extended family support': that 'the family' would agree to carry the physical and psychological burdens of care. Certain patterns of dependencies and obligations are implicitly presumed to be 'natural' and 'normal' and legislation and social policy both reflect and reinforce a number of assumptions about the structure and content of 'familial' relationships. Most social policies are based on assumptions about the pattern and nature of 'normal' relationships 'within the family'.[2,3]

One mother of triplets wrote advising triplet mothers-to-be:

'Don't panic! Get yourself a sympathetic mother or mother-in-law.'

The assumption is that mothers, in particular, can be readily mobilised to assist and support their adult daughters with childrearing in the ways reported in community studies in the 1950s and 1960s.[4,5]. In contrast, more recent research shows that such help is neither extensive nor unproblematic.[6,7,8] The day time child care of just under one third of three year old singletons was shared to some extent for all three years of their lives by their grandparents in one study in Edinburgh.[9] Other research suggests that grandparents share the care of their grandchildren only on an occasional basis, for babysitting or in an emergency.[10] The response from relatives to sharing early child care varies greatly. Furthermore, the day to day care of children with disabilities is unlikely to be shared to any extent by relatives outside the household.[11] The burden of responsibility for pre-school age triplets, quadruplets or quintuplets is daunting, and even more so if one or more child has disabilities which require constant vigilance.

Sixty eight per cent of parents in the parents' study indicated that they had at least one relative on whom they had relied for support and practical help in the crucial early months after some or all of their triplets or quadruplets came come from hospital. In the majority of cases, these relatives were female. Most often the mother's mother was described as a helper followed by father's mother, mother's sisters, aunts and cousins. Parents' fathers were included as equal helpmates in only a small percentage of these instances, although sometimes their financial help or their role in providing transport was acknowledged separately.

A quarter of the parents reported that they had received a remarkable level of care and concern from relatives, in particular from the mother's relatives. Four mothers of triplets commented:

'Without my mother's help we would not have survived the first year. I dread to think what would have happened to our marriage and health if she had not helped as she did.'

'Mother, sister, and partner have been wonderful. We could not have coped adequately without them. Mother and father come any time, and always at least five times a week for four or five hours at a time. Sister comes most weekends.'

'My mother was extremely good and fortunately she had a car and was able to drive over and help whenever needed. I don't think I would have been sane without her. She came over every day while they were very young (and still does). My mother-in-law was also quite good but unfortunately (she) became very ill during their second year and died.'

'My parents have provided the most practical help and moral support. I think without them I would have given up long ago! They live 10 miles away but make the journey at least three days a week and every day in the first year.'

The range of activities undertaken by relatives and the timing and duration of this help depended on such factors as their age, their physical and mental health, their employment situation, how far away they lived, the form of transport available to them, and their inclination to help. In nine instances, the parents had relatives who were dependent on them. Fifty eight per cent of all the parents in the parents' study reported that their relatives had difficulties helping them, although this did not necessarily prevent those relatives from providing practical assistance. For instance, if the distance was not too great, and convenient transport was available, frail health or age did not prevent some mothers' mothers providing what help they could.

Five per cent of parents' parents had moved house to be nearer to help with the care of their triplet or quadruplet grandchildren. Usually it was the mother's parents who had moved. In addition, at least four households had moved house so as to be nearer their relatives.

Several mothers wrote on their questionnaire that neither they, nor any of their relatives, could drive. All were therefore dependent on alternative forms of transport, with the accompanying inconveniences. The help some parents had received from their relatives had been intermittent. Others made it clear that their relatives had withdrawn, even moved house, to escape the weight of shared responsibility. A few explained in interview that their mothers had always maintained a distant attitude to their children and grandchildren. One mother of quadruplets described her mother as not 'that sort of mother and grandmother'. There was not as a result, she said, 'that generation support' for herself and her children.

Whether or not relatives were available to help inevitably also depended upon the tasks and timing involved, as well as their circumstances. Only a few were able and willing to help through the night or to share responsibility for the children on a regular basis. Most of the parents in the study had at least one relative who rallied round to help in some way in the early months, but such help was limited by the relative's coping ability and resources. Subsequent offers of assistance were qualified and constrained by practicalities. Few could rely on relatives for sustained long-term support on a daily basis, although the knowledge of their encouragement and concern was emotionally supportive:

'Moral support and encouragement from parents – plus their guilt because they were so helpless and far away. They worried when they visited and saw the hassles, and had to leave us again. No real friends because we only moved to that house a month before they were born so we knew no-one and couldn't get out to make friends.'

Help from friends and neighbours

Forty one per cent of the parents in the study recorded that they had at least one friend or neighbour from whom they received regular support and practical help during the first year. Eighteen per cent, including eight parents of quadruplets, mentioned several friends and neighbours, who, in some instances, had organised themselves into a rota to help with feeding the babies or with domestic tasks. Other friends literally went out of their way to take older children to school. Some comments about friends and neighbours were very positive indeed:

'To be honest we have had more practical and emotional help from friends and neighbours than from family who tend to come for a cuddle and think that three babies "is fun". Friends and neighbours all come in on a rota and are always willing to either feed a baby or wash the kitchen floor.'

Occasional help at a particular stage, or in an emergency, was also valued. The parents of triplets spoke of the kindness of a neighbour who saw their exhaustion and volunteered to undertake the night-time feeding of their triplets for two nights. Another parent described how friends had driven her to and from the hospital to visit her triplets. Even if friends and neighbours were not available to provide practical help, regular reminders of them just 'being there' were important:

'My neighbour popped round for coffee most days and Mum came over one or two afternoons a week. My friend does not drive so I used to go and see her with the babies once a week for a couple of hours.'

'A few friends were wonderful. I made myself go and visit them at least once a week/fortnight and they accepted me and five children taking over their homes. I received little or no practical help from any friends or neighbours but their "being there" was enough.'

Friends, as one mother put it, provided 'shoulders'.

Intensity of help and support required

'Not much [help]. Disappointed at lack of practical help from relatives/friends although I don't think it was intentional. Pride stopped me from asking for help.'

One mother of four month old triplets and three older children wrote in response to a poignant article in a women's magazine about the plight of a mother of quadruplets who felt unsupported:

'I feel I am in a slightly different position as my friends, family and the social services have been wonderful in providing help for me. In fact I have had to turn down help.'

A few other mothers wrote in similar vein about their satisfaction with the level of help that they had either received without any financial outlay, or that they had obtained for themselves by employing helpers.

About a third of the parents did not acknowledge that they received any help from relatives, friends or neighbours. For some parents, the stresses of caring for three or more children of the same age were magnified by the unexpected social isolation. They reported that caring relationships had broken down, that relatives and friends had withdrawn from their lives, overwhelmed by the reality of their multiple birth children. This withdrawal was clearly particularly distressing. A few had found that relationships had broken down in a critical way which they found difficult either to articulate or fully comprehend. One mother of triplets and two older children described her situation to a newspaper reporter, only to be taken aback when neighbours, who believed they had helped her, reacted with some annoyance to the content of the article which subsequently appeared in their local newspaper:

> 'Looking back on it though (the triplets are now nearly five), it's not the sheer hard grind and exhaustion that accompanied bringing up all those small children which wore [the triplet mother] down so much as being shut out by the community . . . Neighbours would rarely invite them to parties because they couldn't cope with them, baby-sitting groups didn't work for the same reason, swimming pools wouldn't allow her in because there's no-one to help supervise them swimming, health clinics wouldn't let her make an appointment so she had to wait her turn with three, sometimes four small children, and so the list goes on.'

Night nursing help from statutory and other sources

> 'I had a night sitter two nights a week from social services for eight weeks. The help was very good.'

> 'If my husband's parents had not paid for four night nurses for six months for us, I don't know how we'd have managed. Night time help is the most essential thing. If you don't have sleep you can't go on at all.'

Three quarters of the mothers and fathers in the parents' study shared with each other the night time feeding and care of their higher order multiple birth children. Without some respite, this was described as both exhausting and stressful, confirming research findings reported elsewhere.[12] Nevertheless, parents of triplets seldom obtained any help at night and rarely, as shown in Table 7.1, a community night nursing service, or even a night sitter scheme.

In the survey of community nursing provision to households with higher order multiple birth children only a third of directors of community nursing services replied that there was the possibility of night nurse provision. Several directors remarked that it had been possible only in 'extreme' or 'very special' circumstances, where 'parents have been unable to cope or where there were considerable social problems'. The possibility of an unmet 'need' for night nurse provision was not generally acknowledged, unless there were overt social or medical problems in the household. Such a need was mentioned only once in the survey of community nursing provision, in relation to triplets born in 1985 and discharged home from hospital five weeks after delivery:

'Need to have NNEB student or trained nursery nurse who could help evenings and nights for several months. Not able to within budget.'

Households with quintuplets and sextuplets have been provided with nursing support during the nights for as long as a year, however. The cost of providing this care can come either from health authority community nursing services or from social services departments. In some areas there has been collaboration between health and social services after agreement, at a multi-disciplinary case discussion or conference, that it was necessary to provide an offer of special nursing services or to relieve parents in some other way of total responsibility for their children at night. Some authorities had night 'sitters' available within the district nursing service, to be used in exceptional circumstances. Others called on the services of the Red Cross or contacted volunteers from the Volunteer Bureau to provide an overnight feeding service several times a week.

Table 7.1

Provision of local authority night nurse

	Triplets		Quadruplets and Quintuplets	
	Number	Per cent	Number	Per cent
None provided	261	94.9	14	58.3
Brief help in emergency	1	0.4	0	–
A few weeks	3	1.1	0	–
About a month	1	0.4	0	–
About two months	6	2.2	4	16.7
Three months or more	2	0.7	5	20.8
Still continuing	1	0.4	1	4.2
Total	275	100.0	24	100.0

Source: Parents study.

Table 7.1 shows that in the parents' study only five per cent of the 275 triplet households and 42 per cent of the 24 quadruplet and quintuplet households had received health or local authority night nurse provision, or a night sitter, for any period at all. One of the mothers of triplets wrote that she only obtained such assistance in an emergency when the babies were under two months of age:

'Only had a "night sitter" (not a nurse) for two nights when we both had flu.'

The parents of one set of quadruplets were provided with a few weeks' help at night after the second born and fourth born of their quadruplets came home. This was only provided, after a struggle, as the mother of the quadruplets described:

'It was a terrible fight to start with, and when [first-born and third-born quadruplet] came home with their tracheotomies the AHA (Area Health Authority) supplied night nurses for a further 13 nights. We then went on TV and had public donations to pay for night nurses. This has since run out.'

She wrote subsequently with the tragic news that her first-born quadruplet had died and that she again had the help of night nurses paid for by the health authority:

'. . . the Area Health Authority have stopped fighting over things and supplied nurses seven nights a week . . . they won't take them away until [third-born quad's] trachi [tracheotomy] is removed.'

Five women reported that they had found no difficulty with the night nurse assistance they received. However, 14 mothers did describe stressful difficulties in obtaining the service in the first place, in establishing a trusting relationship with the person provided, or of experiencing disappointment in the provision received. Sometimes considerable pressure was brought to bear before the service was provided:

'I had to threaten to have a nervous breakdown (I was very close to it) and it took my doctor, my neighbour (who is in the social services), my health visitor, my midwife, my mother-in-law and my husband to secure this service.'

Mothers who each obtained about two months' help at night wrote:

'[Service] was not arranged until the triplets had been home for six weeks after which time I was ill with exhaustion.'

'I was originally promised three months cover, five nights per week. Unfortunately this did not materialise and only 46 nights were provided over the period 20.2.86 to 1.5.86 inclusive. The night cover was from 12.00 midnight to 6.00 am, which meant we were up till past midnight and again at 5.45 am to relieve the nurse as the babies were kept downstairs and we would not leave them unattended at any time . . . was never any weekend cover even if my husband had to work over the weekend. There was no cover if there was a bank holiday, or if the nurse was ill for a night.'

'The lady who helped was an ex home help (social services) employed especially to work with us [as a night sitter] but not trained in any way. She had fixed ideas about how to deal with babies. totally opposite to our own ideas. She left the babies to cry, thereby waking the whole household because she believed they'd got into the habit of waking.'

This last mother subsequently paid a friend of a friend £15 for one night a week to come and help through the night over a three month period. Other mothers described a variety of partial arrangements to obtain some sleep:

'We didn't have any [help at night] to begin with, at all. One of the nurses on the special care unit used to come [to our house] about once every two weeks I suppose, and I would feed her and in return she would do the night shift because it was her night off from the hospital. She would come out and she would just sit all night waiting for them to wake up, which was great. That was the only time we got sleep.'

In a handful of cases, the provision of an untrained 'night sitter', on an emergency basis, for one or two nights a week did much to alleviate the chronic exhaustion and tiredness of the mother and often of both parents. Nevertheless some of these mothers told how they had to reach breaking point before the possibility of such assistance was seriously discussed.

Help from local authority social services

Newly-delivered mothers may be supported by hospital-based social workers attached to maternity or neonatal wards. These 'hospital social workers' are well placed to attempt to ensure that practical help is forthcoming when a mother is discharged home from hospital. They can make enquiries from the hospital, liaise with health authorities and social services departments and establish what level of provision is likely to be available. In addition, these social workers are positively associated with the health services. The perceived stigma of being 'known to social services' seems to be avoided. Elsewhere, liaison health visitors working in neonatal units serve a similar function.

Most local authorities are able to provide some 'home help' or 'home care' services to newly-delivered mothers on a means-tested basis. In fact, this service originated in child welfare legislation and was first introduced in 1918 as a supplement to domiciliary maternity services. The breakdown of statistics about home helps' work by client group was discontinued following the Rayner review of Government Statistical Services in 1981 but there is no doubt that 'maternity cases' now constitute only a very small part of the workload of home helps and home carers. The emphasis is on homecare services designed to meet the needs of elderly, disabled and housebound people.[13] Mothers of young infants are seldom regarded as being housebound. Services are provided, for the most part, to people aged 65 and over. Home helps may sometimes be called upon to provide a single parent with another pair of hands or to monitor a situation for a social worker, for example where there is a suspected case of non-accidental injury to a child, but the service is usually targeted on elderly people living alone.[14] Also, the service typically continues until the elderly person dies.

The home help service is, nonetheless, the main route by which the social services channel support and domiciliary care to households which include children from a higher order multiple birth. The official reason given for allocating the service in the first place may be because a mother of triplets who is about to be discharged from hospital has already one other young child at home, or because she has had a caesarean delivery or a hysterectomy. The fact that she has delivered triplets may not come into the administrative reckoning and she may receive a very short term contract service.

In the early 1980s, one of the mothers of triplets included in the study compiled a series of 'Supertwins' newsletters, which were circulated to mothers of higher order multiple birth children. In the summer 1983 issue of the newsletter she offered advice about home helps:

'I have recently had contact with lots of mothers of triplets and quadruplets who have either not had a home help or have had very little help. This is an awful situation as I do feel that you just cannot cope alone. Perhaps you gave up the fight to have one too easily. I know of one mother who refused to take her babies home until she was promised a home help at a reasonable price. Whilst I am not advocating that you all resort to such tactics, she was successful. I do appreciate that you don't feel emotionally up to the hassle when you have just had the babies. Another problem has been that some have had an unsuitable home help and stopped the service because of this. Please don't do this. I had this problem and it was very awkward but a discreet phone-call to the H.H. [home-help] supervisor was again successful and the result was that I had a superb person who has become a family friend. If all else fails you can write to your M.P. or local councillor.'[15]

As shown in Table 7.2, all but one household with quadruplets and 61 per cent of the households with triplets were provided with at least some help from a local authority home help. In the majority of cases the time allocated to these households was spent doing cleaning, hoovering and ironing. The details provided about the nature and extent of this help was seldom similar. Not only were there variations from authority to authority in terms of the tasks undertaken, and particularly whether home helps could include child care tasks, but also in terms of the flexibility over the timing of the help, the number of hours per week and the length of time for which the service was provided. Indeed, the nature and extent of help provided varied in different areas of the same authority. Much depended upon the discretionary assessment of 'needs' by the home help organiser. The period of time a home help is allocated to a household is a matter for the organiser's judgement. These assessments are not standardised. As has already been mentioned, provision may be on medical grounds in the first instance. One mother of triplets explained that the three hours daily help she initially received was because she was recovering from major surgery.

'Award of home help service in first instance was on the grounds of my hysterectomy *not* multiple birth. I may not have received home help otherwise. When service terminated after three months I found I couldn't cope at feed times. GP arranged reinstatement.'

This mother also made arrangements for additional domestic help, on a private basis, for four hours a week, from the time when her triplets were aged three months until they were eight months old.

Where a home help was provided to the mothers of triplets, for almost three quarters of them this help was provided for six months or more. For just over a third, such help provided for a year or more. When appeals for an extension were supported by the mother's health visitor and/or doctor they were often successful. In a few instances the help provided was generous. One mother had a home aide for four hours a day, five days a week for the first two months plus a home help, also for four hours a day, five days a week to help exclusively with the feeding of the triplets. A second home help came twice a week to do shopping for her until the children reached school age. These helpers were provided at no cost to the parents after they had been means-tested.

The range of the work undertaken, the number of hours per week, the time period and the cost of this help to the parents varied considerably. One mother of quadruplets wrote that she received '60 hours a week at first. Cut to 50 hours after six months, then to 40 at about 12 months until down to 15 hours at two years'. Another described how she gave up her home help after about six months because of the cost:

Table 7.2

Provision of local authority home help

	Triplets		Quadruplets	
	Number	Per cent	Number	Per cent
None provided	107	38.9	1	4.2
Still receiving home help service	33	12.0	5	20.8
A few weeks	21	7.6	1	4.2
About three months	25	9.1	2	8.3
About six months	30	10.9	3	12.5
About 1 year but less than 2	36	13.1	1	4.2
About 2 years but less than 3	14	5.1	9	37.5
Three or more years	9	3.3	2	8.3
Total	275	100.0	24	100.0

Source: Parents' study.

> 'Originally two hours per morning and two hours per afternoon, though after the first few weeks, the afternoon session reduced to one hour maximum and sometimes not used at all. After four months, morning reduced to one and one half hours. Nil cost originally, though for last month I had to pay £4.00 per hour [in 1986], which I found too costly for the benefit I obtained from it,'

A handful of mothers with one or more older children had a home help provided by the local authority during their pregnancy as well as after the birth. One of these mothers, with three older children, had a cervical stitch at 28 weeks of pregnancy and had then been allowed to return home until she went into hospital to have her triplets at 37 weeks of pregnancy. During this period she had a home help for two months. Another mother, who had one older child, had just been provided with a home help when she was admitted to hospital for 'bed rest' at 28 weeks of pregnancy.

The problems most frequently mentioned with home helps, or with the home care service in general were inappropriate timing, inflexibility and unreliability of the service. The following comments indicate some of the problems that arose:

> 'Limited to morning visits. First home help was reasonably adaptable re timing [of] help with feeds. Second home help was given strict and regular time therefore not always when I need her most. Had to leave mid-feed!'

> 'Sometimes my home help has been called away to someone else and that has caused havoc in my home with things not getting done.'

> 'To start with home help was changed several times which wasn't good for the babies. 'We have had to fight to keep our home help. They wanted to withdraw her when the girls were 1.'

It is clear that, in the majority of instances, local authority home help organisers, and the home helps themselves, have at least some difficulty accommodating the unusual needs of these households. Such difficulties, however, must be viewed in the context, not only of the numbers of elderly and of the very high work-loads in some areas, but also as one aspect of the long standing debate about how the home help service operates, how organisers order priorities and whether alternative or supplementary help can be provided by, for instance, a family aide. One local authority social services department conveyed in a letter some of the difficulties to be faced in deciding what help can be provided to a household soon to include triplets:

'[The parents-to-be of triplets] were visited by our Home Care Organiser [early in 1989]. Following that visit [the mother-to-be] was offered a minimum of three visits per week between one and a half and two hours, with a possibility of a maximum of five depending on other demands on the Home Care Service, including stresses that will be on it during the summer period due to holidays, sickness, etc. This, of course, will be reviewed when [the mother-to-be] comes out of hospital and also when the children return from hospital. One of the things that we will be looking at is whether we can use a Family Aide, or some other support service. At present we do not have a post filled, but we hope the situation over the next three months will change. It will then be a matter of prioritising [the mother's] needs, together with other people who are requesting the services of a Family Aide. This would have to be a local discussion taken at the time as such a resource became available, if it became available.'

Help from general practitioners

Usually the mother's GP was aware of her higher order multiple pregnancy for many months before delivery. Most doctors have, however, no experience either of such deliveries or of the care of the babies. Unprepared, they may fail to grasp the situation and the extent of the exhaustion and anxiety that confronts the parents.

In answer to a specific question about the care, advice and help received in the first year from their GP, 38 per cent of the parents of triplets and 58 per cent of the parents of quadruplets praised or made very favourable comments, as shown in Table 7.3. These included 'the best', 'excellent', 'great', 'very sympathetic and helpful'. It was notable that 62 per cent of parents of triplets did not make comments of this sort.

Parents were very appreciative if their GP had been supportive from the outset. They welcomed early contact with their GP, if not by regular visits then by phone. Such contact was particularly welcomed in the weeks after one or more baby had been discharged from hospital:

'During the first week he phoned at odd times to see if we were OK.'

'Our GP was super. She called in once a week and I found it reassuring to know someone cared and appeared to understand the problems.'

'Very supportive – would just pop in when passing to check all was well.'

'Came to visit regularly when we just came out of hospital.'

Table 7.3

Parents' views of the care, advice and help received from their GP in first year

	Triplets		Quadruplets	
	Number	Per cent	Number	Per cent
Favourable comments only	105	38.2	14	58.3
Critical comments only	54	19.6	3	12.5
Mixed reaction	9	3.3	1	4.2
'Nothing special'/'just routine'/minimal care	39	14.2	1	4.2
None received	22	8.0	2	8.3
No answer	46	16.7	3	12.5
Total	275	100.0	24	100.0

Source: Parents' study.

Negative responses from parents centred on their doctors' unsympathetic attitude towards their situation and on their reluctance to make home visits. Some of these parents wrote that they had subsequently changed their GP:

'No help was given, and when I did need the doctor I was expected to drag the whole family to surgery.

'Tried to give me anti-depressants when all I really needed was practical help with the babies day and night.'

'Very bad with self, refusing to accept that I had post-natal depression.'

'My GP refused to come on a home visit on one occasion when [second born triplet] was sick and it was snowing and I had no transport to get to the surgery. He said I should get on a bus. I have since changed GPs.'

'[My] GP was extremely unhelpful and unsympathetic and I have since left him.'

The knowledge that their doctor was accessible should the need arise was important to parents. They made comments about their GP such as 'always at hand by phone', 'would see the children any time we needed him to'. One mother wrote a glowing account of the sympathetic care that she and her family had received from their GP:

'He is, and has been fantastic. Other than immediate family, he is the most supportive person. He has called in to check on us every week since they were born. He has come round at weekends and during the night if anyone has been ill and always has time to provide a shoulder for me to cry on. I do not know what I would have done without him at times.'

Most parents found difficulty getting to the surgery and so house calls for vaccinations as well as for bouts of sickness were welcomed. Parents' comments included mention of specific instances of help, particularly where their GP had contacted social services to secure, or restore, practical help and support.

'GP always supportive – extra [home] help due to him.'

In one instance the GP had herself regularly taken a triplet set into her home to care for them for a weekend:

'[Female] Doctor took triplets every 6-9 weeks to give us a break and let us have time to spend with our older daughter who was only two years old.'

The role of health visitors

Health visitors, despite their training in nursing, and their knowledge of child development, are unlikely to have experience with families that include triplets or higher order births. Nor is there any written guidance about the best ways to support these families. Most importantly, in many districts staffing levels within the health visiting service do not permit the provision of the kind of intensive service often required.

Table 7.4

Visits from health visitor

Frequency of visits	Triplets		Quadruplets and quintuplets		Total	
	Number	Per cent	Number	Per cent	Number	Per cent
Did not visit	3	1.1	0	–	3	1.0
Once or twice	50	18.2	5	20.8	55	18.4
Regular over several weeks	12	4.4	1	4.2	13	4.3
Regular over several months	101	36.7	6	25.0	107	35.8
Regular over first year	89	32.4	10	41.7	99	33.1
Visits over longer period	7	2.5	2	8.3	9	3.0
No answer	13	4.7	0	–	13	4.3
Total	275	100.0	24	100.0	299	100.0

Source: Parents' study.

All but three of the households in the parents' survey had been visited by a health visitor after one or more triplet, quadruplet, or quintuplet came home from hospital. After the initial home visit, the number and frequency of subsequent visits to these households differed considerably, as is shown in Table 7.4. Three quarters had been visited by one or more health visitors for at least several months of the first year. A third were visited regularly over the first year and a few for many months longer.

In contrast, 19 per cent of mothers indicated that their health visitors had called only on one or two occasions and a further four per cent reported that their health visitors had visited frequently but only in the first few weeks. Almost a quarter of mothers, therefore, were visited only at the outset of their first year with their triplet, quadruplet, or quintuplet babies. In a few of these cases this was because the health visitor had become ill or had left and not been replaced. Only sometimes could the mother turn to another person in the health service. Comments on the help received from health visitors included:

'Helped organise prior to birth. Contacted social services; local playschool for a place for my son; reps. [sales representatives] at clinic etc. Unfortunately she left not long after the birth, so I received really no help. No health visitor called regularly to check how I was coping physically and mentally.'

'My health visitor left to have a baby herself and was not replaced, so I only saw relief health visitors when I went to the baby clinic.'

'[Health visitor] Useless – hadn't a clue. But the paediatric liaison officer at the hospital was marvellous. She let me ring whenever I wanted. She visited quite often, and if I asked her to come because I was desperate, she came.'

As Table 7.5 shows, those who had been visited more frequently by their health visitors were more likely to have had no criticism or to be very satisfied indeed with the help provided:

Table 7.5

Parents' comments about help provided by health visitor, by frequency of visits

	Frequency of visits by health visitor			
	Once or twice/ regular visits over several weeks	Regular visits over several months	Regular visits over first year	Visits over longer period
Percentage with:				
Positive comment about help provided	13.2	49.5	67.7	100.0
No positive comment	86.8	50.5	33.3	–
Total	100.0	100.0	100.0	100.0
Number	68	107	99	9

Source: Parents' study.

'My health visitor was invaluable in that she would help in any way at all at any time of the day.'

'I couldn't have survived without her. She would call at least once a day at first, then as often as she could. She became a friend to be relied on.'

'She took an interest in me as well as the children.'

One mother described her first health visitor very critically, reporting that eventually she was 'banned from their home' by her husband and herself because of the upset she caused. She commented about this woman's successor:

'Second HV [health visitor] did development tests at home, booked immunisation appointments half hour before everyone else to avoid waiting. Helped move the babies from car to surgery and back.'

Where parents did expand on the positive help provided by their health visitor it was in terms of the ready provision of helpful advice, practical help and encouragement given, as one mother put it, 'in a friendly, not overbearing way'. Another mother conveyed her appreciation that her health visitor had both made her feel that she could cope with the situation and had included her husband in discussions. Words like 'reassuring' and 'supportive' appeared frequently in accounts:

'Mainly moral help – plus the usual visits to the Clinic. She called for me and drove me there when necessary. She informed me of benefits available.'

'She was the same HV I'd had for my son so I already knew her. She was very practical and knowledgeable and supportive and arranged nappies, a few boxes of baby food and even found two night nurses for us! Unfortunately we changed our GP and lost her and the next health visitor was out of her depth and useless.'

'The HV was a godsend. She was in her fifties and single. She was prepared to come at any time of day or night to help. Over a Bank Holiday she came to bath and feed all three so that we could have a meal by ourselves, uninterrupted. She gave us much practical advice and help (providing us with incontinence roll to use as disposable nappies). She was always encouraging and practical about their progress. I worried over their weight and height but she always pointed out that I was only 5'2" and they'd never lost weight. I cannot praise her enough – her obvious care about the babies and ourselves as well as her very practical approach made her a great friend and ally. Her retirement was our loss and her successor doesn't live up to her standards.'

'She came regularly and never seemed in a hurry to go; she weighed them at home for several weeks and was always ready with help and support. She was the first to admit that she had no experience with triplets and never thrust advice at me or laid down her rules. She always said "They're your children and you will know them best". She has also done several checks and assessments at home to save me the trouble of going to the clinic. I don't think I would have survived without her. She gave me her phone number in case of emergency which I have used a couple of times.'

The potential significance of the health visitor is clear, not only as a source of reassurance, but also as a mediator and facilitator. She can act as a link, not only by informing the prospective parents about the services that are available but in arranging the provision of a home help antenatally, or arranging for the service to be extended or re-instated after the birth. She can provide an ear within the home and, outside, a medium for the stressed and vulnerable mother and her children. 'Mrs W was my voice', wrote one mother. It is also clear that to avoid distressing crisis management in the first year sensitive and sustained contact is necessary in the first few months, rather than a few fleeting visits 'to view', sometimes with students in tow. Some health visitors seemed insufficiently aware of parents' anxiety and the restrictions placed on their lives by the care of their higher order multiple birth children.

There seems good reason, at the very least, for health visitors to take portable scales to weigh the babies in their homes to avoid the considerable difficulties for the mother in taking them and possibly other young children as well, to the child health clinic. Positive comments provided by the parents indicated that their needs were quite straightforwardly for advice, support and reassurance so that they could overcome day to day problems and cope confidently with their situation.

Nevertheless, only 31 per cent of the respondents to the survey of community nursing services envisaged any special health visitor provision. One mother of triplets, a health visitor herself, spoke of her disquiet:

> 'Having talked to other mothers of triplets throughout the country, I am quite horrified at the lack of health visitor input. That they've had to struggle to a clinic. Not had support at home from the health visitor. Not had support from the midwife. Really been left to get on with it.'

She emphasised the particular importance of a follow-up visit after diagnosis of a triplet or higher order birth, as an essential first step for the well being of the mother.

Anticipated needs and possible strategies for the care of the babies could be discussed in the antenatal period with women with higher order multiple pregnancies, but the responses to the parents' study suggest that they seldom were. Difficulty arose when there was uncertainty as to who would provide help, when they could provide it and at what cost. As a consequence, some parents, bitterly disappointed that their expectations of help were not being met, vented their anger on their health visitor. One health authority manager described the level of help eventually negotiated for one household with quadruplets, but not until the relationships between the health authority and the parents of the quadruplets had become strained to the limit:

> 'Nursery Nurse 9am-5pm weekdays (Social Services provision); Private Nursery Nurse 9am-5pm weekends at cost of £80. After this became too expensive for family, Health Authority took responsibility for payments – employing a 'bank' contract. One home help from 7pm-8am for three nights. One home help from 1am-8am for other four nights. One home help from 9am- 5pm Fridays. College student one day per week. Making a total of 139 hours per week extra help. This was in addition to the health visitor who was going into the house several times a week and helping to feed, etc.'

The health visitor, in particular, had been distressed to meet with increasing hostility during the early months, as the parents felt that the health authority was not responding adequately to their needs. There is a need for a 'named person' of sufficient authority such as a health visitor to take responsibility for acting as an initial point of contact and to co-ordinate the various services and help provided. Parents are not in a position to take on this co-ordinating role themselves.

Help from students, trainees, volunteers and support groups

In all these households, child care in the early years is likely to be shared with others, not necessarily smoothly or with continuity. Usually, the administrative and budgetary arrangements of the health and social services cannot accommodate their needs readily, as has been illustrated earlier in this chapter. As a result, supplementary, complementary or alternative sources of practical help and support may need to be negotiated. These are not 'ordinary' households under temporary pressure. Parents require some form of respite from the care of and responsibility for their children as well as practical help, but before they are born and when they first come home from hospital there may be reluctance to admit the need for help.

Help and support to parents of triplets, quadruplets and quintuplets came, not only from relatives, friends, neighbours and the statutory services, but also from volunteers. Individuals also helped because they were engaged in community service or were in some kind of training. When asked, 'Are you aware of other sources of support (e.g. volunteer schemes) in your area to which parents of these children might be referred?', the respondents to the survey of community nursing services identified a number of such sources. Ten per cent of respondents mentioned the voluntary initiative Home-Start, in which volunteers from local schemes, all mothers themselves, visit, and offer to parents with children aged under five, support and practical help in their own homes.[15,16] A similar proportion identified trainee nursery nurses as an additional resource. Just under half mentioned a twins club or the Twins and Multiple Births Association (TAMBA) which is a national multiple birth support organisation. Over a third identified other provision, including community and good neighbour schemes, church organisations and mothers' self-help groups.

Such helpers may come forward on an *ad hoc* basis. They may be recruited by the parents themselves or, more usually, by the health visitor or another health professional. Previously unknown individuals and voluntary agencies have provided a level and quality of support and practical help that some parents have reported in glowing terms. In some instances, support and help with feeding from members of the National Childbirth Trust, or the arrival of a volunteer from Home-Start or telephone contact with another mother of triplets through TAMBA has provided a lifeline at a crucial time.

Apart from friends, neighbours and the occasional relative, people mentioned by parents in response to the question, 'Did you receive any regular support and practical help from friends and other people during the first year?' were described as nursery nurse trainees, community work or social care students from local schools, and Youth Training Scheme trainees. Also listed, however, were a handful of individuals to whom mothers gave the designation 'volunteer' or 'voluntary worker' under the heading 'relationship to you'. Sometimes the individuals were not given any designated relationship at all. Two mothers mentioned 'National Childbirth Trust supporters' who 'came in to help with feeds' in this way, as did two of the five mothers who listed Home-Start. Other mothers in the study were known to have received the assistance of Home-Start volunteers but not in the first year after the birth. One mother listed Home-Support, a local community programme project. Students, trainees and volunteers from these various sources at best provided a mother with a regular personal contact. When well suited, such individuals provided a qualitatively different kind of help to that usually provided by the statutory services, in terms of time or priorities or both.

The major criticisms raised by the mothers in the parents' survey in relation to these sources of help were firstly, the provision of students, trainees or volunteers who were unsuitable, in the sense that they could not cope with the situation in which they found themselves. Secondly, such individuals were sometimes unreliable. Volunteers who offered to help with feeding, for instance, sometimes either cancelled at short notice or just did not turn up. Also several mothers made the point that busy mothers cannot supervise. Parents under stress are vulnerable because when offered help they are more likely to accept. Initial qualms about the suitability of a carer may be overridden if no other source of help is offered.

A questionnaire survey undertaken by Home-Start Consultancy in July 1989 showed the scale of the task of attempting to meet the diverse needs and demands of mothers who were caring for their higher order multiple birth children, and some of the difficulties of voluntary agency involvement. Twenty-five Home-Start schemes reported that they were currently providing, or had provided, volunteers for 40 households which include triplets or quadruplets. One of these schemes also expected to find volunteers for a further two sets of triplets in the near future. In addition, one Home-Start scheme anticipates that it will shortly provide such support for the first time. Twenty six Home-Start schemes reported that they had no experience of such involvement.

Most of the households who had been placed with a Home-Start volunteer were referred to Home-Start when the higher order multiple birth children were less than a year old. Over half had been referred either prior to delivery or in the early weeks following the birth. In the majority of cases, the source of referral was a health visitor, although a handful were from hospital social workers. Two were self-referrals and there was also one referral each from a twins club, child guidance clinic and a social services home help organiser. In total, 52 volunteers currently are or have been involved. They either visited sequentially or worked together in pairs to provide help with feeding, for instance. Sometimes as many as five volunteers were involved with one household. The volunteers provided an average of between six and eight hours per week per household. Two Home-Start organisers however reported cases where volunteers had provided help for up to 18 and 20 hours per week respectively. In general, however, the time needed to provide help to some families was far more than one volunteer could offer. One organiser had found it necessary to set up a rota of volunteers. However, these volunteers felt 'programmed in' and missed the establishment of a mother/volunteer relationship, which is one of the fundamental objectives of this voluntary initiative.

Over half the organisers of Home-Start had not found difficulties in matching volunteers with families with multiple births, but, as one organiser commented, the task centred on 'finding volunteers able to give the amount of time required, at the time when required e.g. tea-times, bath times, bed times'. Organisers drew attention to the need for volunteers to be fit and to have strong backs to cope with all the lifting, carrying and manoeuvring prams and pushchairs. Others pointed out that some volunteers found that they were effectively 'on call' and that this was a considerable pressure when little other help was forthcoming. Volunteers also had to attend to their own families' needs and could not always provide the time that was required.

Beyond this urgent problem of securing practical help, many parents valued the sympathy, support and advice of other parents of higher order multiple birth children. Of the 24 parents of quadruplets and quintuplets, half had been at some time a member of a twins club and/or TAMBA and over a third were members at the time of completing their questionnaire. Fifty four per cent of parents of triplets had belonged to a twins club and/or TAMBA and 35 per cent were currently members. TAMBA gave the parents' study publicity and therefore these proportions reflect the fact that TAMBA members not already included in the study contacted OPCS and were sent a questionnaire.

Overall, positive comments predominated, both about twins' clubs and about TAMBA. Some mothers mentioned that they held some position of responsibility in their local club or in TAMBA. Others mentioned that they had helped to found their local twins club. A mother who was an enthusiastic founding member of a two month old twins club expressed what, for her, was the supportive feature:

'It helps to know that the problems you are having are not just you. It also helps you just to talk about problems and learn what help, if any, others are receiving.

Other mothers echoed this 'shared experience' aspect of their club:

'I felt the Twins Club immensely helpful – mainly moral help – giving encouragement and unconscious support – when one sees other mothers finding life a little stressful and difficult one draws support and encouragement from this.'

'Good to be able to discuss and help other people with any problems.

'Great for letting off steam – still believe hospitals, baby clinics, GPs, etc are *very* bad in general at encouraging people to join. Mums, especially, if at home with three plus babies really need to get out for a couple of hours – if just to have a moan – and feel 'normal' for once!'

For some parents the experience of learning to cope with three, four or five infants born of the same delivery and sharing experiences supportively with other parents in a similar situation are closely interwoven. Supertwins, as a support and contact group, can, and does, provide a sense of solidarity. For some, membership can facilitate lifeline contacts with other parents and, especially, a voice and a listening ear at the end of the phone in times of crisis. This form of support is invaluable.

Nevertheless, given the extraordinary child care situation, there are certain tensions surrounding the roles of mutual support, particularly if the higher order multiple birth children in the households concerned are close together in age. Parents are seldom in a position in the early years to offer practical help in emergencies to others in the same situation. Also, a support group such as Supertwins has difficulty reaching out beyond those who can be in contact by telephone, who are confidently mobile, can arrange baby-sitting and can make time to travel to meetings:

'When the children were very small I never seemed to have the time to phone or go to the club and also I have never wanted to spend my free time talking about my children or anyone else's.'

'Although I was asked to join the local twins club, I had very little spare time to attend any meeting and did not have transport during the day.'

'I did not join, mainly because I had no time to, until two years after the birth and I think by that time I had struggled through the worst period. I only went to three meetings and, as I was not finding them beneficial and my time was precious, I stopped going.'

Members of twins clubs and Supertwins welcomed the financial savings which resulted from sales of clothing and equipment. In addition, many benefited from advice about what sources of help might be available if requested.

Conclusions

Parents needed additional help to care for their triplets, quadruplets and quintuplets. Initially, they needed to get some sleep, and to ensure that their children were fed with the minimum of stress. Later, they also needed to have some time to themselves. Mothers, in particular, needed some hours of respite from the continuous care of their children. The difficulties arose when there was uncertainty as to who would provide such help, when and at what cost.

It could not be presumed that relatives would rally round. Relatives were not always able, or willing, to help carry the physical and psychological burdens of care. The majority of parents in the parents' study had at least one relative on whom they had relied for support and practical help in the crucial early months after some or all of their triplets or quadruplets came home from hospital. Few relatives could provide sustained help and support beyond this time. Over half of the parents reported that their relatives had difficulty providing assistance because of their age, infirmity, distance or lack of transport. Not many parents could rely on relatives for long-term help and support on a daily basis. In addition, fewer than half of the parents recorded that they had one or more friends or neighbours who had provided regular support and practical help during the first year. About a third of the parents did not acknowledge any help from relatives, friends or neighbours in the first year after the birth.

The level of practical help and support required, at night and during the day, is more than it is normal to expect other people to volunteer to provide. As a result, many parents asked for help from the health and social services. The needs and demands associated with the care of these children is an exacting test, not only of relationships, commitments and priorities, but also of the effectiveness of the health and social services in providing appropriate help and support.

Parents seldom received help at night with feeding and child care. A very small proportion of the households which included triplets, and less than half of the quadruplet and quintuplet households, had received health or local authority night nurse provision, or a night sitter, for any period at all. On the other hand, a local authority home help was provided for all but one household which included quadruplets and over half of the households with triplets. Most households with triplets received this service for at least six months, although the number of hours per week per household varied greatly. Where appeals for extension of the service were supported by the mother's health visitor and/or general practitioner, they were often successful.

Parents' accounts suggest that, particularly in relation to triplets, some general practitioners failed to appreciate the stresses of the situation and offered neither sympathetic nor accessible care. Parents were very appreciative if their general practitioners had been supportive from the outset. They welcomed early contact after one or more baby had been discharged from hospital and regular reassurance about the well-being of their children. House calls for vaccinations as well as for bouts of illness were welcomed as most parents found difficulty getting to the surgery with their children. Where parents did expand on the positive help provided by their health visitor it was in terms of the ready provision of helpful advice, practical help and encouragement.

Help and support was also received from other sources: from nursery nurse trainees, community work or social care students, Youth Training Scheme trainees and voluntary initiatives such as Home-Start and the National Childbirth Trust. However each trainee, student or volunteer, could not usually provide more than supplementary or complementary assistance and support over an extended period. In addition, shared membership of a twins club or of the TAMBA support group, Supertwins, provided some parents with the sympathy, support and advice of other parents of higher order multiple birth children and access to sales of secondhand clothing and equipment for their children.

Mothers themselves suggested that they would have welcomed a home visit by a midwife or health visitor antenatally to talk through their concerns, to reassure. and to identify potential problems in securing practical help and support. Anticipated need and strategies of care could be discussed with women with higher order multiple pregnancies in the antenatal period, but seldom are. Specific problems at the individual and the local level could then be anticipated, alternatives researched beforehand and potential gaps in support and help mapped out. Parents and also local authority health and social service managers identified as a priority assistance with child care, from whatever source, particularly with night and day time feeding in the first year, with help to get out of the house to parks and play areas and to participate in supervised play and preschool in the second and third year. Mothers of higher order multiple births risk becoming isolated and housebound, particularly in the first two to three years, if they have no-one to share the responsibility of the children nor a companion to accompany them on outings with their children. This, not only has consequences for a mother's use of child health services, but has consequences for the mother's well being.

There is a need for a 'named person', such as a health visitor, to take responsibility and to act as a co-ordinator for the services required. Otherwise sympathetic contact by professionals may not be maintained and community resources may not be made available. Anticipatory work is particularly necessary as it is evident that there are continuing problems in identifying budgets to fund services to these households. Furthermore, to avoid stigmatising these households as 'at risk' in the attempt to secure resources, flexibility is needed when interpreting local authority guidelines and legislation. It may be the case that supplementary, complementary or alternative sources of practical help and support, particularly with feeding, may be satisfactorily negotiated by the health visitor to meet some of the diverse needs of these households. Several mothers made the point, however, that busy mothers cannot supervise those who are helping her and that sometimes the helper proves unreliable. These households become 'high need' by virtue of the sheer number of young children of the same age. The parents are potentially vulnerable because they may hesitate to turn away any source of help. A 'named person' attuned to the particular circumstances could renegotiate the situation.

Parents seek the assurance of reliable practical help. They need resources in terms of time, people and money to ensure that they can continue to carry out their responsibilities. They also need support on a day-to-day basis; and appropriate professional intervention in times of emergency. In order for parents to request practical help and support, they need to know of, or to be able to conceive of, particular sources of help or services that would meet their sense of need. In practice such services may be unavailable or have yet to be devised.

References

1. Australian Multiple Birth Association Inc. Proposal submitted to the federal government concerning 'Act of Grace' payments for triplets and quadruplet families. Coogee, Australia: AMBA, 1984.

2. Land H, Parker R A. 'Family policies in the United Kingdom: the hidden dimensions'. In: Kamerman S. Kahn A (eds) Family policy: government and families in fourteen countries. New York: Columbia University Press: 1978.

3. Morgan D H J. The family, politics and social theory. London: Routledge and Kegan Paul, 1985.

4. Young M, Willmott P. Family and kinship in East London. London: Routledge and Kegan Paul, 1957.

5. Rosser C, Harris C C. The family and social change. London: Routledge and Kegan Paul, 1965.

6. O'Connor P, Brown G W. Supportive relationships: fact or fancy? Journal of Social and Personal Relationships 1984; 1: 159-175.

7. Curtice L. The first year of life: promoting the health of babies in the community. London: Maternity Alliance, 1989.

8. Cornwell J. Hard-earned lives: accounts of health and illness from East London. London: Tavistock, 1984.

9. Hill M. Sharing child care in early parenthood. London: Routledge and Kegan Paul, 1987.

10. Wilson G. Women's work: the role of grandparents in intergenerational transfers. Sociological Review 1987; 35: 703-720.

11. Glendinning C. Unshared care: Parents and their disabled children. London: Routledge and Kegan Paul, 1983.

12. Editorial. The dangers of not going to bed. Lancet 1989; i: 138-139.

13. Mitchell S, Middleton L. Local authority research on home help services: A review of aims, methods and conclusions for service management. Social Services Research 1988; 17: 1-11.

14. McKeganey N. The role of home help organisers. Social Policy and Administration 1989; 23: 171-188.

15. 'Supertwins' Newsletter No 4. August 1983.

16. Gibbons J, Thorpe S. Can voluntary support projects help vulnerable families? The work of Home-Start. British Journal of Social Work. 1989; 19: 189-202.

17. Van der Eyken W. Home-Start: A four year evaluation. Leicester: Home-Start Consultancy, 1982.

Chapter 8 – Disabilities and health problems in childhood

Alison J Macfarlane, Ann Johnson, Patrick Bower

'I was born one of triplets on Sunday sixth of July, 1958 . . . It was not until I was twelve months old it was discovered by our family doctor's relief that I was a cerebral palsy case. That particular evening when [he] examined me he stood me up in my cot. I over-balanced and fell over in a heap . . .

Whilst my brothers were soon into everything, I was the first to talk, to the surprise of both my parents. I spoke in full sentences, for instance, "I want to go to the toilet". As you can appreciate, by now we were over twelve months of age and I was not developing for a child of my age. It was at that time the local child specialist advised my parents that I was a spastic of normal intelligence . . .

When my parents were informed of my handicap they did not understand the extent of my brain damage nor what the future form would be.'

Paul Cain[1]

These extracts come from an unpublished autobiography, sent to us in response to press publicity about our study. In it, the author, who has right hemiplegia, describes his memories of his childhood development and compares it with that of his identical triplet brothers who do not have cerebral palsy.

In Chapter 6, we discussed congenital anomalies and other problems apparent at delivery. This chapter uses data from the survey of general practitioners to look at the extent to which impairments and other health problems were diagnosed and treated in childhood. It then goes on to discuss these findings in the light of the problems which arose with response to the survey of general practitioners.

After excluding two replies where information about the children was missing and nine replies where questionnaires had been inadvertently sent out even though fewer than three children had been discharged from hospital alive, data were available about 460 children from 137 sets of triplets, 11 sets of quadruplets and one set of quintuplets.

Cerebral palsy

Eight of the children were reported as having cerebral palsy. This gave a rate of 17.4 per thousand children from triplet and higher order births which is high compared with the rate of two per thousand usual in the general population.[2] All of the children for whom replies were received had weighed under 2,500 grams at birth and seven had weighed under 1,500 grams, giving a cerebral palsy rate of 68.0 per thousand of these children weighing under 1,500 grams at birth.

Three of the eight children with cerebral palsy came from the same triplet set and they are shown in the photograph opposite page 162. One of the three is quadriplegic. The other five children were the sole child with cerebral palsy in three sets of triplets and two sets of quadruplets.

Vision, hearing and speech problems

The vision problems reported by general practitioners are shown in Table 8.1. Nearly 10 per cent of the children had some sort of vision problem. Only four children, or one per cent, had serious problems. This rate is not particularly high.[3] Two of these four children were described as having severe vision loss and a further two had retinopathy of prematurity. This is a potentially blinding condition which can affect preterm babies.

Just over six per cent of the children had squints. A study of children in the general population showed that four per cent of children had a squint at the age of six years[4], so the percentage in our survey was marginally higher than would be expected by chance.

Only two children, or four per thousand had the severe and permanent hearing problems associated with sensori-neural deafness. This affects one per thousand of the general population.[2] On the other hand, 22 children (five per cent) had experienced conductive hearing loss or other temporary hearing problems associated with otitis media (middle ear disease) and other ear infections. This is much lower than in the National Study of Morbidity in General Practice, in which 38 per cent of children aged under four years had been seen by their GP for otitis media or other ear infections durinq the study year.[5]

All the children with hearing problems had weighed under 2,500 grams at birth, but the rates for children with birthweights under 1,500 grams were similar to those for children who had weighed between 1,500 and 2,499 grams.

Eighteen children, or four per cent, were reported to have shown some delay in speech development. The percentage was somewhat higher for children who had weighed under 1,500 grams at birth than for those who had weighed between 1,500 and 2,499 grams.

Convulsions

Convulsions were reported in nine children (two per cent). In five children these were associated with epilepsy while the other four had febrile convulsions. Four of the five children with epileptic convulsions had weighed under 1,500 grams at birth, whereas all those with febrile convulsions had weighed between 1,500 and 2,499 grams. Febrile convulsions are often under-reported, so the percentage of children affected may have been higher.

Illness and hospital admissions

Although some general practitioners gave information about consultations for infections, it was clear that this was far from comprehensive as no specific request was made for information about consultations for minor infections. The illness rates reported were far lower than those reported during a single year in the National Morbidity Study.[6]

As Table 8.2 shows, just over a fifth of the children had been admitted to hospital at least once and about three quarters of those admitted had had surgery. Some had been admitted for more than one type of surgery. The types of surgery done are shown in Table 8.3.

Given the reported rate of squints and middle ear problems, it was not surprising to find that two per cent of children had operations for squints and four per cent had myringotomy and/or had grommets inserted. It was more notable that two per cent had operations for pyloric stenosis, which is a partial obstruction of the stomach at the

Table 8.1

Vision problems reported by general practitioners

	Birthweight g								Total	
	Under 1500		1500–2499		2500 and over		Not known			
	Number	Per cent	Number	Per cent	Number	Per cent	Number	Per cent	Number	Per cent
Squint	11	11	13	4	0	–	5	10	29	6.3
Severe vision loss	1	1	1	0.3	0	–	0	–	2	0.4
Retinopathy of prematurity	2	2	0	–	0	–	0	–	2	0.4
Other vision problems	2	2	8	3	1	4	0	–	11	2.4
No problems reported	87	84	264	92	21	96	44	90	416	90.4
Total children	103	100	286	100	22	100	49	100	460	100.0

Source: Survey of general practitioners.

155

Table 8.2

Children who had been admitted to hospital at least once

| | Birthweight g | | | | | | | | Total | |
| | Under 1500 | | 1500–2499 | | 2500 and over | | Not known | | | |
	Number	Per cent	Number	Per cent	Number	Per cent	Number	Per cent	Number	Per cent
Admitted for surgery	26	25	34	12	2	9	10	20	72	16
Admitted for other reasons	6	6	16	6	0	–	3	6	25	5
All children admitted	32	31	50	17	2	9	13	26	97	21
Total children	103	100	286	100	22	100	49	100	460	100

Source: Survey of general practitioners

Table 8.3

Children who had had surgery

	Number	Per cent
Type of surgery		
Hernia	18	3.9
Squint	10	2.2
Pyloric stenosis	7	1.5
Tonsillectomy	7	1.5
Myringotomy/grommets	17	3.7
Other surgery	26	5.6
Total children	460	100.0

Note: Some children had more than one type of surgery, so numbers do not agree with those in Table 8.2
Source: Survey of general practitioners.

point where it joins the small intestine. In the population as a whole this usually affects only three children per thousand.[6]

Hospital admission was more common among children who had been born with very low birthweights. As Table 8.2 shows, 31 per cent of children with birthweights under 1,500 grams had spent some time in hospital, compared with 17 per cent of those who had weighed between 1,500 and 2,500 grams and nine per cent of those who had weighed 2,500 grams or over. This is broadly comparable with findings of a study of children born from 1974 to 1978 to residents of Oxfordshire and West Berkshire. In this, 27 per cent of children weighing under 1,500 grams at birth and nine per cent of those weighing 1,500 grams or over had been re-admitted to hospital by the age of two years.[7]

Congenital malformations

In all, 58 children or 126 per thousand, were said by general practitioners to have congenital malformations. Table 8.4 shows the types of malformations, tabulated by whether or not they had been noted by paediatricians in replies to the obstetric survey. Nineteen per cent of the malformations had been identified at birth, included in the case notes and reported on our questionnaire. On the other hand, 69 per cent had not been. In the remaining 12 per cent of cases there was no information either way on the baby's form in the obstetric survey. Table 6.12 shows that malformations were recorded at birth for 44.7 per thousand babies, some of whom died and were therefore not included in the general practitioners' survey. In contrast, Table 8.4 shows that 116.8 per thousand triplets covered in the general practitioners' survey had a malformation.

The most common malformations were the various cardiovascular malformations, which affected five per cent of the children. As is often the case, only a relatively small percentage of these, 14 per cent in our data, were diagnosed at birth. On the other hand, it is likely that a proportion of malformations were reported heart murmurs which did not reflect underlying congenital malformations.

After these, the most common malformations were talipes (club foot), those of the urogenital system, which include malformations of the genital organs, bladder and

Table 8.4

Comparison of congenital malformations reported by general practitioners and those reported at birth

	Congenital malformations reported by general practitioners			
	Recorded at birth	Not recorded at birth	No infor- mation at birth	Total
Central nervous system		1		1
Ear and eye	1	1	1	3
Alimentary	2	1		3
Cardiovascular (heart and circulatory system)	3	18		21
Respiratory system		3		3
Urogenital	1	5	2	8
Talipes (club foot)	3	5	1	9
Other limb malformations	1	2	2	5
Haemangioma and other skin diseases		3	1	4
Other malformations		2		2
Total malformations	11	41	7	59
Total children with malformations	11	40	7	58
Total children				460
Total children with malformations per 1,000 children				126.1
Total triplets with malformations				48
Total triplets				411
Triplets with malformations per 1,000 triplet children				116.8

Source: Linked general practitioner data and obstetric.

kidneys. Only one of these had been reported in the obstetric survey. A higher proportion of club feet had been diagnosed at birth but there were other limb malformations which were diagnosed later.

Two very serious malformations included in the 'other' category were not apparent at birth. One triplet child was found to have Hirschsprung's disease, an abnormality of the nervous pathway to the large bowel which prevents normal bowel contractions. The other was diagnosed as having albinism, a genetic disorder which can affect the pigmentation of the hair, eyes and skin and can be associated with loss of vision.

Interpretation of the findings

Two major factors need to be taken into account when interpreting these findings. The first is that the design of the study excluded children in higher order births from which fewer than three children left hospital alive. It could well be that morbidity among surviving children in these sets is higher than sets where all the children survived. This has been shown to be the case for monozygotic twins, so it would not be surprising if this was also the case for triplets.[8] This means that our study design is likely to under-estimate the morbidity among triplets as a whole.

The second factor to be considered is the low response rate in the general practitioners' survey and the possibility of response bias. It is possible that general practitioners may have been less likely to reply in respect of families with medical and social problems.

In replies to the general practitioners' survey, 22 per cent of the triplets weighed under 1,500 grams at birth compared with 37 per cent of all triplets in the obstetric survey tabulated in Table 6.3. This reflects the exclusion of babies who died and their fellow triplets from the general practitioners' survey as, in the obstetric survey, 22 per cent of triplets discharged from hospital alive weighed under 1500g.

In the light of these problems it is interesting to compare the high rate of cerebral palsy among triplets in our study with that found in a study based on the Western Australia Cerebral Palsy Register.[9] This contains information about all cases of cerebral palsy among people born in Western Australia since 1956. Over the period 1966–1985 the birth prevalence of cerebral palsy was 2.4 per thousand live births, among singletons, 6.3 among twins and 31.6 among triplets. This was based on five sets of triplets. One of these sets would not have been included in our study at all as one triplet was removed by selective reduction thus reducing the pregnancy to twins and two other sets each contained a stillbirth, so would not have qualified for the general practitioners' survey. Excluding these would have brought the rate much nearer to that in our study, although the unadjusted rate is not significantly different from ours because of the small numbers of triplets involved in each case.

A further factor which makes our data difficult to interpret is that the children were at different ages when the questionnaires were sent to general practitioners in 1988 and 1989. Thus children born in 1980 could have reached the age of nine while those born in 1985 may have been only three years of age.

Assessing the impact of disability on adult triplets

The question arises as to how long a period of follow-up would be needed. The later parts of Paul Cain's autobiography, from which we quoted earlier, illustrate the way that some consequences of his disability did not fully hit him until he was an adult. Despite missing periods of time at school because of operations, he passed three 'O' levels, got a post in local government and obtained professional qualifications in public administration. He learned to drive and took an active part in clubs for disabled people and in his church.

Despite this, at the time he finished his autobiography at the age of 29, he was unemployed, having been retired from local government on grounds of ill-health. He commented:

> 'Over the years, I have met numerous handicapped people who have become unemployed. Today it is a very competitive world and the pressures of the business world are increasing. The Disablement Resettlement Officers can only encourage employers to place us in satisfactory jobs. Unfortunately, the present recession has made market forces relating to job opportunities very sparse indeed!'[1]

Despite this he was determined to put forward a positive view of handicapped people and related this to the advantages and difficulties of being a triplet:

'As we grow older we appreciate the ups and downs of life to test our character. Being one of triplets gave me the determination to face all traumas of life with confidence.

Both my brothers were married within eight months of each other. At the time of their marriages I was unaware of the personal loss due to the separation from them through the natural process of marriage.'[1]

Despite further setbacks, Paul Cain's autobiography closes on a positive note:

'In writing this book I hope it portrays the message that having a handicap does not make you any different from able-bodied people ... My book has shown that by community participation most problems can be faced if not always solved.'[1]

Conclusions

Although the findings of our survey must be regarded as tentative, replies to questionnaires sent to general practitioners showed a raised prevalence of cerebral palsy, squint, pyloric stenosis, congenital malformations and hospital admissions among children from triplet and higher order births. Children from sets of triplet and higher order births where fewer than three children left hospital alive were not included. This, together with a low response rate, may have led to under-estimation of morbidity among children born in triplet and higher order births.

Despite this, high morbidity rates were found and this is a cause for concern. There is, therefore, now a need for a prospective study, using the British Paediatric Surveillance Unit, which had not been set up when our study started, and the National Health Service Central Register. In view of the poor responses to postal questionnaires by general practitioners, it would be desirable to use paid interviewers preferably with a nursing training so that they could make clinical observations.

References

1. Cain P. Where there is a will there is a way. Unpublished autobiography.

2. Johnson A, King R. A regional register of early childhood impairments: a discussion paper. Community Medicine 1989; 11: 352–363.

3. Kohler L, Stigmar G. Visual disorders in seven year old children with and without previous vision screening: an epidemiological study. Acta Paediatrica Scandinavica 1978; 67: 373–377.

4. Kendall J A, Stayte M A, Wortham C. Ocular defects in children from birth to six years of age. British Orthoptic Journal 1989; 46: 326.

5. Royal College of General Practitioners, Office of Population Censuses and Surveys, Department of Health and Social Security. Morbidity Statistics from General Practice 1981–82. Third national study. Series MB5 No 1. London: HMSO, 1986.

6. Forfar J O, Arneil G C, eds. Textbook of Paediatrics, Third edition, Vol 1. Edinburgh: Churchill Livingstone, 1984.

7. Mutch L, Newdick M, Lodwick A, Chalmers I. Secular changes in rehospitalisation of very low birthweight infants. Paediatrics 1986; 78. 164–171.

8. Szymonowicz W, Preston H, Yu V Y H. The surviving monozygotic twin. Archives of Disease in Childhood 1986; 61: 454–458.

9. Patterson B, Stanley F J, Henderson D. Cerebral palsy in multiple births in Western Australia. American Journal of Medical Genetics (In press).

Chapter 9 – Consequences

Frances V Price

'In the first 12 months of their life, I didn't go out. My husband did my supermarket shopping. I shopped for clothes by post.'

'One great difficulty when the babies were nine months to 18 months was getting out with them without having to rely on a friend or neighbour to push one of the pushchairs'

'In the last two and a half years my wife has only had one day off from looking after the children – for her grandmother's funeral! The financial strain and the burden of having no car means that I have to work as much overtime as possible, and do most of the shopping on foot, which means even less time helping at home. I only wish there was some means by which we could afford and arrange a well deserved holiday for my wife.'

Introduction

It is not simply having three or more children of the same age which is unusual but also the cumulative effects of arrangements which have to be made for their care. This chapter traces the effects on the day to day circumstances of the parents, in particular the publicity which followed the delivery, the efforts needed to provide enough living space, and the many practical difficulties in getting out to the shops, the clinic and the playgroup, and in getting away for a break. Underlying these themes, however, are the sleeplessness, the critical time management problems, the risk of isolation and the consequences of these problems in the longer term, not only for the optimum development of the children, but also for the parents, any siblings and for other relationships way beyond the household.

Publicity

'TV wanted to portray us as a large poor family at Christmas. We declined.'

Higher order multiple births are news. Three quarters of parents reported that they had experienced exposure to some form of publicity about the birth of their triplets, quadruplets or quintuplets in the national or local press, on radio or on television. With hospital co-operation, a few had actively and successfully managed to avoid any public disclosure whatsoever. This was not always without a struggle. On occasion, press reporters even claimed to be relatives. The identity of the parents of the first IVF triplets born in the UK in 1983 was kept secret. By contrast, the birth in 1984 of the first IVF quadruplets in the UK received front-page publicity in the national press. This had turbulent consequences for their mother, father and two older sisters.

Table 9.1 shows that publicity surrounded all but two quadruplet deliveries and 73

Table 9.1

Publicity and its consequences

Publicity and its consequences	Triplets		Quadruplets and quintuplets	
	Number	Per cent	Number	Per cent
No publicity	72	26.2	2	8.3
Publicity:				
Favourable consequences	27	9.8	5	20.8
Negative consequences	17	6.2	6	25.0
Mixed/neutral conequences	26	9.5	2	8.3
No consequences	110	40.0	6	25.0
Not stated	20	7.2	3	12.5
No response	3	1.1	0	–
Total	275	100.0	24	100.0

Source: Parents' study.

per cent of triplet deliveries. Overall, in 58 per cent of these households, such publicity was not found to be of any consequence one way or the other. A mother of triplets and an older child wrote that publicity had encouraged a greater awareness amongst her friends and neighbours of the problems she faced but she regretted the unwelcome comments made to the children. Only 27 parents of triplets and five parents of quads described favourable consequences:

> '£5 from a pensioner who wished us luck but did not give her name, just "80 years old".'

> 'An offer of a photograph by a local photographer.'

> 'Television appearances were really good fun.'

Local press coverage had resulted in the gift of a second-hand twin pram to one of the mothers of triplets. Two others wrote that they had received friendly letters of advice and congratulation after their multiple birth was reported in the press. Just occasionally, publicity brought an unsolicited gift, an offer of help, or renewed contact with friends from the past. On the other hand, there were sometimes negative consequences. Parents mentioned the irritation arising from frequent curious visitors, insensitively expecting to be provided with tea or coffee, and staying too long. Some received unwanted mail. One mother reported:

> 'I had two rather nasty letters. One lady accused me of sexual discrimination as she thought I had breastfed the boys only. One lady thought I had put my children in a pushchair prematurely.'

A poison pen letter was posted to a mother of triplets after full page newspaper coverage of the family's housing needs. One or more crank phone calls were received by five mothers and obscene phone calls by two mothers. These consequences proved

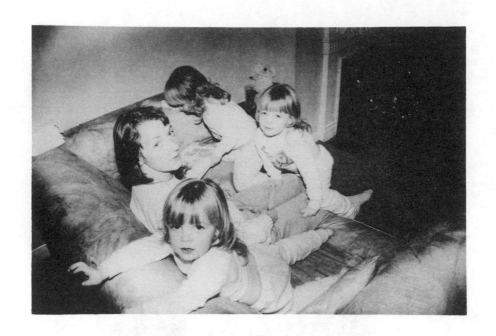

deeply disturbing. Some parents had changed their telephone number to an ex-directory number.

Frequent visitors, the persistence of the press and of insurance salesmen on the telephone and the doorstep, following publicity, were mentioned, as was the exclusion of older brothers and sisters from the press photographs of triplets, quadruplets or quintuplets. Reports in one paper were syndicated to others. A mother of quadruplets described how a report about their birth in the local paper had subsequently been used in the popular national press:

> 'After the story had appeared in the local press we were pestered by other papers and magazines and one or two used our story and pictures, without our permission or even any mention to us beforehand.'

Like several other mothers, she complained about irritatingly frequent phone calls by the press, the inaccuracy of the press coverage and the upset and turmoil that misreporting had caused them.

While some parents of quadruplets did benefit financially from exclusive reports about them in newspapers and magazines, these reports generated further articles and publicity with which they were often ill-prepared to cope. During one interview for the parents' study the father of IVF quadruplets handed over a black briefcase, full of newspaper cuttings from all over the world about the controversies surrounding the birth of the quadruplets. He said he never wanted to see its contents again. A few mothers said that in the early weeks after hospital discharge they became reluctant to answer the front door.

Benefits, gifts and loans

> 'Absolutely no commercial sponsorship offered – we were told over and over that triplets are "too common" or "not enough babies nowadays – must be quads or more".'

> 'The first time the health visitor came she said what a pity I hadn't had five. I would have got free milk! You only get free milk if you have five babies or more.'

> 'My father asked [commercial company] if we could bulk buy the baby milk. We were told they did not do this and [they] sent one free tin.'

Parents spoke and wrote about the widespread assumption that having triplets, quadruplets or more brought financial benefits from the state. Strangers in the street would ask, 'How much do you get for them?' and seemed reluctant to believe that there are no special payments, apart from child benefit for each child. Some fathers encountered difficulties obtaining state benefits because they had voluntarily given up employment to help care for their children. The income that several mothers obtained from their part-time work took some households just over the threshold above which they were not entitled to state benefits. A few described their distress at discovering that they were entitled to financial assistance about which they had not previously known. For example, one mother wrote that she had not received Family Income Supplement until her triplets' third year as no-one had informed her about this particular state benefit. Another mother of triplets wrote:

'My husband was off work for three months sick. The children were only three months old. We lived off our savings as his employers were only paying sick (£49 per week) for nine weeks. However, we went to the social services after this period and found out we were entitled to £50 per week plus milk tokens. They wouldn't back-date the payments. This was our fault as we should have approached them immediately. However, it never entered our minds as we were both in full-time employment and have never claimed off the State.'

Parents confirmed that there was a misleading but widespread assumption, often encouraged by hospital staff and health visitors, that charities and commercial firms are willing to provide generous gifts and sponsorship for triplet and higher order births. In a few instances, a hospital social worker or health visitor managed to secure funds from a local charity to purchase a washing machine or tumble drier for households without one. Letters were written to commercial firms and charities by or on behalf of 59 per cent of the parents of triplets and 83 per cent of the parents of quadruplets or quintuplets. Three quarters of the households which included quadruplets and half of those which included triplets, received a gift of a quantity of milk powder in tins or sachets. One mother received milk free because she agreed to take part in a research project organised in conjunction with a commercial firm.

The quantities of milk donated varied enormously. One mother was supplied with free milk for a year, another for six months and yet another for six weeks. Sometimes the health visitor made a gift of free samples of milk and babyfood she had been given. Offers to supply a particular brand of milk was always tantalising but not always suitable for the babies. One mother of quadruplets told how she was asked by a sales representative visiting the neonatal unit if she would like a free supply of milk for her children. She accepted this offer of free milk 'dangling in my face', as she put it, despite advice from the neonatal nursing sister that the brand of milk offered to her was unsuitable for such young babies. She gave the babies this milk for three weeks but it became clear that they were not thriving on it. She then approached another firm who donated a six month supply of milk, which she used until this milk proved also to be unsuitable. She then gave the babies the same milk that they had been given whilst in hospital, buying it with the milk tokens to which she was entitled.

Fewer households had received sizeable gifts of baby food, and again there was considerable disparity in the quantities provided. These ranged from 24 tins of baby food to a year's supply. Gifts of nappies ranged from one nappy for each triplet baby in one instance and a total of three nappies for quadruplets in another, to gifts of one or even two thousand disposable nappies at the other end of the scale. Apart from the milk, which often came from a sales representative visiting the neonatal unit, most gifts of food usually took the form of small sachet samples supplied after some request or initiative by hospital staff, or by a health visitor passing on her free samples. Thirty nine per cent of parents of triplets and just under a half of parents of quadruplets had obtained their gifts by writing as one of them put it, 'begging letters'. Sometimes, during interviews, the considerable effort and skilful humour which had gone into the composition of such letters was described. Parents of quadruplets, however, were more likely than parents of triplets to feel that all these efforts had been worthwhile. Other parents made it quite clear that they had never been prepared to parade their plight in this way to potential donors.[1]

Accounts of sponsorship or an abundance of gifts from shops and commercial companies were very much the exception. One company supplying pregnancy clothing and children's wear consistently responded to letters from or on behalf of parents of triplets and quadruplets by sending gift vouchers valued at between £20 and £50. No other individual company responded on such a scale.

Only a fifth of the parents mentioned gifts or loans from relatives and friends but those described were usually substantial:

'Much of the most expensive items were gifts from family, eg pram £240 buggies £120 [and] £75.'

In some households, a relative or, in one instance, a friend met the cost of disposable nappies for a year or more. It seemed to be the case that gifts from friends and relatives were not mentioned unless they were regarded in some sense as unusual, or not likely to have been given except in the special circumstances of a higher order multiple birth. For instance, parents or parents-in-law paid for shoes for the children or met the cost of a home extension. The parents-in-law of one mother of quadruplets gave £1,200 so that she and her husband could buy a larger vehicle and thus be able to get out with their quadruplets. Sometimes parents referred to gifts and loans when describing the help and support received from friends or when providing their estimate of the financial costs of bringing-up multiple birth children. One mother of triplets wrote, after giving her estimate of costs:

'We were very lucky in having cots, high chairs and a lot of other equipment given to us.'

Another wrote:

'Friends gave and lent me a lot of clothes and equipment.'

Probably the variety of such sources of benefit is under-reported. Sometimes, the source was unknown. A packet of washing powder or a bag of clothes would simply appear on the doorstep.

As shown in Table 9.2, most of the households with quadruplets received a number of substantial gifts. What is more, these gifts, especially the donations of milk, nappies, baby food, equipment and money and discounts from firms, were dispropor-tionately greater than those received by households with triplets. The quantities of milk, baby food, toiletries, pushchairs and shoes donated to the quadruplets in several households were the direct consequence of numerous letters sent by their parents to a variety of firms requesting help. In addition to numerous free gifts of milk, jars of strained and junior foods, baby toiletries, shoes and equipment, including two double pushchairs and one extra large pushchair, one household with quadruplets benefited because their health visitor arranged a year's supply of free nappies. The father's parents paid for night nurses for six months as well as paying for a dishwasher. Also the mother's parents paid their fees for nursery school.

Several mothers of quadruplets, however, had written letters to firms supplying food, equipment and clothing, but had not asked for their products as outright gifts. Instead they had enquired whether the firms would provide discounts on bulk

Table 9.2

Gifts received from commercial companies

	Triplets		Quadruplets and quintuplets	
	Number	Per cent	Number	Per cent
One or more gift of milk	77	28.0	14	58.3
One or more gift of nappies	67	24.4	9	37.5
One or more gift of baby and/or junior food	60	21.8	9	37.5
One or more gift token or purchase discount	45	16.4	10	41.7
One or more gift of equipment	17	6.2	9	37.5
Total number of households	275	100.0	24	100.0

Source: Parents' study.

purchases as they would always be buying for four. All the firms to which they wrote declined.

Housing status, moves and extensions

'We moved three weeks before the birth.'

At the time when the triplet or higher order multiple pregnancy was diagnosed, some parents-to-be were living in one or two bedroom accommodation, or living with their parents or in-laws. The parents' study questionnaire did not directly cover the issue of living space, but parents wrote and spoke of confined space as an issue of great consequence, particularly when there was literally no extra room to spare. Existing space was managed, often with great ingenuity, and furniture and mattresses manoeuvred around. Albums of photographs were produced during some interviews which showed how crowded things had been before moving house or building an extension, or whilst one or more relatives were staying to provide round-the-clock help.

The financial costs of moving house and building extensions were considerable and inevitably threw the household into some turmoil. Long drawn out negotiations for house sales could complicate matters and add to the stress. Planning permission to extend was not always granted, either the first or second time around. The number of bedrooms was not the only important issue in the decision to move, or to extend. Many decided that a safe play place for their children was first priority, particularly in their second year of life:

'Of all the problems in coping with triplets my main problem has been in providing an adequate safe play area for the children who are now 16 months old. In desperation I am trying to apply for a grant from the council to enable me to extend a room in my house.'

Space and privacy were often sacrificed in an effort to get help from relatives. One mother reported that she, her husband and their triplets had moved in with her parents so that they could help with childcare. Another household, which included quadruplets, moved to a smaller house to be near the mother's mother:

'Confined space is a real problem, particularly bedroom and playroom-wise. The four sleep in one bedroom, and apart from the obviously cramped arrangements for sleeping (two in a bed, top and tail ends), they obviously create discipline problems as they keep each other awake. Particularly between two to three years, they would get straight out of bed as soon as I had left them and get all their toys out. When I removed the toy basket, they would tip out all their chest of drawers. They soon got around the problem of 'child proof' locks, and worked out a co-operation system whereby one would hold the door/drawer slightly ajar, whilst another would slide in his hand and unhook the lock. It's far more exciting to run riot in a bedroom (and acting together, they have the confidence to do it) than to settle down to sleep. And if there simply is nowhere else to put them to sleep (our house is only an average three bedroomed semi) this problem can continue for a long time. They never go to bed before 8pm, so they should be tired, but they seem to be able to keep each other going.

We are hoping to extend to provide another bedroom and enlarged kitchen but this will create an added financial burden, and one which every higher order birth family must face. There is a fear of financially overstretching because you know that if things do get tight, you will not be free to get paid work to help with the family budget. Our home is right near my mother's and this proximity of my only source of help does outweigh the fact that the house is far from ideal space-wise. Our children are being brought up within a close extended family relationship even though that extension is just my parents and I think this is just as important as having enough bedrooms.'

The majority of parents in the study were owner occupiers. This accounted for 83 per cent of the parents of triplets and all but the parents of one set of quadruplets who were renting local authority housing. By comparison, 14 per cent of the parents of triplets were renting from the local authority. In addition, six households which included triplets were in privately rented accommodation, and three other households were in tied housing.

Eleven households which included quadruplets, 46 per cent, had moved house since the birth, and a further three households with quadruplets intended to go through this upheaval. Forty two per cent of the households which included triplets had moved house and a further 33 families, or 11 per cent, were planning to do so. Those parents who were renting local authority accommodation were obliged to wait until the babies were born before they could begin to negotiate for a transfer to a larger house or to a ground floor instead of a high rise flat.

Of those who had moved house, three quarters of the parents of triplets and nine of the 11 parents of quadruplets had moved only once. All the parents of quadruplets and nearly three quarters of the parents of triplets had moved for more space in the first instance. Three households, one including quadruplets and two including triplets, had emigrated and subsequently returned. Eighteen per cent of parents of triplets who had moved once or twice, had done so because of a change of job and eight per cent had moved to be nearer to relatives. Other reasons for moving were the quest for better facilities, particularly schools, or a forced house sale or repossession following a marital breakdown.

Half of the parents of quadruplets had built extensions to their homes and another three households were planning an extension. At least two fathers of quadruplets had undertaken all the building work themselves. In one case, the fee paid by a newspaper for publicity about the birth paid for a playroom extension to a two bedroomed house. Just over a quarter of the parents of triplets had extended their homes. The cost of the extension was met by a charity in only one instance, and this was because the triplets had disabilities.

Transport

> 'Only went for weekend walks with husband. Week-days [nursery nurse] students occasionally took children out.'

Transport difficulties were frequently mentioned by parents. These were an impediment to outings, whether for visits to clinics, mother and toddler groups, shopping or just to get out of the house. One mother of six year old triplets wrote:

> 'I did not get out a lot when they were little. I only learned to drive three years ago.'

In the early months, some parents managed to transport their triplets in one pram. The parents of one set of quadruplets hired a 'quad' pram from the Supertwins Club at a cost, in the early 1980s, of £1 a week. A large twin pram sufficed for two months for several sets of triplets until their parents bought a triple buggy. One mother struggled alone with two of her triplets in a twin pram and one in a single pram until the children were eight months old, when she was given an old fashioned coach built twin pram, into which she fitted all three. Thirteen per cent of triplet sets were carried in two prams for some months.

At a later stage, complications with unwieldy pushchairs were mentioned in interviews, as was the difficulty of clamping two together. A few fathers made special pushchairs themselves. During the study, wholesalers ceased to import a quadruplet pushchair because of complaints that its back suspension could not reliably take the weight of four infants. Few mothers mentioned sometimes using a sling to carry one of their triplets whilst pushing the other two in a pushchair. A quarter of the triplet sets were transported in triple buggies. The design of some versions of these specially made, and expensive, pushchairs met with criticism however. They were too wide for most pavements and shop entrances. Most parents of triplets had used a double and a single pushchair and most parents of quadruplets used two double pushchairs.

Difficulties over the transport of their children were exacerbated for those mothers with no companion to accompany them regularly when they went out with their children. This was the situation on weekdays for 39 per cent of the mothers of triplets and also for a quarter of the mothers of quadruplets. Just a few of the mothers mentioned that their home help or family aide or their older children were able to help them on outings. When one of the mothers of quadruplets had to make hospital visits with her children her home help went with her, but this was unusual. In another instance, a Home-Start volunteer helped a mother to get her triplets to their appointment with a speech therapist. In 10 per cent of households a nursery nurse or nanny, employed privately, acted as helper. Several mothers of quadruplets reported that the nanny often took two of the four children out in one double pushchair whilst they cared for the other two at home. This practice had the advantage both of greater mobility for the nanny and also of concealing the two children's quadruplet status, thus avoiding the time-consuming questions of passers-by.

Access to car or van

'This is probably the biggest practical problem in caring for the babies and getting them about.'

'It is very hard to go anywhere, without the car, without someone to help.'

'We in fact have two cars. Public transport with many babies is unthinkable.'

All the parents of quadruplets and quintuplets, and 90 per cent of the parents of triplets in the parents' study owned a car or van. Some had purchased this vehicle outright, others with a loan from a bank or a relative. For some this was a gift. The remaining 10 per cent, all parents of triplets, did not have access to a vehicle at the time they completed the study questionnaire. Also some parents made it clear that their car or van was used exclusively for work purposes, or was only available at weekends. Some vehicles were very recent acquisitions. In other cases, cars were sold as an economy, round about the time of the higher order multiple birth. One couple, who sold their car when their triplets were born, were only later able to borrow a relatives' car.

Available cars were not always suitable, however, for carrying triplets, quadruplets or quintuplets in safety. This was a source of both stress and anxiety for parents. Despite the widespread belief that it is 'safer in the back', there is evidence that back seat passengers without seat belts have more numerous and more severe injuries than those who are restrained in the front seat: they are twice as likely to require admission to hospital.[2,3] Eleven per cent of parents commented on the inadequate size and resulting safety risk of their present car. A few mentioned their concern as to how they would manage when the Motor Vehicles (wearing of seat belts by children) Act 1988 came into effect.

'I have a car which is not suitable for five children to travel. But I have no choice as I have to take them to and from nursery.'

'Husband has various cars from work therefore it is not feasible to fix suitable child seats.'

'Desperately need a van with sufficient seats for everyone. We have an old [estate car]. Three baby seats take up all the back seat. The two other children have to manage in space remaining which is uncomfortable and not very safe. If we bought an old van we can't afford garage bills but we have no extra money to buy a newer van. Catch 22!'

Fifty six per cent of all the parents in the parents' study and three quarters of the parents of quadruplets and quintuplets reported that they had bought, or been given, a larger vehicle since the multiple birth.

'When the children were 18 months old ... we changed our car from a [small 4-seater] to a 12-seater mini-bus and I can honestly say it was a lifesaver. Once (again) we were mobile as a normal family, not having to rely on an extra person to help to hold the children while driving. We have found the mini-bus the ideal transport.'

'We had to buy a [mini-bus] as no other vehicle would house the triple pram. The pram was an absolute must for me so as to enable me to take them out by myself.'

'Could not have afforded larger van without father's financial help.'

'My parents bought us an 8-seater minibus as a gift – their life-savings.'

The larger vehicle certainly was not always new, however, and seldom in pristine condition. Once the money has been raised to buy a multi-seater vehicle new, the tendency seems to be to keep it longer than might usually be the case, and it may have been subject to the ravages of a large family for some years. Sometimes, before very long, it had to be replaced by a smaller vehicle, as one mother of quadruplets explained:

'We have a large saloon car, but it is impossible to fit four seat belts in the rear. When the kids were younger we had a 7-seater [car] but it was 14 years old – and fell to bits! We had a [small saloon car] at the birth which we could only fit three seats in and had to trade it for the decrepit [7-seater car].'

The opportunity of a larger company car was available to some parents:

'Our car was a company car for my husband's job, and was a saloon. He was due to change it and was able to persuade the company to allow us to have an estate car as a special concession. We have to pay to put in an extra row of seats.'

Nevertheless, not all company employees were entitled to higher mileage and expenses allowances to cover the costs of running a larger car. Nor was it always possible to provide safety restraints for all the children:

'My husband has to use the car for work two days a week. The employer's policy is to pay mileage and other expenses on the basis that the car's engine is no bigger than 1300cc. We have to have a bigger vehicle for the seven of us (currently 2000cc) so every time my husband uses the car for work we lose out.'

'It is impossible to restrain all five children safely in the car (we have restraints for three, the other two travel unrestrained).'

Only certain makes of car or van were large enough to carry prams and pushchairs and to enable enough car seats and seat belts to be fitted. Many of these vehicles are designed to accommodate seven or eight people in three, rather than the usual two,

170

rows of seats. All were very costly to buy. Prices start at about £12,000 and they are expensive also to run and insure.

> 'We bought a [large estate car] as it was only one of a very few cars that would take three children's car seats at the rear together with the large pushchair etc. Insurance is not cheap. But the car is no luxury. It is a necessity.'

> 'We have a [large estate car] – eight seats. This is necessary since we need 4×3 point seat belts to strap in our children – current legislation prohibits use of front seat. The car was our most expensive special purchase but the freedom was worth it!'

> 'It was absolutely essential to have a three tiered car with space for three adults, one child and three babies.'

At least 53 mothers in the parents' study, 18 per cent, reported that they could not drive. This figure may be higher as, in general, only those who currently had a car available to them answered this question. A car or van was only of use to these women when someone was available to drive them and their children from place to place.

People with a 'mobility handicap' include, not only those with disabilities and the frail elderly, but also 'those coping with children (with or without pushchairs or prams), carrying shopping or luggage'.[4] For parents without a car, the time and energy spent walking with cumbersome pushchairs in all weathers stretched emotional and physical resources to the limit. Some mothers of triplets seldom emerged from their homes in the first eighteen months after their multiple birth. Traffic dangers when walking alone with their young children were a constant source of anxiety to parents. Several alarming, near fatal, incidents were graphically described in interviews. One mother abandoned her toddlers on the pavement as she rushed towards her older child who had been knocked down by a car.

Table 9.3

Access to telephone

Location of telephone	Triplets		Quadruplets and quintuplets	
	Number	Per cent	Number	Per cent
In home	260	94.5	23	95.8
No phone in home, use phone				
in a neighbour's house	4	1.5	0	–
a short walk away	8	2.9	0	–
a distance away	2	0.7	0	–
not stated	1	0.4	1	4.2
Total	275	100.0	24	100.0

Source: Parents' study.

Access to telephone

Ninety-five per cent of all the households in the parents' study were currently on the telephone as shown in Table 9.3. Eight per cent, however, were not connected at the time of the higher order multiple birth. Several parents wrote that their telephone had only recently been connected. With one exception, all households which included quadruplets were on the phone at the time of enquiry. Four households relied on a neighbour's phone, eight on a public phone a short walk away, two on a phone some distance away. Two parents without phones did not answer this question.

Getting out: visits to clinic

> 'I had managed to get the children to the Health Centre for immunisation (at that stage we didn't have a big enough car for three baby seats and a set of straps, so my mother held two babies while one was in a basket and [her older child], aged just 9 in his safety seat, all on the back seat). I asked could they also be weighed – she said no, as there was an antenatal class – but come in "whenever you're passing". I explained I never did (with all the babies). She said, "But what about when you're shopping?". I explained my husband did some shopping and I did the rest at the weekend while my husband minded the babies.'

Although 71 per cent of parents of triplets indicated that they had used their child health clinic at least once the first year, only 42 per cent of the parents of quadruplets did so. Four fifths of parents who did not use the clinic had made other arrangements instead. Of those who managed to get their children to the clinic, 72 per cent reported that they had used it to have their children weighed. Forty one per cent mentioned vaccination and 34 per cent hearing and development tests.

Many mothers overcame considerable difficulties getting to the clinic, sometimes going a mile or more on foot. They then had to cope with long waits, followed by undressing, nappy changing and redressing their babies in crowded rooms. They reported a lack of response from busy clinic staff to their exceptional situation. Several described the mounting stress of waiting for an indeterminate time whilst coping alone with at least three infants, sometimes with other pressing commitments to fulfill:

> 'Impossible to get three babies through the system without a lot of hassle. Not enough time to get them all weighed and home in time to collect my eldest child from school.'

> 'I sometimes had to wait a long time – it would have helped, if we could have been given some preference to others waiting in the clinic because it is no joke sitting with three babies waiting your turn.'

> 'Very crowded, no room for three babies or prams etc. Nobody seemed able to really help me or to understand how hard the visits were. I was always exhausted by the time I got home and never went alone – always took my mother. The long waits were awful with three babies.'

> 'Fitting in the visit and the wait between feeds etc and the older child's needs. A visit made on one occasion aroused so much curiosity that I could hardly attend to the children's needs due to people asking questions.'

'I found that everyone sat and watched me struggle in with the triple buggy and my elder child, without much offer of assistance (there were exceptions). I had quite long waits on a couple of occasions, so my elder child would play up a bit, and I was unable to do much about it, as I was dealing with the babies.'

'Waiting with three babies (sometimes very hungry) was no joke, so after a while I stopped going as it was just too much rushing back home with three hungry babies, trying to feed all three. Appointment system failed to work and at one time I was there for two hours five minutes.'

Babysitting

Expeditions out of the house without the children were only possible where someone could be found who would take charge, if only for an hour. In the first year, 84 per cent of parents had been able to arrange for someone other than each other to 'babysit'. There were, however, great variations in the extent to which they had the opportunity to make such arrangements. The parents of one quadruplet set had only managed to arrange for babysitting on a single occasion, when they took their children to the mother's mother's house to be looked after for the evening. Ten per cent of parents had used their nanny to babysit or had employed a minder. Several had used their home help for this purpose. Almost three quarters of these parents had used one of their mothers as a babysitter. Some of these parents were also among the 19 per cent who indicated that they had used a friend as a babysitter in the first year. Members of the local 'ladies circle' had provided babysitters for the parents of one set of triplets who otherwise relied on a friend. Only two parents mentioned being part of an active babysitting circle. Some, in desperation, took up offers from their health visitor to babysit. For instance, one mother went, belatedly, to her post-natal check up, leaving her health visitor in charge of her triplets.

Holidays in the first year

In the first year, a quarter of the parents of quadruplets and 41 per cent of the parents of triplets had taken a break of two days or more away from their home. Only 22 per cent had not taken any of their children with them. Two thirds had been accompanied by all their children:

'Husband's parents had us all to stay for one week. Very hectic! Not repeated.'

One mother who had not had such a break, commented:

'A holiday would have been nice, but really needed an extra pair of hands.'

Another wrote on her postcard, whilst on a first holiday provided by members of Rotary Club, with her sixteen month old triplets and older daughter:

'The holiday is going well, but we should have brought an extra pair of hands.'

The desirability, but complexity, of arranging such a break for the mother in the first year was raised frequently as an issue. Several mothers referred to such a break as essential, as did the father who was quoted at the beginning of this chapter. A mother of quadrupletss who had first 'successfully' holidayed with her husband, their seventeen month old quadruplets and older son commented:

'Holidays are possible if well planned in advance. As with everything else, put your wishes for a holiday secondary to your children, because if they are not happy on holiday, you will not be. Beach holidays are the order of the day and do not expect them to enjoy sightseeing or shopping. Try to get a big cottage/farmhouse preferably detached with a garden, then they can make as much noise as they like. Ensure there are no dangers before you book ie the house must be fully fenced in, away from main roads, and must not have ponds, wells, outbuildings with dangerous equipment in. Avoid a caravan/chalet park as apart from the obvious space restrictions, you do not want to find that your family has become the major tourist attraction. Above all, do not expect a holiday to be a rest, settle for a change and you will have minimal problems and you will not need an army of helpers. My husband and I have managed our five on four holidays since the quads were seventeen months old.'

Overnight visits by children away from home

'One stayed with a friend, one stayed with mother-in-law, one stayed with grandma ... It was a disaster. They were all unhappy.'

'[Second-born triplet] had feeding problems in the first 10 months so she spent three to four nights a week with [triplet mother's] parents for about five months which eased the pressure considerably.'

In 42 per cent of triplets and half the sets of quadruplets, one child or more had stayed away from home with another person for at least one night. A variety of arrangements had been made and such visits were usually brief, infrequent and likely to be to a relative's house. A mother of six year old triplets wrote:

'When the children were little no-one would babysit in case there were problems. My sister will have them for the odd night now they are older but she does not have children of her own and they wear her out! So not very often.'

For several of the parents, such a visit had been a development in the past year. Few triplet sets had nights away from home as a regular arrangement with relatives; but individual children did go to stay, without their siblings, with a friend, god-parent, or relative.

When child care is needed for a week or more and there is no relative or friend who can have the children to stay, it becomes very expensive:

'Triplets stayed at [a nursery nurse training college] for one week [in May 1986] while we moved house. Cost us approximately £300.'

Another mother who wrote in December 1988 quoted the cost to her of a similar arrangement:

174

'We are just off on holiday for three weeks so the babies are off to [a nursery nurse training college] – cost £892.'

Conclusions

Most of the births in the parents' study had been featured in the local or national press, but few parents reported any particular consequence. Free copies of press photographs were welcomed, but not always offered. Just occasionally, publicity brought an unsolicited gift, an offer of help, or renewed contact with friends from the past. On the other hand, there were sometimes negative consequences. There were complaints about curious vistors and the persistence with which journalists pursued their story. Far greater distress, however, resulted from the strange or even obscene phone calls received by a very few parents. Some changed their telephone number to an ex-directory number.

Overall, the findings of the parents' study did not support the apparently widespread assumption that commercial companies are willing to provide generous gifts and sponsorship for triplets as well as for children of higher order birth. Whereas most of the households with quadruplets and quintuplets received several substantial donations from commercial companies, usually of milk, nappies, equipment or gift tokens, such donations were far less likely for households with triplets. About a quarter of all the households with triplets received one or more gifts of milk or nappies. These donations, however, were seldom sizeable and included the free samples passed on by nursing staff and health visitors.

Many households sought new accommodation after the birth: about half had moved house or shortly intended to do so. A few had moved after the diagnosis of the multiple birth. Over half the parents of quadruplets and just over a quarter of parents of triplets had built home extensions.

Many parents reported problems getting out of the house, with or without their children and in transporting them in safety. Specially designed pushchairs were costly, cumbersome and generally too wide for pavements and doorways. Most parents used two pushchairs, a double and a single one for triplets and two double pushchairs for quadruplets. Inevitably, preparations to go out took time, especially in winter weather. Those parents without a regular companion to accompany them faced additional hurdles. The struggle to get out to shops, clinics and pre-school facilities was a continuing problem, especially for those who could not drive, were without a car, or whose car could not carry all their children adequately restrained. When things went wrong some households did not have a telephone connection to summon help.

Not all parents managed to get to their local child health clinic in the first year and a few had no alternative arrangements either. Those who did use their local clinic reported the difficulties, not only of getting there, but also of the long waits in crowded rooms with fretful children.

Parents emphasised their need for regular breaks, even if only for an hour or so. Most parents had used babysitters on at least one occasion in their children's first year, but some parents had only managed to do so once or twice.

Few parents envisaged the extent to which their circumstances would change: the sheer exhaustion, the weight of the responsibility for three, four or more children of the same age and the difficulty of getting out with them in comfort and safety. Access to people and to places outside the home may be restricted, or quite literally prevented, particularly if there is no regular helper available.

Much discussion about individual circumstances could, to advantage, take place in the antenatal period. Many difficulties could be anticipated at this stage, advice sought, and possible options to resolve them considered. For instance, mothers and fathers welcomed early advice on how to be and stay mobile. For those who cannot drive or who have no access to a vehicle, it is important to consider ways and means for them to get out with their children.

If visits to the child health clinic are likely to be difficult, health visitors can usually arrange both to take portable scales to weigh triplets and quadruplets in their own homes. Various immunisations and development tests can sometimes be done at home. Even if the latter is not always possible, there are ways for health professionals to remove or alleviate some of the difficulties that parents have reported that they faced in crowded clinics.

Parents in the study also emphasised the vital long-term importance of regular breaks, if only of a few hours a week, when the responsibility for the triplets, quadruplets or quintuplets and any other siblings is shared. Various possibilities can be discussed during the pregnancy, as to who might be asked to take charge.

A telephone connection in the home for the first three years seems a sensible, if not vital, precaution. Not only is there reason to believe that three, four or five infants of the same age are likely to be at greater risk of accidents within the home but also when there is an accident or an emergency there is an obvious difficulty in getting to a phone in a street some distance away with three, four or five youngsters in tow.

The financial circumstances of higher order multiple birth households require careful consideration. Cash grants and loans would alleviate problems caused by the need for home extensions and larger cars, as well as the considerable child care costs to be faced. In the longer term there is a strong case for a higher rate of child benefit payment.

References
1. Raphael T, Roll J. Carrying the can: charities and the welfare state. London: Child Poverty Action Group/Family Welfare Association, 1984.
2. Dreghorn C R. The effect of seat belt legislation on a district general hospital. Injury 1985; 16: 415–418.
3. Yates D. Rear seat belts. British Medical Journal 1989; 299: 341–342.
4. National Consumer Council. What's wrong with walking? London: HMSO, 1984.

Chapter 10 – Pre-schooling

Frances V Price

'I walk to playschool. Sometimes it takes 40 minutes. If one child is ill we don't go at all.'

'The education authority only provides two full-time nursery places per family. So I either *divide* the hours between them, which I can do, or just two will go and one [will go] to paid nursery. But how could I decide how to split them?'

Introduction

Sometime after their children passed their second birthday, if not before, most parents in the study sought some form of organised activity for them. They wanted somewhere for them to meet and play with other children, elsewhere than in their home, before they started school. Some triplets and quadruplets, of course, require more specialised provision because of their disabilities or health problems, Mother and toddler groups, various playgroups, day nurseries, nursery schools and nursery classes in infant schools all provide preschool experience of different kinds and with varying levels of shared responsibility for child care.[1,2,3] Local authorities' duties to provide nursery education have in recent years been limited to children with special educational needs.[4]

This chapter is about the pre-school provision which was used by parents in the parents' study for their children. It describes their experience of it, including gaining access, journeying there and back, and the difficulties they encountered.

Pre-school provision

All but two of the 103 sets of triplets, quadruplets and quintuplets who were five years or over at the time that their parents completed the parents' questionnaire had made use of some form of pre-school provision for two or more of their higher order multiple birth children. One of the two exceptions had four older children, including twins only 14 months older than her triplets. The second mother wrote:

'As a non-driver I was unable to take them to playgroup'.

The number and proportions of children who ever used a mother and toddler group, a playgroup, a nursery school or a nursery class in a primary school are shown in Tables 10.1, 10.2, 10.3 and 10.4 respectively. Higher order multiple birth children aged less than one were seldom taken to any form of pre-school facility, except sometimes to a mother and toddler group. About half of the children who were aged between two and three when their parents completed their questionnaire had used a

Table 10.1

Use of mother and toddler group by age of children time of survey

Age in years when questionnaire completed	Children who had ever been to mother and toddler group										Total households
	None went		Two went		Three went		Four went		Five went		
	Number	Per cent	Number	Per cent	Number	Per cent	Number	Per cent	Number	Per cent	
Less than 1	39	95.1	0	–	2	4.9	0	–	0	–	41
One and over but less than 2	20	57.1	0	–	15	42.9	0	–	0	–	35
Two and over but less than 3	18	42.8	0	–	22	52.4	2	4.8	0	–	42
Three and over but less than 5	38	48.7	0	–	38	48.7	2	2.6	0	–	78
Five and over	58	56.3	1	1.0	40	38.8	4	3.9	0	–	103
Total	173	57.8	1	0.3	117	39.1	8	2.7	0	–	299

Source: Parents' study.

Table 10.2

Use of playgroup by age of children at time of survey

Age in years when questionnaire completed	Children who had ever been to playgroup										Total households
	None went		Two went		Three went		Four went		Five went		
	Number	Per cent	Number	Per cent	Number	Per cent	Number	Per cent	Number	Per cent	
Less than 1	41	100.0	–	–	–	–	–	–	–	–	41
One and over but less than 2	33	94.3	–	–	2	5.7	–	–	–	–	35
Two and over but less than 3	28	66.7	–	–	14	33.3	–	–	–	–	42
Three and over but less than 5	37	47.4	1	1.3	38	48.7	2	2.6	–	–	78
Five and over	31	30.1	2	1.9	64	62.1	5	4.9	1	1.0	103
Total	170	56.9	3	1.0	118	39.5	7	2.3	1	0.3	299

Source: Parents' study.

Table 10.3

Use of nursery school by age of children at time of survey

Age in years when questionnaire completed	Children who had ever been to nursery school										Total households
	None went		Two went		Three went		Four went		Five went		
	Number	Per cent	Number	Per cent	Number	Per cent	Number	Per cent	Number	Per cent	
Less than 1	41	100.0	–	–	–	–	–	–	–	–	41
One and over but less than 2	34	97.1	1	2.9	–	–	–	–	–	–	35
Two and over but less than 3	36	85.7	–	–	5	11.9	1	2.4	–	–	42
Three and over but less than 5	40	51.3	–	–	38	48.7	–	–	–	–	78
Five and over	62	60.2	–	–	35	34.0	6	5.8	–	–	103
Total	123	71.2	2	0.3	78	26.1	7	2.3	–	–	299

Source: Parents' study.

Table 10.4

Use of nursery class by age of children at time of survey

Age in years when questionnaire completed	None went		Two went		Three went		Four went		Five went		Total households
	Number	Per cent	Number	Per cent	Number	Per cent	Number	Per cent	Number	Per cent	
Less than 3	118	100.0	–	–	–	–	–	–	–	–	118
Three and over but less than 4	30	83.3	–	–	6	16.7	–	–	–	–	36
Four and over but less than 5	31	73.8	1	2.4	10	23.8	–	–	–	–	42
Five and over	84	81.6	–	–	17	16.5	2	1.9	–	–	103
Total	263	88.0	1	0.3	33	11.0	2	0.6	–	–	299

Source: Parents' study.

mother and toddler group. Regrettably, for some of these children, the actual provision was minimal and consisted only of one or two hours once a week or once a fortnight. About half of those aged between three and five had experience of a playgroup, and over two thirds of those aged five and over. Just under half of those who were aged between three and five had ever been to a nursery school.

A number of children were too young to take advantage of the facilities available, although some mothers were anticipating the opportunity. A mother of six month old triplets wrote:

'I hope to attend a mother and toddler group when they are about eight months. I have their names down to attend nursery school.'

Mother and toddler groups are a first option at the toddler stage and are often regarded as a preparation for playgroup or nursery school. The mother has to accompany and stay with her children, however. This is because the objective of such groups is to bring mothers and their young children together regularly under one roof, sharing space and facilities at little cost. Nevertheless, many mothers admitted that they found mother and toddler groups a difficult experience without a companion to accompany them:

'Couldn't practically go unless someone could come with me (carrying babies upstairs to hall, watching four at once). Then lack of car when we moved further away.

A few made it clear that they went to mother and toddler group for the benefit of their children:

'I joined a mother and toddler group mainly for the children's sake, to encourage them to play and mix with other children more, and also to play with them which I didn't do at home – there was always work at home.'

Other mothers decided that this was not a facility that they wanted to try:

'There is a local mother and toddler group. The cost is £1 per session per child. It is held once a week for one and a half hours. It would mean me staying with and coping with the three children. I have never felt prepared to do this.'

In interviews, several mothers spoke of feelings of loneliness when describing their experience of a mother and toddler group. They did not feel included in the general group ethos of comparing and sharing experiences and making arrangements to meet. A mother of triplets observed, 'You can't just say, "Oh come round to play" or "We'll come round and see you"'. Her experience was of feeling 'quite lonely'. She felt unable to do the things that she believed were normally expected of mothers at mother and toddler groups. The sheer weight of responsibility for the care and control of three or four lively toddlers, and sometimes also an older child, concentrates the mind powerfully. Nor did it help matters to be introduced as the local 'Supermum'. Mothers pointed to the difficulty of even finding time to be included in the briefest of conversations when attempting to supervise play activities. One mother commented:

'No real problems, other than transport, except the common feeling of "Is it worth it?". By the time you have got them ready, and arrived, it seems to be time to start getting ready to leave.'

By comparison with mother and toddler groups, securing access to places in other supervised forms of pre-school provision often proved both difficult and costly. Children's names must be added in good time to waiting lists for playgroups and nursery schools. Places in day nurseries require a recommendation by health visitors or health and social service professionals on grounds of need. If there is no state nursery provision locally then private pre-school playgroups or nursery schools may be the only option, provided they have three, four or five places available. Playgroups or 'playschools' vary greatly, with respect both to cost and to the time period of supervised provision available. They may be run at social services day centres, by volunteers as part of a charitable venture or by a combination of the two. Some playgroups, set up as self-help and community projects, may come under the umbrella of the Pre-School Playgroups Association (PPA). Others are fiercely competitive profit-seeking ventures. Parents wrote of costs, in early 1988, of £100 per child per term for a private playgroup place, and £200 to £400 per child per term for a private nursery school place. For some parents the financial problems of meeting the cost of the three or more places at such establishments is considerable, and may prove insurmountable, unless either some reduction in fees is allowed or the local authority agrees to bear some, or all, of the cost.

An analysis of British data comparing the learning ability of children who had some pre-school experience and those who who did not suggests that most forms of such experience are beneficial in this respect.[6] The stories and songs learnt in playgroups and nursery schools, for instance, are likely to encourage verbal and cognitive development.[7] However, for some mothers, the pre-school provision they sought was as much to provide a brief respite for themselves from full-time responsibility for their young children as to provide the children with pre-school experience. One mother described how, after months of confinement in the back room of their small house, she went to her health visitor and told her that she had finally reached the end of her tether. The health visitor responded by arranging for her triplet boys to go to nursery school some six weeks before they reached the age of three. Another mother felt that she could not do without the costly two mornings a week that her triplets and older son went to playgroup. She made it quite clear that this provision was a necessity for her sake and for her children. Arrangements were made for the two and a half year old triplets of another mother to go to a playgroup after she reached breaking point. She and her children were collected in a car by volunteers and driven across the city to spend about two hours at the playgroup one day a week. Once there, the volunteers looked after her children in one room whilst, in another, she had a cup of coffee and talked to other mothers and volunteers.

The benefits of preferential nursery places were summed up by a mother of quadruplets:

'I feel nursery placement from the quadruplets being three years old has been my saviour. Not only does it give me two hours alone for shopping etc. It also enables the children to mix with others, something they had not done before. For several months, they went around nursery in a pack. If one moved to the slide, they all went, but they will now play with others and go their own separate ways. I had no problem getting them into nursery. The nursery teacher is very understanding of our needs and allowed me to decide whether they all came together or not, and whether I wanted morning or afternoon sessions. (For practical reasons of getting there to nursery – 25 minutes walk pushing them in prams with my mother – chose mornings and all together.) They did get preferential treatment in securing the places as other children seem to be six months older than the quads when they start nursery. They are treated as individuals and just like the other pupils.

I impressed upon the nursery staff that I would want them to be treated in exactly the same way as any other child. I wanted the fact they were quads ignored as much as possible so that they felt just the same as everyone else. Although I have referred to them here as "the quads", it is something I have never done at home. I feel the labelling creates a barrier between the four and [her older child]: sort of "them and him" situation which I find unacceptable. I've tried to foster the idea of five individuals, and the fact that four were born on the same day has been of no great importance. Group identity of the four is not something I want to encourage, and the nursery is allowing them to go along at their own individual pace. I think higher order birth parents should be given state nursery places as a priority.'

Costs and difficulties encountered

The costs of pre-school provision and the help parents obtained in meeting them varied considerably from place to place and between different forms of provision. For instance, the mothers of two sets of triplets born in 1983 reported obtaining a reduction only in the fees for nursery school:

'Mother and toddler group was 20p per child – no reduction. Playgroup was £1 a session per child – no reduction. Nursery school (one term only) was £5 per session (morning 9-1pm) for all three – a reduction of £4. This was a nursery attached to my place of employment and they were very sympathetic.'

'Mother and toddler group: 20p per morning per child. Playgroup: 75p per morning per child. Nursery School: £200 per term per child. Reduction on Nursery School fees.'

The nursery school fees also were effectively waived for one child of another triplet set born in 1984:

'Mother and toddler: 55p per session 10–12.00 (for three children plus mum). Nursery: £3 per child per morning 9–12.30pm. However the organiser gave me a one third discount! So a seven week session of two mornings a week cost £84 instead of £126.'

The fees for playgroup for one child of a triplet set born in 1984 were met by the local branch of the Pre-School Playgroup Association:

'Mother and toddler group: 25p per family per session. Playgroup: actually an Opportunity Group – £2.25 per child per week (total £6.75). Pre-School Playgroup Association (local branch) meets the cost of one child.'

Triplets born in 1985 also obtained a one third reduction of their playgroup fees:

'Toddler group: 50p per family, regardless of size. Playgroup: £1 per child per morning which is two thirds of usual price. Special reduction subsidised by the (community-run) playgroup funds.'

A few mothers of triplets secured a reduction by helping at the playgroup themselves:

'Playgroup £1 per child per session. They had one session free as I used to assist one day a seek to help defray the cost!'

In some areas a private playgroup was the only pre-school facility in the locality. To send three or more children was beyond the means of some parents, unless there was some reduction in, or sharing of the cost:

'Our girls will start playgroup in September. We have written to social services asking if we can have help with the fees. We have to fill in a form and wait and see.'

For some parents there were no affordable local pre-school facilities until the children were over three years old:

'They have been guaranteed places five mornings a week from the age of three and a quarter in the nursery class of the local state infants school – free. Head makes a point of giving preference to twins or more.'

Thirty per cent of all the parents who obtained some form of preschool provision for their higher order multiple birth children secured some form of reduction of fee for one or more of their children. In addition, the costs of either one or more child, or a proportion of the hours allocated were met by Social Services funding in eight per cent of cases. However, with the exception of triplets with special needs, this form of subsidy was more likely to be available to quadruplets and above than for triplets. For instance, a mother of quintuplets described the financial arrangements made by her local authority social services department for her children to go to playgroup:

'Social Services paid for two years. We paid the third year, 75p each per child per morning. (2 mornings at first, then three per week).'

In another local authority, the social services department met part of the nursery school fees of a set of quadruplets:

'It is £35 a week for each child. Total £140 a week [for] which I get £60 from the Authority which is not enough.'

In another, the social services department met half of the cost of sending a set of triplets to playgroup.

> 'The mother and toddler group was 20p for first child and 10p for subsequent children. I asked the local council for help to send them to playgroup and they paid half the price. Nursery school is free.'

Access to pre-school

Forty five per cent of those parents who had looked for preschool facilities had experienced difficulties obtaining access to them. Twenty per cent reported no difficulties. It was not always possible, for instance, to secure enough places in playgroup for three or more children. As a result, parents either accepted the place or places that they were offered and sent their children on a rota basis, or they waited:

> 'Had to wait longer for places at playschool because of needing three placed together on same days.'

> There were not enough places at the local playschool so I waited six months until I got them all in together on the same day.'

> 'Difficult to get three places at once until Social Services stepped in.'

> 'We were not entitled to a nursery place at the local school but the health visitor wrote a letter to help us.'

Sometimes it proved necessary to make other arrangements:

> 'We had to split attendance between two playgroups because of placement problems for three children at once. No other problems. There were advantages in their going to two different groups.'

> 'It was very difficult to find groups with places available for three children. Two groups did agree to help us after me contacting social services and then social services said that they would allow the groups to take three extra in exchange. No financial help. They started at two years three months.'

A few mothers commented that they met with criticism from other mothers because of the number of places they had secured for their children:

> 'Some mothers moaned that my children took four places. So, for the first year, until they were [aged] four, I only sent them [for] one morning [a week]. Could not stand the moaning.'

A handful of mothers reported that they had decided not to send all their higher order multiple birth children to playgroup or nursery school at the same time:

> 'I wanted to send my triplets to playgroup two at a time to give each a morning alone with me and two mornings out. The local playgroup couldn't cope with this arrangement. Nor was it open four days [a week], which I needed if they were

eventually all to go for a third day together, giving me one morning off. So we have to use one further away and less ideal in other ways.'

The timing of the placement was the problem for some mothers:

'Only problem was older child at different school. He needed picking up at same time.'

'They allowed the triplets to start a few months early but gave them afternoon placements. Being young children they were very tired and it was a difficult beginning, particularly with the older siblings in another school three quarters of a mile away finishing at the same time. I had no offers of help.'

For others, the cost of transport to preschool was the main difficulty:

'At first the public transport made me pay for the fourth child underage as "three plus a family, four a school group". After complaining, the bus company provided me with an exemption.'

Those who had no car were very worried about road safety:

'Difficult to walk alone with three young children.'

'Playgroups etc all within walking distance but pavements too narrow for triple buggy so I would need help to attend.'

If the mother went out to work, whoever looked after the children had to be able to get them to playgroup or nursery school:

'I work part of the week so I had to obtain places within walking distance of my mother-in-law's home. Eventually I did but it was hard work.'

Other parents either could not use a bus, or could not afford bus fares:

'There are no nursery facilities (apart from privately run establishments) where I live. I could have gained a place in a city school nursery, but distance and travel costs ruled this out. Bus fares would have been £2.20 per day.'

'Transport is always a problem as it has to be in walking distance as I cannot get on a bus and cannot afford taxis.'

Conclusions

Mother and toddler groups, various playgroups, day nurseries, nursery schools and nursery classes in infant schools all provide pre-school experience, but of different kinds, costs and levels of shared responsibility for the care of triplets, quadruplets and quintuplets. All offer an alternative to home, at a regular time. What is crucially different, apart from cost, is the time period of provision and whether or not, as in all mother and toddler groups and some playgroups, the mother is required to stay with her children whilst they are there and to retain total responsibility for their charge. For some mothers the pre-school provision they sought was as much to provide a brief respite for themselves from the full time responsibility for their higher order multiple birth children as to provide pre-school experience for the children. In this respect, mother and toddler groups were a difficult, and sometimes stressful, option, even with a companion. The large majority of parents sought at least some hours of supervised child care at a playgroup or nursery school and, if necessary, assistance with fees or with transport there. The combined issue of cost, distance, transport, and particularly the cost of transport, loomed large in descriptions of the difficulties encountered, however. Also, unfortunately, some obtained this kind of provision only when they reached breaking point. Given that research with twins has indicated delays in the development of language,[8] the social and developmental benefits for higher order multiple birth children of providing some hours of supervised pre-school provision would seem to be a priority.

References
1. Blatchford P, Battle S and Mays J. The first transition – home to pre-school. Windsor, Berks: NFER-Nelson, 1982.
2. Haystead J, Howarth V, Strachan A. Pre-school education and care. Edinburgh: Hodder and Stoughton, 1980.
3. Hill M. Sharing child care in early parenthood. London: Routledge and Kegan Paul, 1987.
4. Pugh G. Services for under-fives. London: National Children's Bureau, 1988.
5. Van der Eyken W. Mother and toddler groups. Where No 134 London: Advisory Centre for Education 1978.
6. Osborn A F, Milbank J E. The effects of early education. Oxford: Clarendon Press, 1987.
7. Hayes D S, Chemelski B E and Palmer M. Nursery rhymes and prose passages: pre-schoolers' liking and short-term retention of story events. Developmental Psychology 1982; 18: 49–56.
8. Hay D A et al. Speech and language development in pre-school twins. Acta Genetica Medica Gemellologica 1987; 36: 213–223.

Chapter 11 – Schooling

Frances V Price, Sarah Moores, Eileen Ockwell, Bride Stokes

The education authority even agreed to accept them earlier than usual, ie at Christmas instead of Easter and the headmistress asked me whether I wanted them together or separated.'

'Teachers and fellow pupils find it difficult to remember which is which.'

'One is not so academic and has lost some confidence. They tell tales of each other.'

Introduction

Some parents wrote, 'They are now at school' in response to the question requesting information about current sources of help not previously available. In general, at about the age of five, the care and control of their triplets, quadruplets or quintuplets became officially shared by others, and in a place other than home. Entry to school was a long anticipated landmark in the lives of both parents and children.

This chapter is about some of the difficult issues and specific problems which have been raised by parents in relation to their children's transition to school, their entry to school and their communication and development whilst at school. First of all, parents' survey data is cited to provide an indication of the extent of these problems and the numbers involved. Second, three case-studies written by mothers of triplets serve to highlight and to place in context the various issues and problems.

Table 11.1

Arrangements at school

	Triplets Number	Per cent	Quadruplets and quintuplets Number	Per cent
Same school:	96	92.3	11	91.7
Same class	82	79.8	7	58.3
Different class	14	13.5	5	41.7
Different schools:	8	7.7	1	8.3
Because of impairment	4	3.8	–	
Other reasons	2	1.9	1	8.3
Not stated	2	1.9	–	
Total sets of children at school	104	100.0	12	100.0

Source: Parents' study.

One hundred and four sets of triplets and 12 sets of quadruplets and quintuplets were at school at the time their parent completed the parents' study questionnaire. The statistical information from these 116 households, shown in Table 11.1, forms the basis for this chapter. In addition, 27 mothers whose triplets and quadruplets were born before 1979 also completed a questionnaire and provided welcome additional information about the schooling of their higher order multiple birth children.

Entry to school

Well documented differences exist between local education authorities, both in the education provision that they make, and in the economic resources on which they can draw. Directives concerning numbers to be admitted, age of school entry and, specifically, directives about school entry of 'rising fives' have a considerable impact on households which include triplets, quadruplets or quintuplets. In some instances, local schools were unable to take all three triplets, and parents were offered only one or two places. Few parents were able to make alternative arrangements further afield, not least because of the difficulties and cost of transport which would be involved. In one household in the study an older child of over five was still not at school. His mother had to cope with his need for her attention as well as her boisterous three year old triplets, one of whom was developmentally delayed. At considerable cost, all four children went to a local playgroup for two mornings a week. Their mother regarded this as a vital respite, for herself as much as for her children.

Twenty four per cent of the parents of triplets and 42 per cent of parents of quadruplets and quintuplets who were at school reported that there had been difficulties with their entry to and start of schooling. A mother of nine year old identical triplets wrote:

> 'All the boys got very upset at first because none of the other children could remember their own names. Coping better with it now though.'

One mother vigorously contested arrangements made by her health visitor, without consultation with her, that her triplets should each attend a different primary school. The mother protested that the logistics of getting all her four children to and from these different schools seemed not to have been taken into account by the professionals involved:

> 'Apparently, the health visitor was recommending that we split them up for their own benefit. She obviously had not thought through the implications of such an action.'

As shown in Table 11.1, in most instances the children in each triplet, quadruplet and quintuplet set attended the same school. In six triplet sets and one quadruplet set, however, one child of the set attended a different school. A monozygotic pair of girls in one triplet set had heart and hearing problems which made it necessary for them to go to a school for children with special needs. Two girls and one boy from different triplet sets who had cerebral palsy also attended a special school as did a triplet boy who had ocular albinism and was developmentally delayed. Several parents, all of whose higher order multiple birth children were already at school, were confronting the idea that it might be in the best interests of their children to send them to different

190

schools. One quadruplet boy was required to repeat a school year. His parents decided, however, to send him to a different school to his brother and two sisters. The parents of a triplet set comprising a boy and two girls decided to send their son to a different school to his two sisters 'to give him more independence'.

Separate or together?

'Headmistress of their second school wanted to split them up into three different classes.'

'They did ask if I wanted them separated. I said "No".'

Some teachers and parents advocate the separation of triplets, quadruplets and quintuplets into different classes at the outset of their schooling. There is no formally collected evidence either to support this strategy, or to indicate if and when there might be a better time to separate them. For the children, the benefit of separation is seen to be a greater sense of 'self' and independence in learning, less competition and comparison with siblings, and a greater opportunity to make individual friends and develop communication skills. The advantages of separation which are claimed for the teacher are not only a greater opportunity to recognise and treat each child as an individual, and to build on particular strengths and abilities, but also the chance to allocate separate tasks and projects.

It is unusual for three or more parallel classes for the children in each age group to be available within one school, at least at infant school level. Thus, in most schools, the separation of triplets, quadruplets and quintuplets into different classes is not a realistic strategy in the first few years. Of course, in theory, the children could be sent to different primary schools. This is likely to be extraordinarily difficult to implement, unless one or more child is allocated a place in a school for children with special needs. In such cases, the local education authority usually arranges transport by taxi or minibus. In practical terms, sending the children to different primary schools is not an option for most parents, particularly as almost half the parents in the study had one or more older child and some took their children to and from school on foot.

In 15 per cent of all triplet sets attending the same school and 45 per cent of quadruplet sets attending the same school, at least one child from the set was in a different class at school from the rest of the set. The great majority of the children in triplet sets were not separated into different classes at the time of completion of the parents' study questionnaire. Several parents wrote comments which indicated how troubled they were by the lack of separation:

'Not a good idea all being in same class. The identical girls became as one. Nobody seems to know which is which. This applies to teachers too!'

'Teachers seemed to lump them together as a trio. Not much effort made to see them as separate individuals.'

Some parents in interview reported a problematic self sufficiency in their triplets or quadruplets. In certain circumstances the children were markedly dependent on one another and found difficulty in developing relationships with other children. Constant 'togetherness' may hinder, not only language development, but also recognition of the children as individuals, and is likely to make it difficult for each child to accept responsibility for herself or himself. A division of labour may be fostered between the children whereby one child speaks for the others. Teachers may reinforce this pattern of behaviour. In one instance the taller and more articulate triplet was always given the messages and greetings cards from the school to take home. In some situations the children in the set may be fiercely competitive and vie with each other for their teachers' attention.

Language development and communication

The question, 'Have there been any problems arising from differences in language and communication skills between your multiple birth children and other children?' was on the page of the questionnaire headed 'Schooling'. Consequently it was seldom completed by parents of children who were not yet at school. One mother summed up why she believed this to be an unfortunate error of questionnaire design:

> 'It is no good leaving enquiries about speech delay for the school section as they can become a big worry well before then (not only for the parents). Ours had less than one-year-level development of language at 2½ years and had been receiving attention for this since just over two years old.'

Not all children with early language delays turn out to have later problems.[1] Language development is remarkably robust. Many children who have language delays in the early years overcome them, although there is some evidence that they are more likely to have difficulties with language-related cognitive skills such as reading and also behavioural problems in their primary school years.[2] Most recent studies of the prevalence of language delay focus on three year old children and are not easy to interpret.[1-5] There is, as yet, no general agreement as to the definition of normality.[1]

There has been no systematic research into the language development of triplets and higher order birth children. Even with twins it is not known how extensive language and articulation problems can be, or how early in childhood they become evident.[2-7] People tend to assume that the process of language development in twins is essentially the same as in singletons.[2,3] Research suggests that the process may be different in twins and that they tend to be disadvantaged in their language development.[2,3] Certain features in the social environment of multiple birth children may increase the likelihood of developmental delay in expressive language or poor articulation. Multiple birth children spend much time together. The attachment that develops between these children may hinder the development of their language. Each has at least two others with which to share, to reinforce and to maintain invented words and mistakes in articulation. Twins are reported as sometimes developing an autonomous secret language, usually with a different syntax and different learning patterns to the model language of their parents, although this development is usually short-lived as the children adapt their language to that of their parents.[4] As has been observed:

> 'The phenomenon of twins using a private language together has frequently been described, but is not very well documented, and it is unclear whether it actually interferes with normal language acquisition. Certainly, many twins go through only a brief phase of using private language'.[7]

Recently, researchers have suggested that the division of time and attention between two or more infants may be a critical factor in the environment in which multiple birth children learn language. Delays in the development of language and poor articulation may arise, it is suggested, from each child's reduced opportunity for individual time with a parent or adult carer. Furthermore, multiple birth children may compete with each other for adult attention. As a result they not only may speak very fast but also leave out consonants, and even syllables, to get their message across speedily.[6] One adult alone will have difficulty dividing attention between, monitoring and responding to the constant utterances of two, three or more language learning infants. This is a suggested source of language delay in twins.[3] However, the dynamics of the situation, as a factor affecting language development, are as yet unclear. Nor is there evidence to suggest that language delay can be prevented by modifying child care arrangements. Biological explanations such as birth complications, or the possibility of slowed maturation before birth, cannot be excluded from consideration.[7] A combination of adverse factors is likely to be involved.

Mothers and fathers of higher order multiple birth children are unlikely to be any less active than parents of singletons in promoting the welfare and optimum development of all their children. Their circumstances are significantly different from the parents of singletons. There are three, four or more capricious language-learning infants of the same age all clamouring for adult attention. The notion of turn-taking has to be developed over the years. The situation is different from one where there is one adult and one child, or one adult and children of different ages. Parents reported how stressful it was attempting to develop coping strategies to provide each child with individual attention. This was particularly so when one or more child had special needs, or needed sustained extra help with speech therapy exercises, reading or numeracy. Several parents expressed the view that the teachers at their children's school did not readily appreciate the situation they confronted or the sheer impact of attending to, caring for and stimulating three or more youngsters of the same age.

Parents can become acutely worried about behavioural problems or the unequal progress of their children. They readily sense the feelings of inadequacy, and sometimes of depression, in one or more of their children, if she or he is slower to learn than the others, or not as good at games or at making friends. Parents are likely to communicate their worries to the children and, without sensitive teacher-parent discussions, the situation may be perpetuated in a cycle of anxiety.

Involvement of specialists

Twenty one of the 104 parents of triplets and six of the 12 parents of quadruplets who were at school reported that one or more of their children had been seen by a speech therapist:

> 'Two need speech therapy – certain sounds are mispronounced "f" and "p", ends of words not sounded. Both have a different speech pattern – picked up at three year check up. [Second born triplet] has been to therapy for a short while but the sessions were stopped. She should be recalled after her first half term to see if her speech has matured any.'

Some health visitors helped with getting particular children referred to a speech therapist. Waiting lists were long, however, and some children did not receive specialist attention in time to benefit before starting school. One mother wrote on her questionnaire:

'[Health visitor] has helped in arranging speech therapy (after a wait of 10 months) for [two of her triplet daughters].'

This mother provided further information some months later:

'The speech therapist was very pleased with [first born triplet] yesterday. She behaved herself for one and a half hours. But she does not think that she has time to make enough progress with [second born triplet] before commencement of school. However, I am sure she will be OK. She has made such marvellous progress in the few weeks that she has been attending, that we can only guess at how well she would have done if she had got the help 12 months ago.'

A few parents reported that their children had overcome a reluctance to use language by the time they started school. A mother of triplets wrote:

'When they were three and under they communicated more with their hands etc and didn't speak very much, but, by the time they were four they had caught up with everybody'

On the other hand, some children started primary school with marked communication difficulties. Twenty four per cent of parents whose higher order multiple birth children were at school, 22 of whom had triplets and three of whom had quadruplets, reported that their children had problems with language development and communication. Furthermore, a few parents reported that the neglect or mismanagement of this situation by school staff and other professionals had led to further difficulties and caused additional stress for all concerned. The following case study provides an illustration.

One mother of triplet daughters described her efforts to obtain expert assistance for two of them who were identical and needed to overcome speech problems, increase their confidence and establish basic literacy skills.

After their assessment at two years old, the health visitor had referred all three children for hearing tests and then for speech therapy. At this stage, as their mother reported, 'They couldn't say a single word'. Some five or six months later an appointment for a hearing test became available and a speech rather than a hearing problem was identified for the two identical triplets. By contrast, their non-identical triplet sister was identified as having a hearing problem. She had overcome this by the time she was four, after two operations within a year for the insertion and reinsertion of grommets. Unfortunately, her identical sisters' speech problem was to prove more intractable.

By the age of three, the identical pair had a vocabulary of a few single words. Both were referred for speech therapy. Once a week for three months both girls and their mother were taken by a Home-Start volunteer by car to a speech therapy treatment group. In this setting, the speech of both girls improved. Both began to use sentences. After three months, speech therapy was made available to just one of them.

Given her particular circumstances, this mother found it difficult to care for her three lively pre-school children and also to attempt to do the 'homework' which was set by the speech therapist for just one child. She found the exercises she was asked to do with her daughter very complex and hard to understand. The 'homework' was seldom done. The speech therapist reacted to her acknowledgement of this by postponing the next appointment until she did attempt some work with her daughter. This greatly increased the mother's sense of anxiety about the situation.

The triplets, at this time, were in separate classes at a city day nursery. All three seemed to their parents to be developing happily and confidently. Subsequently they moved to the local primary school as rising five year olds. Here they were placed in two different classes with no mention of any upset. One identical triplet girl and her non-identical triplet sister were in one class and the other identical triplet in another. However, with the arrival of a new headteacher in their second term at primary school, all three were put in the same class against their parents' wishes. The standard of their work deteriorated and they lost confidence. One of the identical triplets in particular became very nervous and upset. Their headteacher initially said to their mother that she would review the situation. Later, after additional visits by their mother, it was agreed that the school would provide additional teaching support. This, however, had not materialised half-way through the triplets' third term of schooling. Perplexed and upset by her daughters' lack of progress in school, their mother turned to her GP for help. As a consequence, one identical child was referred by the GP to a clinical psychologist and the mother's fears that her daughter had real problems with her language development were confirmed by the psychologist's verbal report.

In the ensuing months, this mother wrote to or telephoned everyone she believed might be able to identify or secure appropriate help for her daughters. Eventually, in the summer following their fourth term of schooling, both her identical triplet girls were assessed by the school psychological service and she was sent a copy of the psychologist's report. One of her identical daughters was described as 'a pleasant and cooperative six year old who appeared quite amenable throughout the test situation' and was assessed as having a verbal intelligence quotient of 114 but 'quite a serious speech problem'. Her identical triplet sister, by comparison described as 'somewhat diffident', was reported as having 'some articulation problems' and a verbal intelligence quotient of 100. It was emphasised that both were at a very early stage of reading.

In the autumn of their fifth term in schooling, and in the light of both their detailed psychological assessment, and also of a second hearing test it was agreed that the identical triplet pair again be separated in different classes, just as they had been in their first term at school. At the time of enquiry, both were receiving three quarters of an hour support in separate groups from a special needs teacher for four days a week and were awaiting appointments for speech therapy. Their mother was pleased with the various developments and hoped that her daughters would soon catch up with their contemporaries in learning to read. Nonetheless, she was aware that, had she not herself become so distressed about her daughters' situation, made frequents visits to the school and contacted all those she believed might be able to intervene to help her, matters might not now look so promising:

'I feel very bitter that I have had to do so much sorting out myself. [The head teacher] didn't even see about getting any extra help until I had been to see the [clinical] psychologist [arranged through her GP].'

In interview, several other parents reported similar difficulties confronting their children's speech and articulation problems within the school.

In total 12 of the 116 parents reported that one or more of their children had been seen by an educational psychologist. Ten were parents of triplets and two were parents of quadruplets.

The principle that 'pupils are to be educated in accordance with the wishes of their parents' was enshrined in the 1944 Education Act. More recently, the 1981 Education Act introduced the concept of 'learning difficulty' and laid down a legislative framework so that, where possible, a child with special educational needs, that is with 'a learning difficulty which calls for special educational provision to be made', can have these needs met in an ordinary rather than a special school. Under the Act, parents have the right in law to request an assessment of their child's special educational needs. This is not only to understand better what learning difficulties are involved, but also to enable a specification of special needs for certain kinds of approaches, facilities or resources within the schooling system and to determine what provision can meet these needs.[8,9] On completion of the formal assessment of the child, the education authority drafts a written statement and provides the parent(s) with a copy. This statement is the legal documentation of the child's needs, as identified by all the professionals from whom advice has been sought, and also of the form of education provision which should be made for the child. In the course of the study, written statements were prepared for two triplet boys in a monozygotic set setting out their special educational needs which were subsequently met by additional teaching support within their primary school.

Conclusions

Most of the triplets, quadruplets and quintuplets started school with some experience of pre-schooling but not necessarily of separation from their mother or from each other. Teachers are unlikely to have experience in dealing with such children, some of whom were reported in the study as being markedly dependent on each other and exhibiting a self-sufficiency which complicated developing relationships, not only with their teachers, but also with other children. Some children also started school with a marked delay in language development. An important but unresolved debate revolves around the issue of whether or not to separate the children into separate classes at some point during their primary schooling to encourage a greater sense of 'self' and independence in learning. Contact and co-operation between parents and teachers enables any difficulties which may affect their learning or social development to be communicated and solutions sought to overcome them. In the three case studies which follow, mothers of triplets draw from their own experiences to describe the problems they confronted and how they were resolved.

Case Studies

Case study 1: Going to school – together or apart?

'The first problem for us was the choice of school for our non-identical triplet boys. No school in our area offered three reception classes, one for each child, which was what we would have preferred. We narrowed the choice down to two schools. The nearest within walking distance was small and had only one class of less than 20 pupils per year group. The other (a car journey away) was much larger with two reception classes each with 25 pupils, who then moved on to larger classes of 35+ pupils of mixed year groups. We chose the latter school for the boys because it seemed to us to offer the option of separating the boys should the need arise. However we decided to start them off together rather than arbitrarily splitting them up, two in one class and one in another from the outset. (It is no easier trying to do this at a later stage – we agonise each year over whether the time for separation has come!)

The boys had no problems settling in. They already knew many of the children from playschool or elsewhere and the three of them took to school well. However, their very different abilities became apparent almost immediately – the least able child at this stage worked at a different table to the others and started to make different friends. At different times all three seemed to go through a stage of neither having particular friends nor turning to his brothers for support, as one might have expected. But before long the first individual party invitation arrived, quickly followed by others. Invitations out to tea 'on their own' became, and still are, a regular occurrence. Although it is interesting to note that some of their friends' mothers still insist on having all three boys (one at a time and in strict rotation) for fear of causing upsets. By the end of their first year they had many friends. Some were friendly with all three boys, some with just one. We have not yet had an invitation out for two boys and not the other one!

In the second year there was a more obvious three way split. Friendships seemed to be more firmly established and their different personalities had drawn them to very different friends. It was at this stage that we had problems with "telling tales" on each other. The most disruptive of the three asked to be moved to a separate class for this reason alone! However, a split in the third year meant putting one of the boys with children of a predominantly younger age group and this idea was abandoned when he (and his brothers) felt he was being "kept down". It was also during their second year that the two more able boys became very competitive. Fortunately they each found other children in the class with whom to compete, thus easing the pressure at home. However, the third child decided not to compete at all and to an extent "gave up". He needed much praise and encouragement to help him realise that his efforts were worthwhile, even though the end result did not seem to him to be as "impressive" as that of his brothers'.

In the third year they found themselves in a class with very few of their friends from the previous two years but settled very quickly into three different groups – those who play football at playtimes, those who play with the girls and those who do neither! Occasionally two will work together on some project in the classroom. This is not discouraged, although a careful eye is kept on the situation lest friends be excluded too often.

All three boys are making good progress, commensurate with their ability. But I would still like to be able to give each of them the opportunity to learn "alone". To sum up, as a parent of triplets I find quite specific problems in relation to the boys' schooling;

(1) At the end of the day the boys have the same news to tell me (and nothing new to tell each other) and the other two will constantly interrupt and add to whatever one tries to tell me.

(2) Tale-telling cases problems, particularly if one individual is more prone to misbehaviour (however minor). If there is a real problem I would rather hear from their teacher than be given a possible exaggerated report from the other children.

(3) Comparison by teachers and friends, and even by us, is inevitable if they are supposedly doing the same work each day. It is easy to just compare the three and forget to praise each for his own achievements, regardless of what the others have done.

(4) Being together at school all day means we, as parents, really need to create as many opportunities as we can for them to be on their own. Separate bedrooms and outings, or even just time on their own with one parent helps a great deal. Staying overnight (one at a time) with grandparents during the holidays has proved to be very successful, as has encouraging them to become involved separately in out of school activities such as Beavers, judo and swimming where the other children they meet do not know them as "one of the triplets" and they have new experiences to tell of to both us and each other.'

Case study 2. Separated, and then together

'I am a twin. When I was a child my sister and I were the only twins in the area. Twins were rare and consequently we were treated as being rather "special" – not by our parents but by our teachers and relatives. Although very different academically we were kept in the same class at school and had always to sit together. I had never discussed education with my sister but I felt we should have been separated. When my triplets were three I was on holiday with my sister and I asked how she felt about our education and if she had any opinion regarding keeping twins together in school and she surprised me with the strength of her conviction that we should have been separated when we were at school.

It was because of this that I followed my instinct and had the triplets separated at nursery school and in their first year at infant school. They loved being apart and having their own friends. In fact not many people knew that they were triplets. They were often invited out to tea on their own and had their own friends home. We did not have too many problems with friends at first as they were used to their older sisters having friends visit. I did find that when it became known that they were triplets they tended to be invited together.

In their first year at infant school it was the best thing that I could have done. One triplet had no difficulties reading and had no other problems. She was keen and competitive and had to be first at everything. She was lucky because she was among the brightest in the class and thoroughly enjoyed her first year at school. Another triplet was quiet but worked hard and had no problem when learning to read, and at the end of her first year she was very competent at reading and writing. The last triplet was a bubbly extrovert little girl. However she clung to me every morning when I took her to school. She had eczema which appeared to get worse in her first term at school and also she had great difficulty learning to read. However, her teacher was wonderful. She was changed to a different reading scheme every time she reached her limit on one and by the end of the spring term she had practically covered every reading scheme that the school used (and they used quite a few). Because she changed books regularly, she did not appear to feel inferior in reading but accepted that she could not read quite as well as her sisters but she had read a lot more books than they had. At the end of their first year at primary school I let them have separate birthday parties – their birthday is in June. It was a wonderful success. They all had their own friends to their parties and there was very little friction.

We then had to decide what to do in their second year. It would be their final year at infant school and it was possible to have them in separate classes again. However, the three top classes were mixed from three reception classes and the middle infants. The possibility existed that they would be separated from their friends. Also the junior school to which they would go was only two form entry so we would have the problem of what to do then.

We decided to put them together to see how they coped in an environment they knew rather than wait until they went to a new school with new teachers and then be "thrown" together. I should say here that they themselves wanted to be apart and if we had separated them two in one class and one apart, the triplet who was on her own would have felt the privileged one and the other two would have felt unfairly treated.

They accepted that they had to be together and all of them had some friends from their first class with them, plus some older children from the middle infant class. They settled in well and academically they progressed quite well. The triplet who was quite bright and competitive found life quite different from class one. Some very bright children were in this class and she had to learn to cope with not being Number One. However she was naturally a very good worker and enjoyed learning so the change of classmates was very good for her. The other two adapted very well also. The slow reader has progessed extremely well and copes well with the classwork. Once because she didn't work she was given easy spellings to learn and this upset her very much. I told her that if she had been good enough she would have had the same as her sisters, consequently she learned both sets of spellings to show her teacher that she could do them.

I found it very difficult teaching them spellings and teaching them their tables. One tries to ensure that adequate time is spent with each child to ensure that they learn but there is just not enough time and what one child finds easy to learn the other will find difficult and vice versa. I find this very difficult and frustrating and also one feels very guilty that one is unable to give enough time to help the child. We also have a problem of one of the triplets finding things easy – partly because she has a wonderful ability of application and also natural ability. She appears to find spelling and tables easier than the other two triplets and consequently they feel it is unfair.

At home the identical pair tend to play together more, probably because the third has a different ability (eg they will play with dolls while she bats/kicks a ball against a wall).

However, all three of them are very athletic and good at sports. They all go to gymnastics and, now, are enjoying it. At first I had to insist that two of them went. I never had any problem with the unidentical triplet, she is the one who found reading easy and appeared to be natural gymnast, ball player, runner, pianist, and general good all rounder. The other two took turns to be difficult, first going to nursery school, to gymnastics, swimming and all other activities to which they were taken. However as they got older they found that they were better than their sister and were quicker at running than her and were better at gymnastics so they became more interested in taking part. The unidentical one and one of the others undertook a course in football skills. They have on a number of occasions asked if they can do ballet. I have consistently refused, until I can be sure that they won't cling to me and refuse to take part. Perhaps this will happen within the next year. They all hope to start Brownies in September. They will join the same pack because a friend of theirs is starting then. They have stayed overnight at friends' houses, on their own and have thoroughly enjoyed themselves. Only one of them showed any signs of being homesick.

We have some jealousies but try to overcome these by discussing each other's good points and pointing out that not everyone is gifted in the same way. One of the greatest disadvantages of being in the same class is that as parents we get the same card from each child, at Christmas, Easter and Mother's Day. Also when they come out of school there is great competition to tell me the news of the day and the exciting things that have happened. We have had problems with "telling tales", and as yet I don't think I have worked out how to deal with this. We also have "friend" problems. One wanted to phone a boy one evening and I made her wait until after dinner. While she was waiting, he phoned and asked to speak to her sister! Problems also occur at Christmas and birthdays. If they are each given the same present, once one triplet has opened hers the other two know what they are getting and feel cheated of the thrill of discovering what is inside the wrapper. I have overcome this in a small way by letting them take turns in unwrapping. We also try to give each child some completely different present, very often what they have asked for – within reason. As I said at the beginning I am a twin. Our birthday was just after Christmas and we both had to share our Christmas and birthday presents. Because of this I am very careful to make sure that each child has her own cards and presents and birthday cakes. Perhaps I am stressing the individuality and fairness too much but the need to share so much during my childhood has made me very aware of each child's needs to have their own things. However all my children have no problem sharing clothes and although my eldest daughter is four years older than the triplets her size differs only in height and her feet. Consequently they can share shorts, t-shirts, jumpers, cardigans and socks, and they do not mind.

One very good outcome from having the girls together in one class is that their friends now know them apart as individuals. This had probably been helped by the fact that I have encouraged and succeeded in the girls having different hairstyles. One of the identical girls has a short bob and the other has medium length hair. The unidentical triplet has long hair.

To sum up, the problems which I have found are: (1) I have not enough time to spend with each child for homework. (2) Tale telling is very annoying and upsetting for the other child. I invariably have at least one tale told as I collect them from school, not always the same child telling the tale. (3) Since they have spent one year together, I have found that they are now more aware of being a "triplet" and therefore being somewhat "special".'

Case study 3: The need for flexibility

'As there was no state nursery provision locally, we approached our local authority for financial support for our triplet boy and identical girls to go to a private playgroup and were given forms to complete. The stigma involved in the form-filling procedures at the playgroup was uncomfortable, even though support towards some of the fees had already been obtained. The entire process was demoralising. The playgroup allowed the triplets to start a few months early but gave them afternoon placements and, being very young children, they were very tired. It was a difficult beginning, not only for this reason, but because their older brother and sister were at another school three quarters of a mile away which finished at the same time. We had a new baby son and I had no offers of help. We made every attempt to persevere with this situation as the children at this playgroup usually went on to the local school where two of our children were already settled: However three is an awkward number of children to slot in for extra sessions and we were aware of the pressure to satisfy the needs of other families in the area who were only requesting extra session places for one child.

Apart from playgroup, the opportunities for them to mix with other children in a wider context were minimal. The isolation we as a family experienced could be directly related to our early difficulties with transport, particularly when trying to get to the local mother and toddler group where we seemed to become more of a spectacle than supported members of the group.

After a while we found the situation intolerable. I approached our very supportive GP and I asked if he would write a letter to the nursery department of a neighbouring primary school. The triplets' energy had become inexhaustible, with the little amount of time I was able to give them. They were even waking each other up in the middle of the night to play. At this stage they certainly communicated with one another, but displayed poor language skills. Their powers of concentration also seemed limited, probably as a result of constantly having their play interrupted by a sibling. They were continually on the go, often collaborating in activities, effectively compensating for each other's strengths and weaknesses. Socialisation in a wider context was almost non-existent as they had such limited opportunities to meet and play with other children.

We were successful with our application for entry to the nursery and we specifically asked for morning sessions as that would make it easier to get the older two children to their school. As it turned out, and as had happened with the playgroup, we were "fitted into" afternoon sessions (which were not as popular as the morning ones) which upset the whole family's routine. Eventually the triplets were allocated morning sessions, and family equilibrium was restored. The triplets' speech improved dramatically as they were given the opportunity for individual expression and to mix with other children under the watchful eye of trained staff.

As school age approached, we were told by the staff at the school to which the nursery department was attached that the triplets would have to leave the nursery and enter the infant department of the school in the summer term of their fifth birthday. They could not remain in the nursery beyond this age. Fortunately, we had already decided that we wanted the children under one roof and, as the older children had experienced four settled years at their church school, we maintained our original decision to send the triplets there also. Another deciding factor was that this school had a uniform which would overcome our difficulties of not having enough hand-me-downs in which to dress them. Matters became difficult when this school informed us that they were not offering any places for the following term. Believing our special situation had not been understood, we appealed but lost. It was particularly difficult to accept the school's decision as a friend of the triplets, who was two days older, had been offered a place at the school a whole term earlier. This would have given her two terms more schooling, and she was fortunate to have a home environment which offered her a one to one relationship within the family. At the appeal we were told that in fact there had been only one place available and we were the next family on the list to receive it. They had not however offered us the place because they thought it would be a dilemma for us knowing which child to send. They made it clear it was impossible to make any exception for our two other children, even for one term, as this might "open the flood gates" for further cases. But for the last 10 years we have been the only triplets in our area! Our options at that point were to take the children away from the nursery, leaving them with a term plus a summer holiday with nothing (ie a total of 20 weeks) or accepting the places in the infant department of the school to which their nursery was attached and facing the problem of two different schools operating similar starting and finishing times. On reflection, one stressful experience replaced another. The whole situation was exacerbated by different sports day events, open days, and display days, with parents sometimes having to be in two places at once. At the beginning of the next term we chose to move the triplets to the church school. This meant that they had only two years in the infant department and a second start to school in two terms.

Once settled under one roof, other issues presented themselves which required several approaches by us to the school. It was clear that after the change of school, the triplets again teamed up to achieve tasks set by the teacher. They cleverly built on each other's strengths. It was no surprise to us that the teacher was unaware of what they individually could or could not achieve. School staff were clearly perceiving the triplets as a group and not as individuals. Consequently we considered the possibilities of separation which, ideally, requires three parallel classes. The option to separate one triplet arose and the decision was made that one of the identical girls should move to a different class. We also asked that her sister and brother, who were still together in the same class, should not be placed in the same work groups. By this stage we were beginning to feel the pressures of being labelled "fussy parents", which made the situation even worse. It was always a question of us approaching the school, never the staff suggesting that we discuss matters with them before crucial decisions were made.

On entering the junior department one of the triplets became extremely unhappy at school. I approached the school to be told, without explanation, that the child was disruptive in class. Fortunately a new multiple births clinic had opened at [a city hospital] which was brought to our attention by the voluntary organisation TAMBA and we booked an appointment for each of the triplets to be seen. Up until this point, apart from one development check at the local child health clinic, they had never experienced a thorough medical check-up from the time they left hospital after their birth to this, their seventh year. The examination revealed no worrying coordination problems which might have presented difficulties with school work. However, it was pointed out to us at the clinic that the problems we were concerned about were not unusual in children who had been premature, and, of course, the triplets had been premature. We received a copy of a thorough report from the clinic and another copy was sent to the head teacher of the children's school. The report was given a serious review by the staff and this brought about a more analytical consideration of the difficulties experienced by our son. It was discovered that he had a serious writing and reading deficit and was unable to apply himself to the set work. Instead he tried to win approval from peers by being the class clown, and in so doing, he diverted the teacher's attention from his learning problems. Our son's mathematics work was extremely good, which influenced the school's eventual decision not to allocate extra support for English tasks. It was explained to us that other children in the class showing all round learning deficits had to be priority. We were offered time with the educational psychologist. In our particular circumstances we considered this inappropriate.

Another worrying issue concerned the child who had been separated from her brother and identical sister. We realised that there were going to be difficulties in rearranging who was in a separate class from whom. When the children reached third year juniors, despite consultations with the head teacher and the first ever opportunity to split the children three ways into three separate classes, we were told that they were all to have the same class. It was explained that the local educational authority's policy was to group children according to their chronological age and that no exceptions could be made – yet another example of the way educational policy is made without any consideration of the needs of multiple birth children.

The triplets are now 10 years old and have shared a classroom for a year. For the first time the identical girls have shown a marked discrepancy between their standard of work, whereas whilst in separate classrooms, their results were very similar. It appears that one has dominated the other throughout the year as a result of sharing the same classroom experiences. We have had to be positive about stopping the collective name of "triplets" or using their surname to identify them as a group in the classroom and the school. The children have been affected by one or other being told off, and have found it difficult to choose between classroom etiquette and loyalty towards a brother or sister in whose company they are constantly, both in the classroom and at home. Our children's educational attainments I believe have been directly affected, not only by a home background where it is difficult to offer enough individual support, but also by the inability of the school to recognise their special needs.

In conclusion, the flexibility needed to ensure a satisfactory schooling for three, four or more children of the same age requires that many exceptions be made to the "norm". From time to time, trying to fit into a system designed for singletons becomes stressful if not impossible. Our experience of nursery schooling in itself was invaluable, providing many opportunities conducive to the triplets' development as individuals. However, the difficulties which arose around trying to fit in with the afternoon sessions at the nursery and the race between our children's different schools remain very painful memories. There is often a need for temporary support to overcome learning difficulties and to encourage these children to become literate and numerate members of society. Such issues must be recognized and extra encouragement provided before the difficulties become magnified – with all that means for the children in their future lives in relation to jobs, careers and to becoming, in their turn, parents themselves.'

References

1. Silva P A. Epidemiology, longitudinal course and some associated factors: an update. In: Yule W, Rutter M, eds. Language development and disorders. Clinics in Developmental Medicine 101–102, London: MacKeith Press, 1988.

2. Hay D A, Prior M, Collett S, Williams M. Speech and language development in preschool twins. Acta Genetica Medica Gemellologica 1987; 36: 213–223.

3. Mogford K. Language development in twins. In: Bishop D, Mogford K, eds. Language development in exceptional circumstances. Edinburgh: Churchill Livingstone, 1988.

4. Bakker P. Autonomous language in twins. Acta Genetica Medica Gemellologica 1987; 36: 233–238.

5. Bishop D, Mogford K, eds. Language development in exceptional circumstances. Edinburgh: Churchill Livingstone, 1988.

6. Savic S. How twins learn to talk: A study of the speech development of twins 1–3. London: Academic Press, 1980.

7. Bishop D. Language development in twins. Multiple Births Foundation Newsletter 1989; 4: 3.

8. Galloway D. Schools, pupils and special educational needs. London: Croom Helen, 1985.

9. Adams E, ed. Special education. London: Longmans, 1986.

Chapter 12 – The costs of a multiple birth

Miranda Mugford

'We have really struggled to survive over the last six years – my husband earning just above the amount required to qualify for any help.'

'Although the absolute number of triplets and higher order births may be relatively small, these babies make disproportionate demands on intensive care services...'[1]

Introduction

Having a baby and childrearing are times when a household has greater needs and reduced earning power. Societies have developed ways to help, particularly through provision of health services and state maternity and child benefits, but such support is usually designed to meet the needs of the majority of parents who have a single baby, and fall short of the increased needs when more than two babies are born at one time. The problem of accommodating the greater needs that arise in triplet and higher order births has led to calls for increased health service facilities to accommodate the upward trend in multiple births. Although there have been precedents for special state funded financial benefits for families with triplets, quadruplets or more, there are no such benefits in the UK at present.

Throughout the preceding chapters, comparisons have been made between aspects of pregnancy and birth for twins, triplets and more. At each stage of pregnancy and afterwards, it is evident that more time, skills and other materials are needed by women who have triplets or quadruplets than is the case where a singleton baby or twins are born.

The aim of this chapter is to quantify some of these costs, and to assess the additional costs for triplet and higher order births, beyond what might be expected for twin births. The following sections consider the costs that arise at different stages of pregnancy, birth and subsequent care, discussing the costs arising for parents, health service, and other agencies. In each section some of the identifiable differences in average NHS costs for twin, triplet and quadruplet births have been estimated, and these are summarised in Tables 12.1 and 12.2. These hospital costs are based on data from various sources, adjusted to 1988 price levels. Of course, these do not represent an accurate picture of the total costs of maternity and childrearing for families with births of different orders. Households also bear considerable costs themselves, and some of the data given by parents of triplets are also presented.

Conception

As was shown in Chapter 3, a higher proportion of parents with triplets and higher order births had had some form of fertility treatment compared to parents of twins or singleton children. Replies to the obstetric questionnaire analysed in Tables 3.1 and 3.2 show that two per cent of singleton pregnancies and eight per cent of twin pregnancies had been preceded by either drug or surgical treatment or both. In contrast over a third of women with triplet pregnancies and nearly two thirds of those with quadruplet pregnancies had had such treatments. On average, therefore, higher order multiple birth is likely to be preceded by increased costs of gynaecological investigation and treatment compared with singleton births. Much of the cost of fertility treatment is likely to have been met by the couples themselves.

Data are not available about the costs of gynaecological investigation of infertility and most subsequent treatments. The costs of running an IVF clinic in an NHS hospital have been investigated in one health authority, and it was estimated that, including capital costs, the charge for a treatment cycle would need to be at least £680 at 1988 prices in order to cover the costs associated with the 400 treatment cycles carried out during the period of the costing study.[2]

Most IVF procedures take place in the private sector, as there are so few clinics using NHS facilities that offer IVF. Of those that do, most make some charge, as district health authorities have not in general agreed to fund IVF and GIFT services. Some of these are subsidised by research or charitable funds. Only four of the 13 IVF pregnancies in the obstetric survey were reported to be the result of NHS treatment. In the case of IVF and GIFT, private treatment charges, including in-patient care, for investigation, oocyte retrieval and one single re-introduction of the embryo or gametes are between £3,000 and £4,000. Where IVF is offered as an out-patient procedure, costs are less, but the couple almost certainly have greater travel and accommodation expenses.[3, 4] Health insurance schemes do not generally cover infertility treatment, and so the cost is met directly by individuals seeking treatment.

Because methods of infertility treatment have been shown to lead to increased numbers of triplet and higher order births, many NHS staff consider that, when a new infertility service is established, allowance should be made for the additional costs to the NHS of subsequent care for the mother and babies.[5] Not only do children from triplet and higher order births need more NHS resources than do singletons, but also, evidence from this survey shows that women with higher order multiple pregnancies after fertility treatment used more hospital resources at every stage than did those who had no fertility treatment. Very few couples in the UK opt for private obstetric care, fewer still for private neonatal care. Thus, whether the direct cost of fertility treatment is met by the NHS or privately, the NHS still faces additional costs if the treatment results in a multiple birth.

Out-patient antenatal care

Any woman with a pregnancy identified to be at high risk is likely to have more antenatal visits and tests than usual. Although the number of out-patient visits was not included in the questionnaire, a question was asked about the number of ultrasound scans women had. Women with triplet pregnancies had more ultrasound scans (an average of 4.8 per triplet pregnancy, and 5.2 for quadruplets and above) than had the twin controls, who had 3.2 scans per pregnancy.

The cost of staff and equipment for a routine ultrasound scanning service has been estimated at one London teaching hospital[6] to be over £13 per scan at 1988 prices. This estimate excludes the overheads of running the antenatal out-patent service. Based on this cost, the cost of the average number of ultrasound scans has been calculated in Table 12.1 for women with twin, triplet or quadruplet pregnancies. This gives an additional cost of ultrasound for a triplet over a twin pregnancy of £20.

Table 12.1

Health service costs of hospital care for mothers in triplet and higher order births

	Costs[+] of hospital obstetric care for women, £ per woman			
	Twins	Triplets	Quadruplets	Difference between trip-lets and twins
Antenatal				
Ultrasound scans				
Cost @£13 per scan	42	62	68	20
Clinic visits for ultrasound				
Cost @£23 per visit	74	110	120	36
Cost @£35 per visit	112	168	182	56
Inpatient stay				
Cost @£88 per day	836	2,596	4,787	1,760
Cost @£122 per day	1,159	3,599	6,637	2,440
Delivery and postnatal care for mother				
Cost of delivery	183	215	236	32
Postnatal stay				
Cost @£88 per day	732	911	1,198	178
Cost @£122 per day	1,016	1,263	1,661	247
Total identified costs of hospital obstetric care				
Lower estimate	1,752	3,722	6,221	1,970
Higher estimate	2,358	5,077	8,534	2,719

Source: Parents' study.
+ 1988 prices.

The average cost per out-patient visit at an NHS hospital has not been separately estimated for maternity clinics. It varies between £23 and £35 for all specialties in acute and maternity hospitals in England at 1988 prices[7]. Assuming that women have at least as many visits as they had ultrasound scans, Table 12.1 shows that the NHS costs of hospital antenatal out-patient care are greater by at least between £36 and £56 for triplet than for twin or singleton pregnancies.

Each visit incurs costs for the woman and the health service. For the women, costs of hospital out-patient visits are dependent on travelling distance, time lost from paid work, and arrangements for other dependents. Women expecting triplets or more are more likely to be referred to regional centres for their care, and the average distance travelled and time women must allow for out-patient appointments is therefore likely to be more than for women with twin or singleton pregnances. A study of the costs of routine antenatal visits[8] found that these 'social costs', that is costs borne by the women and their family and friends, of attending Aberdeen maternity hospital varied between £2.02 and £76.02 per visit, with a median value of £14.19. This includes the cost of childcare arrangements, and valuation of the time of those attending clinics.

A similar proportion of women with singleton, twin and triplet pregnancies had other children to care for, but Table 2.2 shows that women expecting four or more babies were less likely to have other children at home. In this respect, therefore, those with higher order births do not on average face greater costs per visit than is usual. In the study by Meldrum, quoted above, costs of babysitting for routine antenatal visits were estimated to be between £1.80 and £9.60 with a median value of £5.02. The number of antenatal visits was not included in the survey, and so it is not possible to estimate overall costs of out-patient antenatal care.

In-patient antenatal care

Women expecting triplets or more spent longer in hospital than those with twins. Chapter 4 shows that these women had considerable periods in hospital before the delivery. Table 4.15 shows that women with triplet and higher order pregnancies were more likely to be admitted at all, more likely to be admitted more than once, and likely to stay longer at each stay than women expecting twins. The mean number of bed days in hospital per twin pregnancy was 9.5 days, compared with 29.5 days for women expecting triplets and 54.4 days for quadruplets or more. Statistics from the Maternity Hospital In-Patient Enquiry (HIPE) show that the mean antenatal in-patient stay for singleton pregnancies was 1.4 days in 1985. The average cost of NHS in-patient care per day varied for acute hospitals grouped by numbers of beds between £88 and £122 in 1988. Data are not nationally available specifically about maternity costs, but costs for those hospitals where 90 per cent of beds are for maternity care also fall within this range. Based on these data, Table 12.1 shows the estimated average cost for twin, triplet and quadruplet or higher order pregnancies, assuming either the highest or the lowest average daily cost applies. The additional cost of in-patient antenatal care for a set of triplets compared to twins is then between £1,760 and £2,440.

The average hospital cost from national accounting data which was used in Table 12.1 includes the costs of laboratory tests, radiography, ultrasound, and pharmaceuticals, as well as medical and midwifery time and catering, laundry and overhead costs. It is not clear from the available data whether triplet and higher order pregnancies are likely to need more or less of each of the available services than the average. Some of those admitted for bedrest may have incurred little more than 'hotel' costs, and so probably cost less than the average in-patient cost. Others, however, found that they had extra tests and scans which they would not have had as out-patients. Table 4.14 shows that bedrest alone was a more frequent reason for admission for higher order pregnancies than for twins, thus suggesting that in-patient care may have been less costly on average per day for triplets. More than half were admitted for other indications, and were likely to have required additional monitoring, treatments and care that might lead to higher than average in-patient costs. The only indications in Table 4.14 that some higher order pregnancies may require more intensive in-patient care are that measures were taken to suppress labour or delay delivery more frequently for triplet and higher order pregnancies than for twins, and women with quadruplet pregnancies were more likely to be admitted for bleeding.

Household costs arising during pregnancy are less easy to estimate. Although in the UK parents do not have to pay the hospital costs, they do have additional costs as a result of the woman being in hospital, as arrangements for running the home in the woman's absence, and for visiting, are paid for from household budgets. One of the women quoted in Chapter 4 illustrated this in considerable detail. Costs do not only arise as a result of hospital admission: some mothers of triplets who stayed at home during pregnancy pointed out that they could not manage household chores without extra help. Indeed some women were admitted to hospital only because there was no-one to help at home.

Delivery

For all births, costs during labour and delivery are high in proportion to the remaining days of in-patient care[9]. The major cost at this time is staff time, which in singleton births varies according to the length of labour, the type of delivery, and the expected degree of risk for mother or baby. One study has estimated the labour ward costs of singleton vaginal delivery to be £77, and for caesarean section, £154[10], giving a weighted average cost of between £90 and £100 for singleton labour and delivery. As all multiple births are usually seen as potentially at risk, additional staff and equipment are likely to be committed for the delivery which will not then be available for other purposes. The average cost is thus likely to be higher than for singleton births, and may vary less with the type of delivery, as the obstetric, paediatric and anaesthetic staff are likely to be at least on 'standby' whatever the mode of delivery. Tables 5.4 and 5.5 show, however, that there were higher levels of intervention in triplet and higher order births than for twins.

Triplet and higher order births also need more skilled staff present at the delivery, and more equipment available for neonatal resuscitation than twin or singleton births, because there are three or more babies who are also are likely to be before term, with the associated increased likelihood that the babies will have difficulties in breathing. Table 6.6 shows that only 32 per cent of twins needed resuscitation at birth compared with 47 per cent of triplets and 61 per cent of quadruplets. In an article published in 1977 about the delivery of two sets of quadruplets[11], two paediatricians per baby were on standby during the last weeks of pregnancy, and they were all present in the labour ward for the delivery, in addition to the usual staff for a caesarean section. Taking the average cost of care for any high risk delivery to be £154, the extra paediatric, medical and nursing staff and equipment required could add at least £26 for each additional baby to the cost of delivery for a multiple birth.

Health care costs at the time of delivery may be further increased by the need for transfer to another hospital during labour. A survey of transfers for neonatal care[12] showed that in 1986–7 less than one per cent of all deliveries involved a transfer in labour. Although only 10 per cent of mothers of triplets were transferred to another hospital in labour, the health service costs of transfer in labour are likely to be high, as teams of staff from two different units are concerned with the labour and delivery care of the woman. Skilled staff are required to attend the woman in the ambulance, and are therefore not available in their own unit during the transfer. It is likely therefore that the costs of delivery including transfer in labour will be at least half as much again as delivery in the hospital of first admission.

Approximate costs for labour and delivery have been estimated in Table 12.1. These were calculated assuming increased paediatric staffing and using survey data about the proportion of women transferred in labour. This shows an additional cost of at least £36 for triplet deliveries over the cost for twins. This difference seems small in comparison to the high cost difference for antenatal hospital care. It is possible there are greater differences. For example, the estimate does not include the cost of keeping extra staff on standby before the delivery, which is discussed later in the section on neonatal care.

Postnatal hospital care

Mothers of triplets stayed longer in hospital after delivery than did mothers of twins. A higher proportion had caesarean or other operative deliveries, and were therefore more likely to require extra postnatal care from staff on the wards. A study of postnatal care costs after caesarean section at a large teaching hospital in 1988 found that average NHS costs were about £700 if there were no complications, but over £1,400 if there was wound infection[13]. In that study the daily costs of care were 50 per cent higher for women with wound infection. It is clear from Table 6.1 that many mothers were far from well after delivery and the recovery from the delivery involved much more than the usual input of health care resources even given the type of delivery. Mothers of twins had fewer problems than those with higher order births, 81 per cent had no recorded problems, compared to 72 per cent of mothers of triplets and 65 per cent of mothers of quadruplets or more.

In Table 12.1, costs of the postnatal in-patient stay are estimated from the daily in-patient cost of care and the mean length of postnatal stay. This has been weighted to take account of complications. As a minimum estimate it has been assumed that those with the problems reported in Table 6.1 had in-patient costs increased by 50 per cent per day. Once again the cost of hospital care of women with higher order births exceeds that for mothers of twins. Costs of postnatal care are estimated to be between £178 and £247 higher for mothers of triplets than for mothers of twins.

Neonatal care in hospital

NHS costs of neonatal care in regional neonatal intensive care units have been estimated in published studies from three different centres[14, 15]. In all of these studies, the cost of care was found to increase as birthweight decreased. The average cost of neonatal care found in these studies per baby admitted would be between £5,000 and £6,000, adjusted to 1988 prices. As babies from triplet or higher order births were of lower birthweight, and were more likely to be admitted to a neonatal nursery, the cost of care for each baby was likely on average to have been higher than for twins. Applying costs of care by birthweight group from the most recently published study from a UK neonatal unit[15] to the proportion of babies in each weight group admitted to special care baby units, Table 12.2 shows an increasing average cost per baby with the increase in the number born in a set. The expected additional cost per triplet compared to a twin is over £1,500. The differences are much wider when the total cost per multiple birth is calculated, adding up the costs for each of the babies in the set. In this case a triplet set would be expected to lead to additional neonatal costs of over £6,000. In these calculations, it is assumed that the cost for babies not admitted to special care is included in postnatal ward costs for the mother, and it is not therefore counted as an extra cost.

Where it is known in advance that a higher order multiple birth is imminent, the neonatal unit may pay staff to be on 'standby' for a number of days before the delivery, as was discussed above. At a rate of £2 per hour for being on call, the unit will have to find £336 to keep one extra nurse on call for a week. In the study quoted, the staff offered their time voluntarily, and at no cost to the NHS. Service planners could not assume that this would always be the case. A unit which is using existing equipment to full capacity may also have to borrow or hire extra equipment for the care of the babies, and they may even have to train additional staff in intensive care methods[11].

Table 12.2

Health service costs of hospital care for children born in triplet and higher order births

	Costs[+] of hospital neonatal and paediatric care, £			
	Twins	Triplets	Quadruplets+	Difference between triplets and twins
Neonatal care for babies				
Cost per baby‡	1,492	3,018	5,091	1,526
Cost per set	2,984	9,054	20,364	6,070
Re-admissions to hospital during first 2 years after birth*				
Cost per baby	46	59	75	14
	64	82	105	18
Cost per set	92	177	300	85
	128	246	420	118

+ 1988 prices.
‡ Special care baby unit costs assumed to be: £8,900 per baby with birthweight under 1500g, £1,154 per baby with birthweight 1500g or more admitted to special care.
* Based on rehospitalisation rates for births in Oxfordshire and Berkshire, 1980–84. Estimates assume that 44 per cent of babies weighting under 1500g and 14 per cent of babies weighing 1500g or more are readmitted.

The costs to parents of visiting three or more babies in a neonatal unit may be similar to the costs of visiting one baby, if the three babies are in one place. Some sets of triplets were split up and transferred to different hospitals, however. Based on the evidence of a study of travelling costs for parents of babies in one regional neonatal unit[16], costs might range between £3.50 and £890 depending on the distance the family lives from the unit, and the length of time the baby is in the unit. These costs do not include the cost of the parents' time in travelling and visiting. As triplets and higher order births were likely to be cared for in regional centres, and to have longer stays in neonatal nurseries, parents are likely to have had travel costs at the higher end of the scale.

Rehospitalisation

Once the mother and her babies go home, those with triplets and more are more likely to face further admissions to hospital either for themselves or for one or more of the children. Many mothers responding to the parents' study reported rehospitalisation at some time since the multiple birth, with all the problems of arranging for the care of the children multiplied, now that there were three or more added to the family. As was mentioned in Chapter 8, just over a fifth of children covered in the survey of general practitioners had been admitted to hospital at least once.

A study of low birthweight babies born to women living in Oxfordshire and West Berkshire showed that babies weighing less than 1500g were more likely to be rehospitalised than bigger babies and that the rate of rehospitalisation for this group has increased over time[17]. The author found that 44 per cent of survivors born between 1979 and 1983 with birthweight less than 1500g were readmitted at least once before their second birthday, compared to 14 per cent of babies with birthweights of more than 1500g. As triplets and higher order births are on average lighter that other babies, one might expect a high rate of readmission to hospital for these children. The average length of stay for all paediatric admissions was 3.7 days in 1986.[18] Assuming that the cost is close to the average in-patient cost for acute hospitals, the average NHS cost per admission would be between £326 and £451. From these data, expected costs of readmission to hospital per baby born and per multiple set have been estimated for different orders of births in Table 12.2. This represents a minimum estimate as it assumes that babies are readmitted only once. Once again the expected costs per baby are higher for babies in higher order births, and this difference is increased when costs per multiple set are considered. However the costs of readmission to hospital in the first two years are likely to be very small in proportion to neonatal care costs.

At home

The costs of caring for a single child at home were estimated in a study by the Family Policy Studies Centre to be about £30,000 at 1986 prices, or £33,000 at 1988 prices. This includes food, clothes and shoes from birth to 16 years of age, but did not include an estimate of the value of the mother's work in caring for the child[19]. Based on this study, the cost of the first year of life would be about £2,200. There are unlikely to be any economies involved in having three or more babies at the same time. On the contrary, families with multiple births do not have the advantage of 'handing down' clothes and equipment from one child to the next. So the costs for a single baby can be multiplied by the number of babies to estimate a minimum cost.

Not all parents gave details of costs, so it is not possible to calculate average costs for all the families in the survey. However, one mother of triplets gave a very detailed account of monthly outgoings for feeding, sterilising bottles, and nappies which is listed in Table 12.3. For her triplets these costs came to a total of £169.30 per month, that is £2,031 for a year. Other responses suggest that her monthly costs are typical, for example: £28 per month for weaning foods (excluding fresh food), and £56 per month for processed baby milk. Nappies were a major item, costs quoted by parents range between £52 and £88 per month.

The same mother also estimated the cost of baby equipment to have been £1,345. Her list is set out in Table 12.4. Other parents again quoted similar costs. For example: 'a triple pushchair, secondhand: £195'; 'two double buggies (for quadruplets): £300'; 'fridge-freezer: £200'; 'tumble drier: £590'. Although some parents manage without some of these items, or are lucky enough to be given them as presents, there are additional costs that are not listed here, such as extra heating, transport costs, additional childcare or home help. One mother of quadruplets said that the electricity bill had doubled 'due to extra washing, drying etc.' Transport costs included fitting suitable car seats. One parent paid £80 for two car seats, and £195 to fit an extra row of seats in their estate car.

Child care and home help

In Chapters 7, 9 and 10, examples of replies from parents give some indication of the

Table 12.3

Examples of monthly expenditure on food and nappies for triplets

	Monthly cost at February 1989 prices, £	
Food		
Milk, major brand formula		
between 5–10 months old		
1 tin every 2 1/2 days @ £4.09 per tin	49.76	
from 10 months		
1/2 cows milk, 1/2 formula		
1 tin every 5 days £24.88 per month		
Weekly milk bill £5.85 £25.25 per month	50.23	
Average monthly cost of formula milk	50.00	
Dried foods at least 3 packs per week @ 99p each	12.87	
Tinned baby desserts, 7 per week @ 25p each	7.58	
Drinks at least 1 pack per week @ £1.35	5.85	
Sterilising fluid 1 bottle per week @ £1.35 per bottle	4.98	
Average monthly costs of milk and processed baby foods		81.27
Diet also includes meat, fish, chicken, liver, fresh vegetables		
eggs, cheese, milk puddings, yoghurt, pureed fruit, bread,		
yeast extract, honey, porridge oats, cereal. Cost not		
included in above		
Nappies		
Major brand, night time nappies: 21 per week @ £7.35 per		
pack of 44	15.20	
Supermarkets own brand: 105 per week @£7.35 per pack of 60	61.90	
Nappy liners, 546 @ £2.10 per pack of 200	5.73	
Cotton wool, 1,350 gram per week @ £1.20 per pack	5.20	
Average monthly costs of nappies		88.03

resources that are needed for these different purposes. In contrast to the period of pregnancy and birth, when the NHS bears a substantial part of the cost, the public sector contribution to the additional costs of caring for triplets or more children at home is very small. For example, during the difficult early months of night-time feeding, a night nurse or 'sitter' was not readily provided by the community health service: only five per cent of triplet households and under half of households with quadruplets were given any service. Chapter 7 includes the admission of one head of community nursing services that her budget was not sufficient to offer what was needed for a set of triplets who had been discharged from hospital at five weeks. The cost quoted by one private agency for hiring a night nurse is £386 for a qualified nurse or midwife for eight hours a night for a week. An unqualified carer hired through an agency would cost £299 for the same number of hours.

For day-time help with the children, as the previous chapters show, many families depended on the unpaid help of friends and family but not all could rely on this. Wages for a full-time living in trained nanny would be upwards of £70 with board and food extra. Wages for a daily nanny are higher.

For help with housework, local authority home help had been made available for a

Table 12.4

Examples of expenditure on equipment for triplets

	Cost, £, at 1989 prices
Twin pushcair (first size)	70.00
Single pushchair	63.00
Twin pram – second hand	50.00
Twin pushchair (second size)	115.00
Microwave	150.00
3 cots	285.00
3 sets cot quilts & bumpers	60.00
2 moses baskets	40.00
3 moses stands	36.00
2 bouncing chairs	20.00
3 car seats	145.00
1 stair gate	23.00
3 cotton blankets (moses baskets)	11.25
3 pairs sheets	21.00
3 cot blankets	18.00
3 sterilizers	18.00
Bottles (15)	12.75
Bottles (6 × 40z)	5.00
Chest of drawers	50.00
2 pram rugs	8.00
2 high chairs	60.00
2 pair 'Cositoes'	16.00
Total	1,345.00

few hours a week to 61 per cent of triplet households and to all households with quadruplets, which at the time of writing is paid for at a rate between £3.50 and £4.00 per hour, unless family income is below the means test level. One social services department quoted the cost of a community care assistant to be £4.25 per hour.

Paying the costs

Most women in the survey were married or living with employed partners at the time of the survey. However, a significant proportion of their partners had experienced unemployment, redundancy or demotion since their higher order multiple birth. Data presented in Chapter 2 show that the family situation and their employment status did not differ greatly between families with twin and higher order births, although triplets and more were less likely to be born to single parents. Even for those families with average incomes, the additional costs of triplets reduced their ability to provide for themselves and their children as they would wish. For some, cars, telephone, holidays and school 'extras' were out of the question. Insurance against the possibility of multiple birth is available for those who can afford it, but insurance companies are unlikely to accept couples who have had treatment for infertility. Premiums are higher for those with a history of multiple birth. Insurance companies that offer such policies have quoted premiums starting at £25 for a possible cash benefit of between

£1,000 and £2,000 for twins, and more for higher order births[20]. Only one mother in the parents' study mentioned having taken out such insurance.

Chapter 9 made the point that triplets are becoming more common, so that commercial sponsorship is unlikely to be found, although this is sometimes a source of help for higher order births. Gifts from friends and relations, although welcome, were inevitably unpredictable and could not be relied on as a source of support. Some parents emphasised that their parents had used their own life savings to provide them with a suitable vehicle, and a washing machine or a tumble drier. In other instances, a friend or a relative paid for disposable nappies for a long period. Others received loans from relatives, which occasionally led to additional stress when the relative's circumstances changed and the loan was recalled.

There is very little statutory help, in the form of special payments to take account of needs at home, either while the mother is in hospital or after the return home. No extra benefits are available specifically for multiple births. If a family is entitled to family income support, on the basis of low income, then other benefits, such as free milk and school meals, may follow. A family on average earnings would not usually qualify unless there were already other children. Even those on low incomes may be excluded, and there can be disincentives to trying to improve the family situation. For example a family with three other children and a set of triplets was refused Family Credit because the father was on a training scheme rather than in employment.[21]

As was mentioned in Chapter 1, a precedent for a special payment to those with triplet or higher order births was set in the UK in the nineteenth century. Queen Victoria established a Royal Bounty for families with triplets who were in need. The fund was abolished in the 1950s, at a time when the provisions for maternity and child support under the welfare state were relatively generous. These provisions have changed since then, and have not kept up with inflation. More recently, the Australian government responded in 1985 to a campaign by the Australian Multiple Birth Association[22] by giving parents of triplets a cash allowance. At the time of writing, parents of triplets in Australia receive £30–£40 a week, and more for quadruplets, for the first two years from the Commonwealth Department of Community and Health Services, irrespective of family means. In addition, the Commonwealth Department of Social Security pays a means tested benefit of up to £70 a month for triplets, and up to £90 a month for quadruplets, until the children's sixth birthday[23].

Conclusions

Tables 12.1 to 12.4 document some of the increased costs for the NHS hospital services and for households with multiple births. These are fairly crude and incomplete estimates which do not include the costs to social services, community health services and to general practitioners. However, the survey data suggest that nearly all of these costs are likely to be at least as great for triplet and higher order births as for twins.

Tables 12.1 and 12.2 show that the average NHS cost of hospital care is about £5,000 per set of twins, £12,000 for triplets, and over £25,000 for a set of quadruplets or more. Neonatal care accounts for more than 60 per cent of the total cost, and antenatal hospital care for over 20 per cent. It could be argued that a triplet birth might reasonably be allocated the resources that would have been used by three single births. The available evidence suggests that the costs are likely to exceed this amount, even where the singleton births are assumed to be high risk, preterm births. The mean expected costs per baby and per multiple set which have been estimated do not express the considerable variation that is likely to occur between individuals.

Family resources are also disproportionately affected. Although it has not been possible to quantify the social costs associated with the increased hospital costs shown in Tables 12.1 and 12.2, there is enough evidence to support the view that the costs of health care which the family has to meet are also higher for higher order births.

A family which has three children in succession can economise on many costs, including cot, pushchair, car seat and even clothes. For multiple births, each baby will need the equipment of a first baby. In addition, the household may need to meet some major capital expenses which they would not necessarily consider otherwise.

This chapter has demonstrated that, at every stage, triplet or higher order births mean higher costs to families and to the health and personal social services. The increased cost is more than the cost faced when a family has three separate children, as the pregnancy and delivery are more difficult, the babies are more likely to need medical care at birth, and the family cannot easily look after three or more babies or young children simultaneously without extra help and equipment.

Although it is more costly to the public purse than singleton or twin birth, triplet or higher order birth is a rare event. In Leeds, for example, data given in response to the survey of social services shows that 15 sets of triplets and one set of quadruplets were born in the two health authorities between 1983 and 1988. The costs of providing special services for such families would therefore seem to be small in comparison with other groups with special needs, but few authorities appear to budget for higher order births, and official and informal support networks do not usually 'earmark' funds to respond to the added needs of such families.

For the health service, the rational use of resources for antenatal care depends on the effectiveness of hospital bed rest for women expecting triplets. If being in hospital makes no difference to outcome, then the large amount of resources taken up in this way might be better used to provide those women who want it with help in their own homes. The biggest problems for the NHS probably arise in the effect on neonatal services in units with relatively small or very busy neonatal nurseries. For this reason, it is important that new NHS services for treatment of infertility that may also increase the number of triplets or higher order births should be evaluated in terms of the available services for neonatal care, as well as the cost of setting up the service. Evidence from a survey of transfers for neonatal care[12] reinforces the point that it is also important that neonatal and obstetric staff liaise about the facilities required for deliveries of triplets and more, and develop policies for such events.

All households with a new child face a period of tighter budgeting, but the arrival of triplets can upset the household economy more drastically because of disproportionately increased needs coupled with reduced earning capacity. A household with income equivalent to the national average earnings could not meet all the needs at home without extra state support unless they had considerable savings, and an unusually supportive network of friends and relations who live near enough and are physically fit enough to provide practical help.

References
1. Royal College of Physicians. Medical care of the newborn in England and Wales. London: Royal College of Physicians, 1988.

2. Drown J. A financial appraisal of the costs to the health service of an in-vitro fertilisation unit and its associated charging policy. Oxford: Treasurer's Department Oxfordshire Health Authority, 1988.

3. Mathieson D. Infertility services in the NHS: what's going on? London: Frank Dobson MP, 1986.

4. Voluntary Licensing Authority. Fourth Report. London, Voluntary Licensing Authority, 1989.

5. Dunn P. Neonatal implications of IVF programme in Bristol. Personal communication to one of the editors.

6. Campbell S. Personal communication.

7. DHSS. Health Service Costing Returns 1987/8. London: DHSS, 1988.

8. Meldrum P. Costing routine antenatal visits. HERU discussion paper no 02/89 Aberdeen: Health Economics Research Unit, 1989.

9. Gray A, Steele R. The economics of specialist and general practitioner maternity units. Journal of the Royal College of General Practitioners 1981; 31: 586–592.

10. Clark L. Personal communication.

11. Salisbury D M, Jones R W A, Townshend P, Baum J D. Paediatric preparation for multiple births. Early Human Development 1977; 1: 39.

12. British Association of Perinatal Medicine Working Group. Referrals for neonatal medical care in the United Kingdom over one year. British Medical Journal 1989; 298: 169–172.

13. Mugford M, Kingston J, Chalmers I. Reducing the incidence of infection after caesarean section: implications for hospital resources. British Medical Journal 1989; 299: 1003–1006.

14. Mugford M. A review of the economics of the care of sick newborn infants. Community Medicine 1988; 10: 99–111.

15. Ryan S, Sics A, Congdon P. Cost of neonatal care. Archives of Disease in Childhood 1988; 63: 303–306.

16. Smith A, Baum D. Cost of visiting babies in special care baby units. Archives of Disease in Childhood 1983; 58: 56–59.

17. Mutch L. Patterns of rehospitalisation in the first two years of life: the influence of birthweight and changing survival rates. Report to the Department of Health and Social Security August 1987. Oxford: National Perinatal Epidemiology Unit, 1987.

18. Department of Health and Social Security, Hospital Statistics, Form SH3. Regional and national summaries for 1986. London. Department of Health, 1987.

19. Roll J. Babies and money: birth trends and costs. London: Family Policy Studies Centre, 1986.

20. Campbell M. The payoff against double trouble. Guardian, May 20 1989.

21. Brindle D. Social fund allocation cuts feared. Guardian, July 17 1989.

22. TAMBA. Supernews (Supertwins newsletter). Spring 1987, London.

23. Health Department of Western Australia. Triplet support. Chart no. 12 – SAC – 8054. Perth, Australia: Health Department of Western Australia, undated.

Chapter 13 – Conclusions

Alison J Macfarlane, Frances V Price,
Beverley J Botting,

Higher order multiple births remain uncommon and unexpected, but the numbers of these births doubled during the 1980s and more of the babies are surviving. As a result, a greater number of people, both parents and professionals, are faced with the extraordinary demands of caring for triplets, quadruplets, quintuplets and sextuplets. This chapter summarises and discusses our main findings and then makes recommendations for action and for further research.

Before conception

The increase in numbers of triplet and higher order births is largely a consequence of the use of drugs and procedures for the management of infertility. In our obstetric survey cohort, covering the years 1980 and 1982 to 1985, 36 per cent of mothers of triplets and 70 per cent of mothers of quadruplets and above had used drugs for ovulation induction. Statistics produced by the Voluntary Licensing Authority showed a clear association between the increase in the rate of higher order births after 1985 and the rising use of IVF, GIFT and associated procedures. There is a need for research to develop methods of assisted reproduction in a way which will reduce the risk of higher order births. Although our survey did not specifically investigate this issue, it would seem desirable to review the Interim Licensing Authority guideline that a maximum of three (and in exceptional cases four) eggs in the GIFT procedure or embryos in IVF should be transferred in any one cycle. We would draw attention to the subsequent recommendation that this limit be reduced to two.

There is cause for concern about the quality of information given to parents about the risks of multiple births associated with infertility treatment, particularly the methods ovulation induction alone which did not involve IVF and GIFT.

Estimates of the risks of multiple births associated with various drugs vary widely and there are no population based data about their use and outcome. The only circumstances where data are collected routinely is in places licensed for IVF, and the establishment in 1989 of a national IVF register is welcome. There is an urgent need to extend this and collect data about all forms of infertility treatment, in particular GIFT and other related procedures.

This lack of data about infertility treatment is in part a reflection of the patchy nature of the services provided. Much infertility treatment takes place in the private sector, which does not take part in the routine data collection systems operating in the NHS. Many women who become pregnant after private sector infertility treatment subsequently receive NHS antenatal care and delivery. This can mean that people providing infertility services in the private sector do not have to confront the consequences for the NHS of caring for a woman with a higher order pregnancy. Furthermore over-representation of middle class people among users of infertility treatment in our sample may reflect the inability of other people to pay for it privately when it is not provided under the NHS.

Pregnancy

Problems were encountered with the diagnosis of multiple pregnancy. In the majority of cases, the multiple pregnancy was diagnosed by ultrasound and the diagnosis was made before 20 weeks of gestation. Diagnosing the correct number of babies was more of a problem, however. For six per cent of sets of triplets and 16 per cent of sets of quadruplets and above, the correct number was not diagnosed until delivery, and many more were not correctly diagnosed until late in pregnancy.

Problems arose in telling parents of the diagnosis and these could be aggravated by professional restrictions and by lack of communication skills. Parents also felt that they needed more help in the antenatal period to start planning how to cope with their babies after the birth.

Although only a minority of women changed to a different hospital during pregnancy or early labour, problems tended to arise for these women, often as a result of lack of communication and differences between the policies of the two hospitals concerned.

A third of mothers of twins and triplets and half the mothers of quadruplets and above had complications in the antenatal period. All mothers of quadruplets and 95 per cent of mothers of triplets were admitted to hospital at least once during their pregnancy, either for a specific complication or for 'bed rest'.

Women varied in their views about routine admission for 'bed rest'. As there is a lack of evidence that this policy is effective and it involves considerable cost for the NHS, and often also for the parents, there is need for randomised trials to compare it with possible alternatives, including support to enable women to rest at home. It is essential that any such trials include surveys of the views of the women who take part and estimates of the costs for the NHS and for the families.

Delivery

Almost half the quadruplet or higher order births covered by the obstetric survey were born before 32 weeks of gestation, compared with a quarter of triplets and less than a tenth of twins. In contrast, only one per cent of singletons sampled in the Maternity Hospital In-Patient Enquiry during our study years were born before 32 weeks.

The relative advantages and disadvantages of caesarean and vaginal deliveries for higher order births in different circumstances have yet to be systematically assessed. Research is needed so that more informed decisions can be made and caesareans restricted to circumstances where they offer clear advantages. There is also a need for comparisons of the relative benefits and hazards of epidural and general anaesthesia when caesareans are considered necessary.

Given this lack of information, it is perhaps not surprising that many parents considered that they had not been involved in discussions and choices about the method of anaesthesia and delivery. Many reported, more generally, that they did not receive the information and reassurance they needed before the delivery. Where parents had been given information and reassurance and were involved in choices, they welcomed and appreciated it.

Lack of discussion and consultation tended to arise where there was a change of hospital or consultant. Parents were also distressed if partners were excluded from the delivery. The mothers appreciated the presence of their partners as well as familiar faces among the hospital staff.

After the birth
About a quarter of mothers of triplets and a third of mothers of quadruplets experienced problems such as high blood pressure, blood loss, anaemia or wound infection after the birth. Although only very few experienced severe problems, this put them at a disadvantage in starting to care for three or more babies.

For the babies, survival rates were higher for first-born triplets than for the second-born, who, in their turn, had higher survival rates than third-born triplets. Although the congenital malformation rates in our study cannot be compared directly with national statistics, the proportions of babies affected were relatively high, with nearly 5 per cent of triplets having a malformation of some sort.

With over half of the quadruplets and just over a quarter of triplets weighing under 1500 grams at birth, many experienced problems which led to long periods in intensive care. Twenty eight per cent of triplets and 62 per cent of quadruplets stayed in intensive care for a month or more.

Even mothers who did not have specific complications found it took some time to recover after the birth. This sometimes meant that if her babies were in special care some time would elapse before she saw them. In many cases the hospital provided a photograph and this was widely appreciated. Further problems could arise later, particularly if the mother was discharged before the babies or if they were transferred to a distant neonatal unit.

Many parents reported that the immediate postnatal period was a stressful time, with uncertainties about how they would care for their babies once they were discharged. About two thirds of parents reported that no positive plans had been made in advance to ensure that they had help and support when the babies went home.

There is a clear need for better liaison between hospital and primary care and social services. This should involve hospital social workers or liaison health visitors and the mother's own health visitor and general practitioner.

Help for parents after the babies went home
Parents needed additional help to care for their three or more babies. Initially, parents needed to get some sleep and to ensure that their children were fed with the minimum of stress. Later on, parents needed some time to themselves and mothers, in particular, needed some respite from continuously caring for their children.

Difficulties arose when there was uncertainty as to who would provide this help, when they could provide it and at what cost. Few parents had relatives or neighbours on whom they could rely for sustained long term help and support on a daily basis. As a result, help was needed from health and social services, but the extent to which this was forthcoming varied widely.

Help at night was seldom provided for triplets and was provided for less than half the households with quadruplets or quintuplets. On the other hand, all but one household with quadruplets, and over half of those with triplets, received at least some assistance from a local authority home help, in most cases for at least six months.

General practitioners also varied in the help they gave. Some failed to appreciate the parents' problems, others made early contact after the babies were discharged, gave regular reassurances about the children's health and made house calls for vaccinations as well as illness. Where this extra care was given, the parents welcomed and appreciated it. Health visitors were, at best, a source of reassurance and often acted as mediators and facilitators. Advice, support and sensitive and sustained contact was what parents required from their health visitors. Some health visitors were, however, insufficiently aware of parents' anxiety and of the restrictions placed on their lives by caring for the children from the multiple birth and sometimes other young children as well. On the other hand, in common with some GPs and other health workers, some health visitors went beyond the call of duty to provide extra help, often giving up their own time to do so.

Some help was obtained from students and trainees such as those on nursery nursing, community work or social care courses, or Youth Training Schemes. Volunteers came from initiatives such as Home-Start and the National Childbirth Trust. People from these sources seldom could provide the total numbers of hours of help required. Usually they could only supplement and complement help available from other sources.

Membership of a twins club or of TAMBA Supertwins provided sympathy, support and advice from other similarly placed parents and the chance to buy second hand clothing and equipment, but was not a substitute for regular help and support from a paid professional worker.

There is, therefore, a need for a 'named person', such as a health visitor, to take responsibility for acting as an initial point of contact and to co-ordinate the various services and help provided. Mothers with several young children are not in the position to take on this co-ordinating role themselves.

Health and disability in childhood

Although replies by general practitioners had to be interpreted with care because of the poor response, they showed a raised prevalence, of cerebral palsy, squint, congenital malformations, pyloric stenosis and hospital admissions among children from triplet and higher order births compared with the general population. As the survey was confined to cases where three or more children left hospital alive, it may well have under-estimated overall morbidity, as there is reason to believe that morbidity may be higher among surviving children in sets where some babies died.

Despite reservations about the data, the findings area cause for concern. There is, therefore, a need for a prospective study to follow up triplets and higher order multiple births to look at their health and development later in childhood.

Press publicity and gifts

Most of the births included in the parents' study had been featured in the local or national press, but this often did not result in free gifts. Whereas the households which included quadruplets and quintuplets usually received substantial donations from commercial companies or smaller gifts of milk, nappies or tokens, these gifts were far less likely for households with triplets. Only about a quarter of households with triplets received one or more gifts of milk or nappies and this included all those who had free samples passed on to them from health professionals.

Housing and mobility

About half of the parents reported that they had moved house since the multiple birth or intended to do so shortly. A few had moved during the pregnancy after the multiple birth was diagnosed. Over half the parents of quadruplets and just over a quarter of parents of triplets had had their homes extended.

Many parents reported problems in getting out of the house, with or without their children, and in transporting them. Specially designed pushchairs were expensive and too wide for pavements and doorways, so most parents used two pushchairs, a single and a double one for triplets, or two double pushchairs for quadruplets. Car seats were also a problem. The struggle to get out to shops, clinics and preschool facilities was a continuing problem, especially for parents who could not drive, were without a car, or whose car was too small for all their children.

Most parents had used a babysitter on at least one occasion in their children's first year, but some parents had only managed to do so once or twice. Parents emphasised their need for regular breaks, even if for brief periods.

Pre-school provision

Pre-school children benefit from contact with other children of similar ages. One way of providing this is through supervised child care at a playgroup or nursery school. Combined problems of distance, method of transport and costs, particularly those of transport, stood in the way of obtaining this child care at a playgroup or nursery school. Research with twins has shown that there is likely to be some delay in the development of language and subsequent difficulties in learning, so this is also likely to occur with children from triplet and higher order births. This suggests that some hours of supervised pre-school provision should be made a priority. Mothers often also needed some respite from the total responsibility for their children. A few mothers only obtained help when they reached breaking point.

School

Parents mentioned a number of difficult issues and specific problems in relation to their children's entry into school and their communication and development once at school. Local schools were not always able to offer three places at the same time and arrangements had to be made further afield. Although most of the children from triplet and higher order births had some experience of playgroups and nursery school, many had little experience of separation from each other. Some of them were markedly dependent on each other and this posed a problem for teachers who were unlikely to have experience in dealing with higher order multiple birth children. 'Togetherness' may hinder, not only language development but also recognition of the children as individuals. This is likely to make it difficult for each child to accept responsibility for herself or himself. One child may speak for the others and teachers can inadvertently reinforce this pattern of behaviour.

The issue of whether and at which stage it is preferable to put the children into separate classes is important but unresolved. There is no formally collected evidence to suggest that children from triplet and higher order births should be separated into different classes at the start of their school life. The benefit of separation is seen to be a greater sense of 'self' and independence in learning, less competition and comparison with siblings, and a greater opportunity to make individual friends and develop communication skills. Communication between parents and teachers is crucial to enable problems to be discussed and resolved.

Costs

At every stage triplet and higher order births entail higher costs to their parents and to the health and personal social services than the equivalent number of children of different ages.

The estimated average cost to the NHS was £5,000 per set of twins, £12,000 per set of triplets and over £25,000 per set of quadruplets. Neonatal care accounts for over 60 per cent of the total cost and antenatal care in hospital 20 per cent. This factor needs to be taken into account when costing infertility services, given the increased risk of multiple birth they entail. This is true even for infertility services outside the NHS, as most women who use them transfer to NHS care once they know they are pregnant.

For parents, the cost of having three or more children at the same time is greater than that of having them in succession, when it is possible to re-use cots, pushchairs, car seats and some clothes. In addition, many households had major capital expenses for items such as home extensions and larger cars, which they would not otherwise have considered.

The services offered by local authorities varied widely, making them difficult to cost. On the other hand, triplet and higher order births are rare events for any social services authority, so the cost of providing special services for such families would seem to be small in comparison with other groups with special needs. Few authorities appear to budget for higher order births, but it would be desirable for them to do so as part of the process of providing contingency plans for any which may occur.

In conclusion, we have identified many problems which triplet and higher order births pose for their parents and the health and social services. We close by recommending ways in which some of these can be confronted, either by policy initiatives or by further research.

Recommendations

Alison J Macfarlane, Frances V Price, Beverley J Botting

Our study identified many issues on which there is a clear need for action and other areas where there is a lack of information or a need for further research. These recommendations are, therefore, set out in a way which reflects this.

1. Recommendations for action by health and social services

1.1 Before conception

1.1.1 There is a need to improve access to infertility services and to provide them in a setting which is integrated with maternity and neonatal services.

1.1.2 Parents should be provided with more information about the known risks of multiple births associated with ovulation induction and assisted reproduction. This should include both written information and counselling before treatment starts.

1.2 Pregnancy

1.2.1 Attention needs to be given to the communication of diagnoses of multiple pregnancy to parents. Problems arose when the diagnosis was communicated tactlessly and also when professional restrictions stood in the way of immediate discussion about the multiple pregnancy.

1.2.2 Once a triplet or higher order pregnancy is diagnosed, parents need information about the implications, and the opportunity to discuss the type of care to be given in pregnancy and delivery. Particular care needs to be taken to ensure that this happens if the mother is transferred to another hospital. The possibility that the babies will need neonatal intensive care should also be discussed and parents should be offered a chance to visit the neonatal unit.

1.2.3 As soon as the diagnosis is confirmed, parents should also be given help to start planning how they will manage to care for the babies once they leave hospital, although the possibility of miscarriages, stillbirths and neonatal deaths cannot be ignored. A 'named person' should be identified, probably a health visitor or hospital social worker. This person should be responsible for identifying, obtaining and co-ordinating the help the parents will need. Relevant primary health care staff, including the general practitioner, community midwife, health visitor, and paediatric liaison health visitor, should be informed.

1.2.4 Although some mothers were relieved to be admitted routinely to hospital for 'bed rest', others were upset by it, particularly if they had children at home from whom they were separated. Unless firm evidence emerges that this policy is effective, each case should be judged according to circumstances and, where preferred, the possibility of providing help and support to enable mothers to rest at home should be offered as an alternative.

1.3 Delivery

1.3.1   There is no evidence to support the view that all triplet and higher order births should be delivered by caesarean section. Unless such evidence emerges from randomised trials, each case should be judged according to the clinical circumstances and the parents' views about the method of delivery and anaesthesia. Whatever the method of delivery, the woman should be offered the option of a companion being present.

1.4 After the birth

1.4.1   More effort should be made to ensure that the mother sees the babies as soon as possible after the birth. The photographs offered by most hospitals are very welcome but are not a substitute for seeing the babies.

1.4.2   Mothers should be given advice, at as early a stage as possible, about feeding their babies and those who want to breastfeed should be given help in attempting to do so.

1.4.3   Discussions should take place with the 'named person' as soon as possible after birth. Plans should be made for coping with the babies after discharge, in the light of what is known about their likely length of postnatal stay. Later on, there should be discussions between parents, neonatal unit staff, paediatric liaison health visitor and the 'named person' about the timing of the babies' discharge and, if their clinical conditions vary, whether they should all be discharged together.

1.4.5   If the mother is discharged from hospital before the babies she may need help with obtaining or paying for the cost of transport to visit the babies in hospital. Possible sources of help with this should be discussed with the parents.

1.5 After discharge

It is clear that parents need help to an extent which cannot be met by relatives, friends and volunteers, so professional help is required. As Queen Victoria recognised, when she instituted the Royal Bounty for triplets, all but the most affluent parents need financial help to provide this assistance and other costs arising from having three or more babies at once. Although many triplet and higher order births received press publicity, this rarely led to donations from commercial companies or other sources.

1.5.1   In the early months, help is needed at night to ensure that the the parents get some sleep.

1.5.2   Over a longer period, especially the first two to three years, help is needed during the day either with child care or with domestic tasks to enable the parents to give more attention to the babies.

1.5.3   Many parents need larger accommodation, either through moving or home extensions. This means that financial help may be needed to cover the increased mortgage or rent.

1.5.4   Transport is a problem. When using pushchairs a second adult is needed and this may have to be a paid helper. Parents may also need help to buy a car, or a larger car, and to fit it with suitable safety restraints.

1.5.5   Transport problems make it difficult to get the babies to clinics and doctors' surgeries. Doctors and health visitors should try, where possible, to make home visits.

1.5.6   Parents can often become isolated. Those who are not on the phone should be given help to obtain one. Parents also need a break from their children and paid child care may be needed for this.

1.6 Pre-school provision

The majority of parents sought at least some hours of supervised pre-school activities at a playgroup or nursery school for their children, and, where necessary, assistance with fees or with transport fares. The convention that mothers should remain with their children often made mother and toddler groups unsuitable for mothers of triplet and higher order births as they needed a break from the children. Parents who did not receive financial assistance in getting to, and paying for, playgroups and nursery schools often found them too costly. Given that research with twins has indicated delays in the development of language, there is a need to give children from these higher order multiple births priority, and often also financial assistance, to attend playgroups and nursery schools.

1.7 School

Parents welcomed the early reassurance that there were places available for each of their higher order multiple birth children at the school of their choice. They also appreciated discussions with teachers about whether or not to separate their children at the outset into different school classes. Teachers need to realise how important it is to provide each child with individual attention, and not to reinforce a pattern of behaviour where one child speaks for the others. Parents may become anxious about behavioural problems or the unequal progress of their children and the situation may require very sensitive teacher-parent discussions. Teachers should appreciate the sheer impact for parents of attending to, caring for and stimulating triplets, quadruplets and more, especially if one or more child has special needs, or requires sustained extra help with speech therapy exercises, reading or numeracy.

2.   Recommendations for research and data collection

2.1   Research is needed to improve techniques for ovulation induction and assisted reproduction so that fewer triplet and higher order multiple pregnancies occur as a result of using these techniques. The Human Fertilisation and Embryology Authority should keep under continuous review the guidelines set out by the Interim (formerly Voluntary) Licensing Authority.

2.2   Data should be collected routinely about all types of infertility treatment given under the NHS and in the private sector. These should be collated with data from the IVF Register, which should also cover all GIFT procedures, to monitor trends in the use of the relevant drugs and procedures and the associated rates of multiple birth and its outcome. It should also be used to monitor access to infertility treatment.

2.3 Research should be started to investigate whether the various drugs used for infertility have adverse short term or long term effects on people who take them.

2.4 Antenatal admission for bed rest is of unproven effectiveness. It results in expense for the NHS and can cause distress for some women. There is a need for randomised trials to assess its effectiveness and compare this with possible alternative forms of support and help to enable women to rest at home. Such trials should include surveys of women's views.

2.5 Professional views about the extent to which caesarean section should be used for delivering triplet and higher order births diverge widely and there is a lack of firm evidence to support these views. There is, therefore, a need for randomised trials to compare the outcome of caesarean and vaginal delivery in different circumstances and also to compare the use of epidural and general anaesthesia for caesareans. Survey should be done of women's views and the consequences for families of operative deliveries.

2.6 As our survey of general practitioners covered only those triplet and higher order births where three or more babies were discharged home alive, we were unable to attempt an assessment of childhood morbidity for all children from triplet and higher order births. Our findings did, however, give cause for concern. There is, therefore, a need for a full follow-up study. This should be planned prospectively through the British Paediatric Surveillance Unit and the National Health Service Central Register to collect reliable information on impairment, disability and the use of health services.

2.7 Little is known about the best way to tackle the educational problems of triplet and higher order births and, in particular, whether the children should be put in separate classes as far as possible. Research is needed to answer these questions.

Glossary – Technical Terms Used

Abdominal delivery:	Delivery through the abdominal wall – *see* **caesarean section**
Acardia:	Without a heart
Albinism:	An inherited disorder of pigmentation characterised by the lack of pigment in the surface tissues of the body such as the skin, hair and eyes
Alimentary:	Relating to the digestive system, mouth, pharynx, oesophagus, stomach and intestine
Alpha fetoprotein test:	Measurement of the protein in the mother's blood or amniotic fluid produced by the spinal cord, brain and liver of the fetus. A raised level may mean that the baby has spina bifida or some related disorder or that there is more than one fetus
Anaemia:	Too few or poor quality of red blood cells and their oxygen carrying pigment haemoglobin in the blood
Anaesthesia/Analgesia:	Lessening or abolition of sensation to pain or stimuli – may be general (total loss of consciousness and sensation) or local (partial or complete loss of pain sensation in a given area)
Epidural:	Local anaesthesia used in labour and for caesarean sections to anaesthetise the lower body; achieved by injecting an anaesthetic drug through a fine tube sited into the epidural space of the lower spine through which pass the nerves relaying pain sensation
Nitrous oxide and oxygen:	Mixture of gases breathed in through a mask as a form of pain relief during labour
Opiates:	Drugs given for pain relief during labour
Pethidine:	Drug given as an injection for pain relief during labour
Anoxia:	Lack of oxygen
Antepartum:	Before the birth
Antepartum haemorrhage:	Bleeding before delivery
Anti-oestrogen:	Drug acting against the female hormones (eg **Progesterone**)
Apgar score:	A 10 point scoring system for assessing a baby's condition immediately after birth. Scores of 0, 1 or 2 are given for heart rate, breathing, skin colour, muscle tone and reactions (ie best = 5x2 = 10)
Artificial induction of ovulation:	Using hormones to stimulate ovulation
Artificial rupture of membranes:	Artificially breaking the sac containing fluid in which the baby is floating
Betamimetics:	Drugs known as **tocolytics** which reduce contractions of the uterus or womb

228

Breech delivery:	The delivery of a baby bottom or feet first rather than head first
Caesarean section:	Method of delivery via the abdominal wall with an incision into the womb
Cerebral palsy:	Damage to the part of the brain controlling movement and muscle. The child has reduced or no control over movement. Mental development, hearing or sight may also be affected depending on how near the damage is to the parts of the brain controlling these functions
Cervical cerclage:	A stitch placed round the **cervix** to prevent the premature opening of the **cervix** and rupture of the membranes
Cervix:	Neck of the womb – the part of the uterus that opens into the vagina
Chromosomal abnormality:	Disorder arising from an alteration in the number or form of an individual's chromosomes (the part of the cells that carry genetic information)
Conception:	The union of the egg and sperm
Conductive hearing loss:	Deafness due to obstruction to passage of sound waves in external or middle ear, usually as a result of infection in the middle ear
Conjoined twins:	Identical twins from a single egg where separation is not complete so they are joined together by some part of their body
Cost:	Valuation of resources. Monetary valuation at 'market prices' does not always reflect the value of resources
D & C:	Dilatation and Curettage. Opening up of the **cervix** to allow the lining of the womb to be removed by scraping or suction
Dichorionic twins:	Twins who were contained in separate chorion (sacs)
Dilatation:	Opening up (eg of the **cervix**)
Dizygous:	Non-identical twins, the result of two independently fertilised ova
Dopamine agonists:	Drugs which have the same effect as dopamine, which is a neuro-transmitter, or substance involved in the release of chemicals crucial to normal brain function.
Dye perturbation:	A test of fallopian tubal patency, where dye is introduced into the **cervix** under pressure and its emergence via the fallopian tube(s) is checked
Dysfunctional labour:	Labour where either the frequency of contractions or the strength of contractions is not progressive (ie increases over time)
Eclampsia:	A complication of pregnancy comprising fits associated with high blood pressure, the passage of protein in the urine, headaches, visual disturbances, and oedema
Elective caesarean section:	A **caesarean section** which has been planned in advance
Endocrinology:	The study of hormone related conditions
Endotracheal tube:	Plastic tube inserted through the mouth to the trachea (windpipe) to assist breathing and to allow removal of secretions in the airways
Epidural:	*See* **anesthesia/analgesia, epidural**

Epilepsy:	A condition in which the sufferer has recurrent fits/convulsions. There are three main types of epilepsy: grand mal, petit mal and temporal lobe epilepsy (also known as psycho-motor epilepsy)
Essential hypertension:	High blood pressure not necessarily related to pregnancy
Febrile convulsions:	Fits or seizures associated with a high temperature
Fertilisation:	The joining of an egg and sperm
Fetofetus transfusion:	Transfer of blood from the circulation of one fetus to another via linking blood vessel communications in a mono-chorionic placenta
Fetus to fetus transfusion:	See **fetofetus transfusion**
Follicle stimulating hormone (FSH):	Hormone which stimulates the development of ovarian follicles
GIFT:	Gamete Intra-Fallopian Transfer. This assisted conception technique involves the use of drugs to stimulate ovulation. Eggs are collected by **laparoscopy** or **ultrasound** imaging techniques. Sperm are collected and placed together with one or more eggs in the woman's fallopian tubes
Grommets:	Small tubes inserted into the ear-drum to allow drainage of the middle ear
Haemangioma:	Benign malformation of blood vessels which causes 'Strawberry mark' or 'port wine stain' in the skin, often on the face
Haemorrhage:	Bleeding, usually refers to extreme loss of blood
Hemiplegia:	A paralysis that affects one side of the body only
Hirschsprung's disease:	A congenital defect of the large intestine in which the network of nerves in part of the intestine is incomplete and therefore the muscles do not work
Hormone:	A chemical substance which stimulates certain cell processes by taking 'messages' from glands to target organs
Hyaline membrane disease:	A disorder of the lungs causing breathing difficulties due to immaturity of the production of substances which stabilise the airspaces (surfactant). Also known as **respiratory distress syndrome** (RDS). The lungs are unable to retain air, and under a microscope appear to contain membranes in the airspaces
Hyperbilirubinaemia:	Raised bilirubin level in the blood (**jaundice**)
Hyperemesis:	Persistent severe vomiting (an extreme form of 'morning sickness')
Hypertension:	Raised blood pressure
Hysterosalpingography:	A procedure involving the injection of a special dye into the uterus and fallopian tubes, so that structural abnormalities can be identified using radiography
Implantation:	The process of the embryo bedding down into the lining of the womb
Induction (of labour or abortion):	Process by which labour is initiated artificially, either by rupture of the membranes (ARM), or by a prostaglandin, or oxytocin, or by a combination of these
Instrumental delivery:	Delivery effected either by forceps or by vacuum extractor (ventouse/suction cup apparatus)

Intermittent positive pressure ventilation (IPPV):	Administering oxygen under pressure into a baby's airway, intermittently, to aid breathing
Intracranial haemorrhage:	Bleeding within the skull
Intrapartum:	During labour and delivery
Intraventricular haemorrhage:	Bleeding into the ventricles of the brain
IVF:	In vitro fertilisation and embryo transfer. This assisted conception technique typically involves the use of drugs to stimulate ovulation. Eggs are collected by **laparoscopy** or **ultrasound** imaging techniques. Sperm are collected and added to the eggs in culture medium. Fertilised eggs are cultured then transferred back into the womb via the **cervix** several days later
Jaundice:	A condition in which there is a yellowness of the skin and 'whites' of the eyes due to a raised level of bilirubin in the blood. Bilirubin is the yellow pigment in blood from red blood cells which give a yellow colouring to the skin and plasma
Laparoscopic hydrotubation:	Using a laparoscope to check fallopian tubes patency
Laparoscopy:	A technique used to assess the abdominal organs (eg a woman's fallopian tubes) by a laparoscope inserted into the abdomen through a small incision in the abdominal wall.
Malpresentation:	The fetus presenting prior to delivery in a position other than by the head which makes for a difficult delivery
Maternities:	A pregnancy resulting in one or more live and/or still births
Menotrophin:	A drug used to treat infertility
Monochorionic:	Fetuses in a multiple birth sharing one placenta and one outer membrane (chorion)
Monozygous/otic:	Identical twins or higher order births, the result of a single fertilised ovum (egg) dividing to produce two or more identical individuals
Musculoskeletal:	Relating to the muscles or bones
Myringotomy:	A small cut in the ear-drum to allow drainage of middle ear
Naevus (plural naevi):	A skin lesion which may be present at birth or develop later. There are many different forms
'Strawberry' naevus or capillary **haemangioma:**	A bright red 'birthmark' only rarely present at birth, which usually appears in the first week of life
Nitrous oxide and oxygen	*See* **anaesthesia/analgesia, nitrous oxide and oxygen**
Ocular albinism:	An inherited disease with lack of pigment in the eye and associated low vision
Oedema:	Swelling due to excess fluid in tissues beneath the skin
Oestrogen:	**Hormone** produced by ovaries. Essentially the hormone of the female
Oocyte:	**Ovum** prior to ovulation
Opiates:	*See* **anesthesia/analgesia, opiates**
Otitis media:	Inflammation of the middle ear, often caused by bacterial infection spreading from the throat or nose. There are three variations: acute, chronic-secretory ('glue ear') and chronic-suppurative. According to which form it takes, the condition can cause deafness and severe earache

Ovarian follicle:	Within the ovary, an **oocyte** surrounded by a ring of granulosa cells. Each month about 20 follicles begin the process of development; usually one culminates in ovulation, the remainder degenerate
Ovulation:	The release of a ripe **ovum** from one of the ovaries around the 14th day of the menstrual cycle
Ovum (plural ova):	Egg
Oxytocin:	Hormone produced by the pituitary gland that causes the uterus to contract and breasts to 'let down' milk
Perineum:	Area between vagina and anus
Pethidine:	*See* **anesthesia/analgesia, pethidine**
Placenta:	Organ comprising maternal and fetal tissues through which nutrients and oxygen pass to the fetus, and waste products from the fetus pass to the mother via the umbilical cord
Placenta – fused:	Where two or more **placentae** have fused together during their growth in the womb and appear as one
Placenta praevia:	A **placenta** positioned close to or directly over the cervical canal (outlet of the womb)
Placental abruption:	The **placenta** coming away from the uterus before delivery of the baby(ies)
Pre-eclampsia:	Raised blood pressure arising in pregnancy, which may be associated with albumen (protein) in the urine and/or swelling due to extra fluid
Presentations:	Describes the position of the fetus in relation to the pelvic canal
Breech:	*See* **Breech delivery**
Brow:	Brow down; the largest diameter of the fetal head
Cephalic/Vertex OA:	Head down, occupint anterior (with the back of the head facing forwards)
Cephalic/Vertex OP:	Head down, occupint posterior (with the back of the head facing backwards)
Face:	Face down
Transverse:	The longitudinal axis of the baby is at right angles to the maternal axis
Preterm:	Baby born before completion of 37 weeks gestation
Preterm labour:	Onset of labour before completion of 37 weeks gestation
Primigravida:	A woman in her first pregnancy
Progesterone:	**Hormone** produced by the ovary which helps to maintain pregnancy
Prophylaxis:	Care given with a view to prevent illness
Prospective:	Ongoing. May relate to a study which follows a selected population through given events
Prostaglandin:	**Hormone** used in **induction** of labour or abortion (among other uses). Naturally occurring compounds which cause changes in smooth muscle contractility; promote uterine muscle contraction in labour
Pyloric stenosis:	An obstruction of the **pylorus**.
Pylorus:	A strong muscle valve at the outlet of the stomach which controls movement of food down the duodenum and small intestine
Pyrexia:	Raised body temperature

Pyrexia, sepsis:	Raised body temperature due to infection
Quadriplegia:	Paralysis in both arms and both legs. *See* **cerebral palsy**
Randomised trials:	A trial, for example, of a drug or treatment, in which participants are allocated in a random way to one or other of alternative ways of management or treatment
Respiratory distress syndrome:	Condition (usually in preterm babies) resulting from lack of surfactant (necessary for lung expansion) in immature lungs. *See* **Hyaline membrane disease**
Resuscitation:	Active intervention to restore heart and breathing activities
Retinopathy of prematurity:	Damage to the blood vessels in the retina (lining of the eye) caused by high concentrations of oxygen in the blood of **preterm** infants. Reduced vision may result
Ritodrine:	Ritodrine hydrochloride is a **betamimetic** drug used particularly in preterm labour
Rupture of the membranes:	Breaking of the sac containing fluid in which the baby is floating, either spontaneously (natural) or artificially
Salbutamol:	A **betamimetic** drug used previously to prevent pre-term labour but now largely superseded
Sensori-neural deafness:	Hearing loss due to an abnormality of, or damage to, the nerve pathways from the inner ear to the cortex of the brain
Severe vision loss:	Reduced visual acuity (often defined as 6/18 or less in the better eye)
Social costs:	Costs met by families or others. Help is frequently provided in kind, and is not always paid for in money, for example, the time given by people who are not in paid employment
Spontaneous delivery:	A delivery which occurs without instrumental or operative assistance
Squint:	Condition in which the axes of the eyes are intermittently or continuously not parallel when focussed on distant objects
Systolic heart murmur:	A noise detectable through a stethoscope heard during contraction phase of the heart cycle, that is between the two heart sounds
Talipes, club foot:	Usually caused by the position of the feet before birth. One or both feet are misshapen, often being turned in at the ankle. It may be severe or mild
Term:	Delivery between 37 and 42 weeks gestation
Tocolytics:	Drugs which reduce contractions of the uterus or womb
Tracheotomy:	An operation which allows air to reach the lungs without first passing through the upper airways (nose, mouth, pharynx or larynx). A vertical cut is made in the front of the neck below the Adam's apple, through which a small tube, or air pipe is passed
Trauma:	Wound or injury
Trimester of pregnancy:	A period of three months; pregnancy is divided into three trimesters – 1st, 2nd and 3rd
Tubal insufflation:	A test of fallopian tubal patency
Tubal reconstruction:	To reconstruct damaged fallopian tubes
Twin to twin transfusion:	*See* **fetofetus transfusion**

Ultrasound:	High frequency sound waves reflected from tissues of differing density to produce images of body organs and structures. In obstetrics, scanning ultrasound gives a visual display of the area scanned, allowing assessment of fetal position, size and diagnosis of some malformations or of multiple pregnancy. Also used for assessment of extent of neonatal brain damage caused by intracranial or intraventricular haemorrhage
Urogenital:	Relating to the urinary or genital systems
Urino-genitary malformations:	Malformations of the urino-genital system
Vaginal delivery:	A delivery via the vagina
Ventilation:	Mechanical provision of cyclical inflation of a baby's lungs to achieve normal levels of oxygen and carbon dioxide in the baby's blood
Vertex presentation:	The fetal **presentation** in which a specific area of the fetal skull overlies the outlet from the womb. This is the normal presentation at term
Zygosity:	Describing the genetic make-up of children from a multiple birth; may be **monozygous** (identical), **dizygous** (two different genetic compositions) etc

Index

Abdominal delivery – see caesarean section
   definition 228
Aberdeen City, studies of multiple
   births 54
Abortion, induced 21
Acardia 118
   definition 228
Africa 26, 90
Age of mother – see mother
Age, gestational – see gestational age
Albinism 158
   definition 228
Alimentary
   definition 228
   system malformations 118, 158
Alpha fetoprotein tests 60–61
   definition 228
Anaemia 70–72, 99–100, 117, 128
   definition 228
Anaesthesia/Analgesia 23, 80, 92–93, 97,
   219
   definitions 228
   epidural 81–82, 92–93, 97
   fatal accidents during IVF 57
   general 81–82, 92–93, 97
   nitrous oxide and oxygen 92
   opiates 92
   pethidine 92
   spinal 90, 92
Anoxia 23
   definition 228
Antenatal admission to hospital 73–77, 78,
   140, 219
   costs 208–209
Antenatal care 59–79
   costs 206–209
Antepartum
   definition 228
Antepartum haemorrhage 70–74, 75
   definition 228
Anti-oestrogen 52
   definition 228
Apgar scores 110–111, 114–116, 129
   definition 228
Artificial induction of ovulation 46–47,
   50–58
   definition 228
Artificial rupture of membranes 86
   definition 228
Assisted conception 20, 119, 224

See also IVF, GIFT
Assisted induction of ovulation 46–58, 224
   definition 228
Australia 159, 215
Australian Multiple Births Association 215

Babies from multiple birth – see also
   children
   birthweights 41, 98, 101–107, 109–110,
   112, 129
   discharge from hospital 127–128, 225
   problems at birth 107, 110
   problems in neonatal period 113, 117
   separation from mothers 119–122
Baby food 164–166
   costs 212–213
Baby sitting 135, 173, 174, 175, 222
'Bed rest' 74–77, 78
Belgium 54, 90
Benefits 163–166, 214–215, 225
Betamimetics 70, 86
   definitions 228
Bias in response to surveys 45
Birth order 23, 102–115, 118–119
Birth registration 15, 18–19, 21, 31, 35
Births and Deaths Registration Acts 35
Birthweight 41, 98, 101–107, 109–110,
   112, 119, 154–159, 219
Blood loss
   after delivery 99–101, 128
   in pregnancy 70–74
Blood pressure 99–100, 128
Blood transfusions 99–101
Booking for delivery 68–70, 78, 90,
   219–220
Breast feeding 124–125, 162
Breast pumps 124–125
Breech delivery 88
   definition 229
Breech presentation 88–91
British Association of Perinatal Medicine
   survey of triplets 37
British Paediatric Surveillance Unit 37,
   160–227
British Perinatal Mortality Survey 22
Brow presentation 89

Caesarean section 23, 80–82, 86–88, 90–93,
   219, 225, 227
   birthweight 103–106

infertility treatment 91–92
policies about 90–92, 97
resuscitation of babies 112
wound infection 99–102
Cain, Paul 153, 159–160
Cardiovascular system malformations 118, 157–158
Carers 131–152
Cars 169–171, 175, 222, 226
Central nervous system malformations 118, 157–158
Cephalic presentations 88
Cerebral palsy 153, 159–160, 221
definition 229
Cervical cerclage 70, 140
definition 229
Cervix 70
definition 229
Child care 173–175
costs 146, 174–175, 212–213
Child Care and Development Group 14, 34
Child guidance clinics 147
Child health clinics 135, 144–146, 172–173, 203
Child seats in cars 169–171, 222, 226
Children from multiple births – see also babies
costs of readmission to hospital 211–212
disabilities and health
problems 153–160, 221, 227
Chromosomal abnormality 118
definition 229
Class – see social class
Clinical psychologists 195
Clomid – see clomiphene citrate
Clomiphene citrate 27, 51–57
Club foot 118, 157–158
definition of talipes 233
Commercial sponsorship 163–166, 175, 215, 222, 225
Communication problems 55–57, 62–66, 69, 78, 80–82, 90, 96–97, 126, 219, 222, 224
Community nursing services, survey of 35, 41, 135–136, 146
Companies, gifts from 163–166, 175, 215, 225
Company cars 169–170
Comparisons between surveys
GPs and obstetricians 105
GPs, obstetricians and parents 38, 41

obstetricians and parents 62, 64, 65, 101–102
Complications
after delivery 99–102, 128
babies 107, 110, 129
pregnancy 70–74, 78
Conception 20, 24–28
definition 229
Conductive hearing loss 154
definition 229
Confidentiality 31
Congenital malformations 117–119, 129, 157–158, 160, 221
Conjoined twins 118
definition 229
Contraception 18, 27
Control groups 31
Convulsions 100, 154
Costs 205–217, 223
antenatal care 206–209
cars 171, 212, 214
child care 174, 212–214
definition 229
delivery 209
equipment 212, 214
food 212–213
home help 213–214
hospital care 206–212
infertility treatment 205–206
moving house 166
nappies 212–213
neonatal care 210
pre-school facilities 182–188
transport 187, 190, 225
Counselling 224

D and C – see dilatation and curettage
definition 229
Day nurseries 183, 195
Deaths, babies 34–36, 90, 105–111
– see also mortality
parents' experience of 24, 32
statistics 22–23
Deaths, women
associated with IVF 57
Delivery 80–98
– see also caesarean, instrumental, spontaneous, vaginal
booking for 68–70
costs 209
gestational age 82–86

method of 23, 80–82, 86–88, 90–93, 219, 235
 and birthweight 102–106, 112
 unexpected multiple birth at 68–70
Department of Health 14, 33, 37
Depression 101
Design of study 31–36
Detection of multiple pregnancy 59–68, 77–78
Diabetes 126
Diagnosis of multiple pregnancy 59–68, 77–78
Dichorionic twins 23
 definition 229
Diet 76
Dilatation, definition 229
Dilation and curettage (D and C) 46, 50, 51
 definition 229
Disabilities
 adults 159–160
 children 153–160, 221, 227
Disablement Resettlement Officers 159
Discharge from hospital
 babies 127–128
 mothers 122–123
Discussion between parents and staff
 about discharge 127–128, 225
 booking for delivery 68–69, 90, 224
 delivery 80–82, 90, 96–98, 219–220, 224
 diagnosis of multiple birth 62–66, 219, 224
 help with babies at home 176, 225–226
 infertility treatment and risk of multiple birth 55–57, 224
District nurses 123
Dizygous
 definition 229
 twins 23, 24–25, 27, 94
 triplets 26, 94
 quadruplets 26
Doctors – see general practitioners, obstetricians, paediatricians
Dopamine agonists 52
 definition 229
Drugs
 for infertility and sub-fertility 20, 27, 46, 47, 50–58, 218–219, 226
Duncan, J Matthews 15, 26, 59
Dye perturbations 51
 definition 229

Dysfunctional labour 91
 definition 229
Ears
 hearing problems 154, 190, 194
 malformations 118, 158
East Flanders Prospective Twin Study 54
Eclampsia 99–100, 124
 definition 229
Education
 pre-school 177–188, 225
 school 189–204, 225, 227
Educational psychologists 196
Eggs – see ova
Elective caesarean section 86, 88, 90
 definition 229
Embryos 24–25
Emergency caesarean sections 88, 95, 122
Endocrinology
 clinics 51–54
 definition 229
Endotracheal tube
 definition 229
Epidurals 80–82, 92–93, 95–97, 122
 definition 229
Epilepsy 154
 definition 229
Equipment for babies and children 165–166
 costs 212, 214
Essential hypertension 71, 72
 definition 230
Ethnic minorities, under-representation in parents' survey 45
Eyes
 malformations 118, 158
 vision problems 154–155, 158, 160
Eynesbury (St Neots)
 quadruplets 16

Face presentation 89
Fallopian tubes 28, 46, 50
Family Credit 215
Family Practitioner Committees (FPCs) 32
Families
 help for parents 132–134
 presence of parents 41–42
Family Income Supplement 163
Fathers
 exclusion from birth 96
 presence at birth 96–97, 225
 presence in household 41–42

social class   42–43, 45, 48, 50
   unemployment   41–42, 48, 50, 214
Febrile convulsions
   definition   230
Feeding   123–125, 225
   breast   124–125, 225
   problems   117
Fertilisation   20, 24–25, 27–28
   definition   230
Fertility rates   17–19
Fetofetus transfusion   117
   definition   230
Fetus to fetus transfusion   117
   definition   230
Financial problems   163–166, 169–171,
   176, 223, 225
Fisher, Ronald   15
Fits   100, 154
Follicle stimulating hormones (FSH)   27,
   51–57
   definition   230
Forceps delivery   88
Fraternal twins   24–25
Friends, help from   134–135

Gamete intra-fallopian transfer – see GIFT
   definition   230
General anaesthesia   81–82, 92–93, 97
General practitioners
   help for parents   131, 141–143, 195–196,
   220, 221
   relationship with parents   44–45, 65, 129,
   141–143
   role in infertility treatment   51–52, 56,
   58
   survey of   31–34, 36–41, 44–45, 51–52,
   153–160
General practitioner maternity units   68
Genito-urinary malformations   118,
   157–158
Gent, Belgium, study of triplets   90
Gestational age
   delivery   82–86, 90–91, 97
   diagnosis of multiple birth   61–63, 67–68
   onset of labour   71–74
GIFT (gamete intra-fallopian transfer)   20,
   27–28, 55, 56–57, 68, 218, 226
   definition   230
Gifts after multiple birth   163–166, 175,
   215, 225
Gonadotrophins   51–57
Good family quadruplets   17

Grand parents   132–134
Great Ormond Street hospital   16
Grommets   154, 157
   definition   230
Guidelines for GIFT and IVF   28, 218, 226

Haemangioma   118, 158
   definition   230
Haematoma   123
Haemorrhage   99–100
   definition   230
Harrison, E   16
Health authorities   131, 132, 135–138,
   143–146
Health clinics – see child health clinics
Health in childhood   153–160, 221, 227
Health visitors   127, 131, 143–146, 183,
   186, 190, 193–194, 220–221, 224
Hearing problems   154, 190, 194
Heart
   malformations   118, 157–158
   murmurs   157
   problems   190
Help for parents   131–152, 220–224,
   225–226
   friends and relatives   134, 150
   general   131–133
   health services   135–138, 150
   level needed   134–135, 150–151
   night   135–138
   relatives   132–134, 150, 225
   social services   135–141
   students   147–150
   trainees   147–150
   volunteers   147–150, 151
Height (mother's)   27
Hemiplegia   153
   definition   230
Hepworth, Barbara
   triplets   16–17
Hernia   157
High blood pressure   99–100, 128
Hirschsprung's disease   158
   definition   230
Holidays   173–174
Home care   131, 138–141, 146
   organisers   148
Home helps   69, 128, 131, 137, 138–141,
   168, 221, 225
   costs   213–214
Home Start   131, 147, 148, 151, 194
Home visits

GPs   141–143, 151
  health visitors   143–146, 151, 176
  midwives   151
Hormones   27, 46
  definition   230
Hormone implants in beef cattle   27
Hospital
  admissions in childhood   154, 156–157,
    160, 221
  antenatal admission   73–77
  booking for delivery   68–70, 78
  costs of care   206–212
  discharge from   122–123, 127–128
  parents views of neonatal care   125–127
  social workers   129, 138
  visiting   123
House extensions   165, 166–168, 175, 222,
    225
House moves   133, 166–168, 174, 175, 222,
    225
Hospital In-patient Enquiry – see Maternity
  HIPE
Human Fertilisation and Embryology
  Authority   28, 226
Human Fertilisation and Embryology
  Bill   28
Human menopausal gonadotrophin   27,
    51–57
Hyaline membrane disease   117
  definition   230
Hyperbilirubinaemia   117
  definition   230
Hyperemesis   74
  definition   230
Hypertension   70–72, 99–100, 128
  definition   230
Hysterectomy   100, 121, 139
Hysterosalpingography   51
  definition   230

Identical
  twins   24–25
  triplets   25
Illness in childhood   154, 156–157, 160,
    221, 227
Immaturity   22
Implantation   24
  definition   230
Induction of abortion   21
  definition   230
Induction of labour   86, 97
  definition   230

Infant mortality   22–23, 34, 107–110
Infections   99–102, 154
Infertility
  clinics   51–54, shortage of   57
  investigation of   46, 47, 51
Infertility treatment   27–28, 46–58, 224,
    226
  antenatal hospital stays   77
  complications in pregnancy   70, 72
  congenital malformations   119
  costs   205–206
  detection of multiple pregnancies   66–68,
    78
  gestational age at delivery   83, 85
  induction of labour   86
  lack of statistics   54, 57, 218, 226
  method of delivery   91–92
  possible risks for women   57, 227
  quality   58
  trends in   53
Inhibitors of gonadotrophin   52
Instrumental delivery   87, 88, 92–93
  definition   230
Insurance against multiple births   214–215
Interim Licensing Authority (ILA)   28, 55,
    218, 226
  guidelines for GIFT and IVF   28, 218,
    226
Intermittent positive pressure ventilation
  (IPPV)   110, 113
  definition   231
International Society for Twin Studies   90
Interpreters, lack of
  bias due to   45
Interviews with parents   35, 98
Intracranial haemorrhage, definition   230
Intrapartum
  definition   231
Intraventricular haemorrhage,
  definition   231
Investigations of infertility   46, 47, 51
In vitro fertilisation – see IVF
Iowa USA, study of triplets   91
IPPV – see Intermittent positive pressure
  ventilation
Iron tablets   52
IVF (In vitro fertilisation)   20, 27–28, 51,
    55, 56, 68, 161, 163, 218
  congenital malformations   119
  costs   206
  possible risks for women   57
  registers   57, 218, 226

Jaundice 117
  definition 231

Kidney failure 100, 124 – see also
  urogenital
King's bounty for triplets 15
  – see also Queen's Bounty

Labour 71–74, 75, 84–89, 92–93
Language development 192–196, 201–202
Laparoscopic hydrotubation 50, 51
  definition 231
Laparoscopy 50, 51
Last menstrual period 61
Limb malformations 118
Loans of money 163–166
Local registrars' industrial action 31

Malpresentation, definition 231
Maternities
  definition 231
  numbers of 19–21, 34, 39
Maternity Hospital In-patient Enquiry
  (HIPE) 32, 75, 85, 86, 97, 103, 219
Maternity Services Liaison Committees 37
Media publicity 33, 35, 45, 136, 161–163,
  168, 175, 221, 225
Menstrual periods 25, 61
Menotrophin, definition 231
Methods used in study 32–35
Middle ear disease 154
Midwives 37, 44, 96, 124
Milk 123–125, 163–166, 175, 221
  costs 212–213
Minibuses 170
Miscarriages 21, 25, 48, 49
  threatened 70–72
Monochorionic 23, 94
  definition 231
Monozygous/otic
  definition 231
  twins 23, 25, 94, 158
  triplets 26, 94
Morbidity
  children 107–119, 153–160, 221, 227
  mothers 57, 70–76, 99–102, 128, 220
  quadruplets 26
Mortality 22–24, 34, 35–36, 105–111
Mother and toddler groups 177–178,
  182–188
Mothers
  age 41

before birth 70–76
discharge from hospital 122–123, 220,
  225
experience of birth 93–98
medical problems after birth 99–102,
  128, 220
morbidity 57, 70–76, 99–102, 128, 220
readjustment problems after birth 129,
  220
separation from babies 119–122, 225
previous living children 43–44
previous pregnancies 43–44
social class 48, 50
visiting babies in hospital 123, 124
Motor Vehicles Act 1988 169
Moving house 133, 166–168, 174, 175,
  222, 225, 226
Multiple births – see also twins, triplets,
  quadruplets, quintuplets, sextuplet and
  nonuplets
  birthweights 102–107, 109–110, 129
  congenital malformations 117–119
  delivery 80–98, 219
  diagnosis 59–68
  gestational age at delivery 82–86
  help for parents after birth 131–152,
  220–224, 225–226
  incidence 19–21, 26
  infertility treatment 46–58
  morbidity 107–119, 153–160, 221, 227
  mortality 22–24, 34, 35–36, 105–110
  numbers of 13, 15, 19, 20, 34
  pregnancy 59–79
  publicity 161–163, 221, 225
  reasons for 24–28
  statistics about 15, 18–21, 31, 35–36
  trends in rate 14, 17–21, 55, 57
Musculoskeletal
  definition 231
  malformations 118
Myringotomy 154, 157
  definition 231

Naevus (plural naevi) 118
  definition 231
'Named person', need for 146, 151, 221,
  224, 235
Namibia, study of triplets 90
Nannies, trainee 128
Nappies 164–165, 175, 221
  costs 212–213
National Childbirth Trust 125, 147, 151

National Health Service (NHS)   57
  Central Register   32, 160, 227
National perinatal Epidemiology Unit   14, 32
National Survey of Morbidity in General
  Practice   154
Neighbours, help from   134–135, 220
Neonatal care   81, 119–122, 125–127, 129, 220
  costs   210–211
Neonatal intensive care units (NICUs)   81, 119–122
  – see also neonatal care
Neonatal mortality   23, 34, 107–111
Newspapers   161–163, 168
Nicholson, Ben
  triplets   16–17
Night care for babies   133, 135–138
Night nurses   69, 135–138, 220, 225
Night 'sitters'   136
Nitrous oxide and oxygen for analgesia   92
  definition   231
Nonuplets   26
Northern Ireland   31, 36–37
Nottinghamshire, ovulation induction   54
Nursery classes   177, 181, 183–188, 201, 202
Nursery nurses   136
Nursery schools   177, 180, 183–188, 222, 226
Nurses   123–127

Obstetricians   80–82, 90, 96
  survey of   31, 33, 36, 37–44, 46–55, 59–65, 66–68, 70–75, 77, 82–94, 99–121
Ocular albinism   158
  definition   231
Oedema   99–100
  definition   231
Oestrogen   52
Office of Population Censuses and Surveys –
  see OPCS
Oocyte, definition   231
OPCS (Office of Population Censuses and
  Surveys)   14, 31, 32
Opiates for general anaesthesia   92
Oral contraceptives   27
Otitis media   154
  definition   231
Ovarian cancer   57
Ovarian follicle   27
  definition   231

Ovarian stimulants   20, 46–47, 50–55, 224, 226
  investigation of possible adverse
  effects   227
  possible risk of ovarian cancer   57
Ovulation   24–25
  definition   232
  stimulating drugs   20, 27, 46–47, 50–55, 57, 224
Ovum (plural ova)   24–25, 27–28
  definition   232
Oxytocin   86

Paediatric liaison health visitors   129, 144, 220, 225
Paediatricians   32, 96, 113, 126–128, 157
Parents – see also mother and father
  communication problems with
  staff   55–57, 62–66, 69, 78, 95–98, 126, 219, 222, 224
  discussion about birth   80–82, 95–98, 126, 219, 222, 224
  discussion of infertility treatment   55–57, 224
  experiences of birth   93–98
  experiences of death of babies   24, 32
  help after birth   131–152, 220–224, 225–226
  interviews with   35
  lack of sleep   131, 150
  postal surveys   32–35, 36, 38–40, 44, 55–57, 62–66, 68–70, 76–78, 80–82, 90, 93, 95–97, 119–128, 131–152, 161–196
  views about neonatal care   125–127
Paris, study of triplets   90
Parity (previous live and still births)   48, 49
Patent ductus arteriosus   118
Pergonal – see human menopausal
  gonadotrophin
Perinatal mortality   22, 23
Perineum
  definition   232
  wound infections   99
Pethidine   92
  definition   228
Photographs
  babies   97, 220, 225
  publicity   162–163, 175
  ultrasound scans   62
Placenta   93–94
  definition   232
  fused   93–94

Placenta praevia
   definition   232
Placental abruption   70
   definition   232
Playgroups   177, 179, 183–188, 201, 222, 226
Polyhydramnios   70–72
Population differences in multiple births   26
Population (Statistics) Act   19
Postneonatal mortality   23, 34, 107–111
Post partum eclampsia   99–100
Post partum haemorrhage   99–101, 121
Prams   168, 170
Pre-eclampsia   70–74, 140
   definition   232
Premature rupture of membranes   91
Prematurity   11
Pre-school facilities   177–188, 222, 226
Pre-school Playgroups Association   183–184
Pregnancy   59–79, 140
Presentations   88–90
   breech   89
   brow   89
   cephalic/Vertex OA   89
   cephalic/Vertex OP   89
   definitions   232
   face   89
   transverse   232
Preterm – see also gestational age
   birth   22, 98
   definition   232
   delivery   98
   labour   71–74, 75, 85–86, 96
Previous living children   44, 47–49, 122
Previous pregnancies   43–44, 47, 49
Primary health care   127, 129, 224
Primigravida   70
   definition   232
Private medicine   54, 57, 218–219
Progesterone, definition   232
Prophylaxis, definition   232
Prospective
   definition   232
   randomised trials   91
Prostaglandin   86
   definition   232
Psychologists   195, 196
Publicity   33, 35, 45, 136, 161–163, 168, 175, 221, 225
Public transport   169, 187

Pushchairs   161, 165, 168–169, 170–171, 175, 187, 222, 225
Pyloric stenosis   154, 157, 221
   definition   232
Pylorus, definition   232
Pyrexia   99–102
   definition   232
   sepsis   99–102

Quadriplegia   153
   definition
Quadrizygotic quadruplets   26
Quadruplets
   birthweights   101–103
   booking for delivery   68–69
   complications in pregnancy   70–75, 78
   delivery   80–98
   diagnosis   59–68, 218
   gestational age at birth   82–86
   gifts   161–163
   Good family   17
   Hamilton, Scotland   15–16
   help for parents   131–152
   incidence   19–21
   infertility treatment   46–58
   morbidity in childhood   153–160
   mortality   22–23
   numbers of   13, 19, 34
   presentation   89
   publicity   161–163
   St Neots   16
   types of   25–26
   zygosity   94
Queen Victoria
   bounty for triplets   15, 215, 225
Queen's bounty for triplets   15, 215, 225
Questionnaires sent to
   community nursing services   35, 41
   general practitioners   31, 32–34, 36, 37–38, 41
   obstetricians   31, 32, 36, 37–41
   paediatricians and other specialists   33
   parents   35, 36, 38–41
   social services   35, 41
Quintuplets
   change in booking   69
   complications in pregnancy   70–75
   diagnosis   59–68
   help for parents after birth   131–152
   night nurses   136
   numbers of   13, 19, 34

Radiographers 63–66
Randomised trials 76, 78, 91–92, 219, 225
   definition 233
   lack of 91, 219
   need for 225, 227
Red Cross 136
Relatives 132–134
Remedial surgery for infertility 50–51
Renal failure 100, 124
Respiratory
   problems 117
   system malformations 118, 158
Respiratory distress syndrome 23, 117
   definition 233
Response to surveys 33, 36–45, 159, 160
   checks for bias 39–45, 159
Resuscitation 107, 110, 112–113
   definition 233
Retinopathy of prematurity 154, 155
   definition 233
Ritodrine 86
   definition 233
Road safety 171, 187
Rupture of the membranes 86
   definition 233

Salbutamol 86
   definition 233
Scans – see ultrasound
Schools 189–204, 222, 226
Scottish Twins Study 37, 74
Scotland 31, 36–37
Seat belts in cars 169–171
'Secret languages' 192–193
Selective reduction 21
Self help groups 131, 147–150
Sensori-neural deafness 154
   definition 233
Separation at school 191–193, 196–204, 221
Sepsis 99–102
Septuplets 19
Severe vision loss 154
   definition 233
Sex of babies 44–45
Sextuplets
   night nurses for 136
   numbers of 19, 34
   Walton 55
Shock 101
Shopping 161, 172
'Siamese' twins 118

Skin diseases 118, 158
Smoking 27
Social class 27, 42–43, 45
   and infertility treatment 48, 50, 57
Social costs 212–215
   definition 233
Social security benefits 163–164, 214–215, 225
Social services 131, 132, 135–141, 143–144, 148, 185–186
   costs 216
   survey of 35, 41, 141, 216
Social workers 129, 220, 224
South Africa, study of triplets 90
'Spastics' – see cerebral palsy
Special care baby units 68, 81, 96, 119–122
   – see also neonatal care
Special educational needs 190, 196
Speech delay 192–196, 201
Speech therapists 193–196
Sperm 24–25, 28
Spinal anaesthesia 90, 92
Spontaneous delivery 88
   definition 233
Spontaneous labour 84–85, 88
Squint 154, 155, 157, 160, 221
   definition 233
St Neots
   quadruplets 16
Statistics, collection of
   infertility treatment 54, 57, 218, 226
   home helps 138
   multiple birth 15, 18–21, 31, 35–36
Sterilisation 80
Stillbirths 22–23, 34, 107–111
'Strawberry stains' 118
   definition 231
Students 147–150, 151, 221
   community work 147
   nursery nursing 136
   nursing 147
Study of triplet and higher order births
   design 31–45
   population covered 31–32, 35–36
   questionnaires 31
   response 33, 36–45
Subfertility
   treatment for 27–28, 46–58
Supertwins group 138–139, 168, 149–150, 221
Support groups 147–150

243

Suppression of preterm labour   70,
    85–86, 96
Surgery
    children from multiple birth   154, 156–
    157
    procedures for infertility   46–47, 50–55
Surveys of
    community nursing services   35, 41, 135–
    136
    general practitioners   31–34, 36–41,
    44–45, 51–52, 153–160
    obstetricians   31, 33, 36, 37–44, 46–55,
    59–65, 66–68, 70–75, 77, 82–94, 99–121
    paediatricians and other specialists   33,
    153–160
    parents   32–35, 36, 38–40, 44, 55–57,
    62–66, 68–70, 76–78, 80–82, 90, 93,
    95–97, 100, 119–128, 131–152, 161–196
    social services   35, 41, 141, 216
Survival of babies from multiple
    births   22–24, 34, 105–111, 129, 220
Swimming pools   135
Systolic heart murmur   157
    definition   233

Talipes (club foot)   118, 157, 158
Tel Aviv, Israel, study of triplets   90
Telephones   171–172, 176, 226
    obscene phone calls   162
Television
    closed circuit   126
    publicity   136, 161, 162
Term, definition   233
Tocolytics – see betamimetics
    definition   233
Tonsillectomy   157
Toxaemia   70–74
Tracheotomy   136–137
    definition   233
Traffic dangers   171, 187
Trainees   128, 131, 147–150, 151, 221
Transport problems   123, 168–171, 183,
    187–188, 190, 191, 221, 226
Trauma, definition   233
Trimester of pregnancy, definition   233
Triplets
    Apgar scores   110–111, 114–116
    'bed rest' in pregnancy   74–77
    birthweights   101–107, 109–110
    complications in pregnancy   70–75, 78
    congenital malformations   117–119
    delivery   80–98

diagnosis   59–68, 77–78, 218
gestational age at delivery   82–86
help for parents after birth   131–152
incidence of   19–21, 26–27
infertility treatment   46–58
morbidity in childhood   153–160
mortality   22–23, 34, 35–36, 105–111
numbers of   13, 15, 19, 20
placenta   93–94
presentation   89
publicity   161–163
types of   25–26
zygosity   93–94
Trizygotic triplets   26, 94
Tubal insufflation   51
    definition   233
Tubal reconstruction   51
    definition   233
Tube feeding   124–125
Twins
    'bed rest'   74–76
    birthweights 101, 103, 105, 109–110
    complications in pregnancy   70–75, 78
    congenital malformations   117–119
    conjoined ('siamese')   118
    diagnosis   59–68
    gestational age at delivery   82–86
    incidence of   19–21
    induction rates   86
    infertility treatment   46–58, 86
    mortality   22–23, 105, 107, 109–110
    placentas   93–94
    presentation   89
    'secret languages'   192–193
    numbers of   19
    vanishing   21
    zygosity   93–94
Twin to twin transfusion, definition   233
Twins and Multiple Births Association
    (TAMBA)   32, 44, 147, 149–150, 151,
    203, 221
    Supertwins group 138–139, 149–150, 168,
    221
    twins clubs   148, 149–150

Ultrasound   59–68, 78, 219
    definition   234
Unemployment   41–42, 48, 50
Urinary complications   71–72
Urino-genitary malformations   118, 157–
    158
    definition   234

Urogenital
  definition 234
  system malformations 118, 157–158

Vacuum extraction 88
Vaginal delivery 81–82, 88–92, 219
  birthweight 102–105
  definition 234
Vanishing twin syndrome 21
Ventilation – see Intermittent Positive
  Pressure Ventilation
  definition 234
Ventolin – see salbutomol
Vertex presentation 88–89
  definition 234
Videos of ultrasound scans 62, 63
Vision problem 154–155, 158, 221
Visiting babies in hospital 123
Visits to friends and relatives 174–175
Voluntary Licensing Authority (VLA) 28,
  55, 218

Volunteer Bureau 136
Volunteers 131, 136, 147–150, 151, 221

Warnock Committee (Committee of Enquiry
  into Human Fertilisation and
  Embryology) 57
Weight, mother's 27
Western Australia Cerebral Palsy
  register 159
Wound infections 99–102, 128

X rays 46, 59–61

Youth Training Schemes 147, 151
Yutopar – see ritodrine

Zygosity 23, 93–94
  definition 234

Addresses of relevant organisations

Twins and Multiple Births Association
51 Thicknall Drive,
Pedmore, Stourbridge,
West Midlands DY9 0YH
Tel 0384 373642

The Twins and Multiple Births Association is a voluntary organisation formed by parents with multiple births. It supports families with twins, triplets and higher order births, both individually and through local twins clubs and its specialist groups. It also works to promote public and professional awareness of their needs. Specialist sub-groups include health and education, supertwins, bereavement, special needs and single parent families.

Multiple Births Foundation
Institute of Obstetrics and Gynaecology,
Queen Charlotte's and Chelsea Hospital,
Goldhawk Road, London W6 0XG
Tel 081 748 4666 ext 5201

The Multiple Births Foundation is a professional organisation which offers support to parents of twins, triplets and higher order births, and also to members of the caring professions who require information and specialised advice. It acts as a resource centre and publishes a newsletter.

National Childbirth Trust
Alexander House, Oldham Terrace,
London W3 6HN
Tel 081 992 8637

The National Childbirth Trust is a national organisation with 350 local groups in the United Kingdom. It offers antenatal classes, breastfeeding counselling and postnatal support and provides a range of information, including leaflets about caesareans, inductions and breastfeeding for babies in special care.

Maternity Alliance
15 Britannia Street, London WC1X 9JP
Tel 071 837 1265

Maternity Alliance campaigns for improvements in rights, benefits and services for mothers, fathers and babies. It has a telephone information service for parents and professionals, dealing with all aspects of pregnancy and new parenthood.

Home Start Consultancy
140 New Walk, Leicester LE1 7JL
Tel 0533 554988

Home Start is a voluntary scheme in which volunteers, all parents themselves, offer support, friendship and practical help to expectant mothers and to families which include at least one pre-school child.

Printed in the United Kingdom for HMSO.
Dd.292638, 7/90, C20, 3385/4, 5673, 94840.